Dedicated to the worldwide wine industry and the great tradition of growing and producing wine throughout time.

THE WORLD OF
WINE

QUIZ BOOK ?

& AMPLIFIED ANSWERS

Dedicated to the worldwide wine industry and the great tradition of growing and producing wine throughout time.

Published in 2021 by
FAIRBANKS KING BOOKS

Kingston upon Thames
London
United Kingdom

Email: fkbooksinfo@gmail.com

+44 (0)7932 670040
+44 (0)7791 511733

www.fairbankskingbooks.co.uk

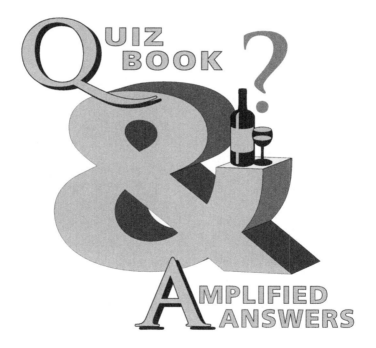

THE WORLD OF
WINE
QUIZ BOOK ?
& AMPLIFIED ANSWERS

**1,000 Questions with explanatory answers
To test and build your wine knowledge**

Roddy Button and Mike Oliver

Design, typography and illustrations: Brian Whitehead

INTRODUCTION TO THE WORLD OF WINE QUIZ BOOK

The World of Wine Quiz Book has 100 quizzes and 1,000 questions which cover all the main wine producing countries of the world. The quizzes then explore iconic wines, grape varieties, wine history, wine culture, production and wine trivia from famous quotations to Hollywood, politics and even literary drunks.

i) Amplified Answers

The unique nature of The World of Wine Quiz Book lies in the Amplified Answers. Instead of a single word answer being provided, they are each a paragraph long. They provide a 'mini wine course' of facts on the diverse wine subjects covered. Over two thirds of the length of The World of Wine Quiz Book is the amplified answers, running to well over 200 pages.

But if you just want the answer very quickly then it is right there, standing out in a bold larger type size. You can read the 'amplified' explanatory part later if you wish.

These amplified answers are designed to explain why your selection was correct, filling in some of the extra backup details and giving more of the surrounding factual information within a paragraph. If your selection of the wine answer was incorrect it will help impart the relevant facts to make sure you know them in the future.

So, as well as a bit of fun, The World of Wine Quiz Book can help build your wine knowledge whatever stage you are at now, from 'I know what I like' wine drinkers to wine adventurers and even testing, and acting as reminders, for professional sommeliers.

ii) Format of the Quiz Groupings

The 100 quizzes are all arranged logically into 8 sections of quiz types. Section 1 is composed of 5 quizzes about testing your general wine knowledge.

Section 2 to section 5 are all country related wine quizzes starting with 8 quizzes on France and French wines, then quizzes on Italy and other 'Old World' wine countries; then moving to the 'New World', starting with the USA and ending with quizzes on New Zealand and South Africa.

Then section 6 has a dozen light-hearted quizzes from celebrities to oddities.

Section 7 is about wine facts from history to grape varieties and wine tasting.

The final section 8 contains quizzes about types of wine and iconic wines of the world.

iii) Quick Signposting from Quizzes to Answers

The comprehensive Contents pages list the page numbers for each separate Quiz, and the corresponding Answer section, as well as inclusive page numbers for each of the 8 Quiz Sections.

The starting page number for each Answer Set is also shown in the Contents pages list. Some amplified answer sets run to 3 pages of facts.

Quick signposting, from Quiz questions to Answer pages, is shown by running the Answer page number down the middle of each outside page edge of every separate Quiz. This will quickly tell you the number of the matching Answer page per Quiz.

iv) Pictorial Signposting from Quizzes to Answers

As well as each Quiz displaying the corresponding Answer page number, every Quiz & Answer Set has at least one black and white matching image.

This is so you can quickly flick through to the Answers section until you see the matching black and white 'main' drawing and that will be the start of the correct set of Answers for your Quiz.

For example, each of the 5 Italian Quizzes (14 to 18) and corresponding Answer sections have a black and white drawing of a different corkscrew type. Just flip through the pages until you recognise the identical corkscrew and you are at the correct Answer set.

v) The Three Types of Quizzes

Most of the 100 quizzes are comprised of traditional multi-choice questions with a choice of three a) b) or c) as the correct answer. Some questions do not need the multi-choice format and just a single answer is needed.

The second type of quiz is matching two connected facts, like matching wine producers with their wine growing region or grape variety. There are 13 of these matching quizzes.

Finally there are 13 anagram quizzes to mystify and intrigue. They sometimes seem quite simple puzzles to solve but turn out to be intricate to pull apart and reassemble.

CONTENTS

SECTION 1 – TESTING YOUR GENERAL WINE KNOWLEDGE

This first section of five introductory quizzes begins with two quizzes on general wine questions to get you started.

Followed by two quizzes asking you to match up famous wines with their countries and wine areas.

Finally, a quiz of wine anagrams which could combine fun with frustration!

The 5 Quizzes are:

QUIZ 1 — GENERAL WINE QUESTIONS – PART 1

QUIZ 2 — GENERAL WINE QUESTIONS – PART 2

QUIZ 3 — MATCH THESE FAMOUS WINES OF THE NEW WORLD
         WITH THEIR COUNTRY/WINE AREA

QUIZ 4 — MATCH THESE FAMOUS WINES OF EUROPE AND THE MIDDLE EAST
         WITH THEIR COUNTRY/WINE AREA

QUIZ 5 — ANAGRAMS – GENERAL

QUIZ 1 – GENERAL WINE QUESTIONS – PART 1

1. Which country produces the wine Vega Sicilia?
   a) *Italy*
   b) *Spain*
   c) *Portugal*
2. What does ABV mean on a wine bottle?
3. Which grape has the tasting characteristics of cedarwood and/or blackcurrants?
   a) *Cabernet Sauvignon*
   b) *Merlot*
   c) *Pinot Noir*
4. True or false – the Sauvignon Blanc grape is used to make white Sancerre?
5. Australia's Barossa Valley is most famous for producing wine from which grape variety?
   a) *Shiraz*
   b) *Malbec*
   c) *Carmenère*
6. Which island is most well-known for growing the Bual and Sercial grapes?
   a) *Sardinia*
   b) *Madeira*
   c) *Sicily*
7. The Pinotage grape was created, and is mostly grown, in which country?
   a) *Australia*
   b) *Chile*
   c) *South Africa*
8. True or false – Prosecco used to be the name of the grape variety which produced the well-known sparkling wine of the same name?
9. Is the Alsace wine region part of France or Germany?
10. Can table wine produced in England be called British Wine?

ANSWERS PAGE 114

2

QUIZ 2 – GENERAL WINE QUESTIONS – PART 2

1. Grauburgunder, Pinot Gris, and Pinot Grigio are all the same grape variety. True or False?

2. Qvevris are widely used in the country of Georgia. What is a qvevri?
   a) *Fermentation/Storage Vessel*
   b) *Harvesting Machine*
   c) *Personalised Secateur*

3. Touriga Nacional and Tinta Roriz are two of the main grapes that can be used to make which type of wine?
   a) *Sherry*
   b) *Port*
   c) *Madeira*

4. Wachau, Kremstal, and Kamptal are important wine regions in which country?
   a) *Germany*
   b) *Austria*
   c) *Switzerland*

5. Part of the longest river in France is one of that country's main wine regions. What is the name of the river?

6. What is the name of the grape variety in Switzerland that is by far the most planted?
   a) *Müller-Thurgau*
   b) *Chasselas*
   c) *Arvine*

7. This famous valley in Cornwall has won multiple awards for its sparkling wine. What is the name of the valley?
   a) *Tamar Valley b) Fowey Valley c) Camel Valley*

8. What is the name of the well-known wine produced in the very north of Portugal, whose style is light-bodied, with relatively low alcohol, and a slight effervescence?

9. The famous red wine Penfolds Grange is produced in which country?
   a) *Australia*
   b) *Canada*
   c) *USA*

10. Côte-Rôtie and Condrieu are in the northern part of which French wine region?
    a) *Burgundy*
    b) *Rhône Valley*
    c) *Alsace*

ANSWERS PAGE 115

3

QUIZ 3 – MATCH THESE FAMOUS WINES OF THE NEW WORLD WITH THEIR COUNTRY/WINE AREA

1. Beringer

2. Brown Brothers

3. Burrowing Owl

4. Monte Xanic

5. Santa Rita

6. Zuccardi

7. Willamette Valley

8. Ata Rangi

9. Vergelegen

10. Etchart

a) *Canada/British Columbia*

b) *Chile/Maipo*

c) *New Zealand/Martinborough*

d) *Argentina/Mendoza*

e) *USA/California*

f) *South Africa/Stellenbosch*

g) *Argentina/Salta*

h) *Australia/Victoria*

i) *Mexico/Guadalupe Valley*

j) *USA/Oregon*

ANSWERS PAGE 117

QUIZ 4 – MATCH THESE FAMOUS WINES OF EUROPE AND THE MIDDLE EAST WITH THEIR COUNTRY/WINE AREA

1. Georges Duboeuf

2. Gaja

3. Dr. Loosen

4. Scala Dei

5. Bernhard Ott

6. Chateau Ksara

7. Carmel

8. Krasno

9. Grof Degenfeld

10. Hatzidakis

a) Austria/Wagram

b) Slovenia/Goriska Brda

c) Israel/Galilee

d) Hungary/Tokaj

e) France/Beaujolais

f) Greece/Santorini

g) Spain/Priorat

h) Italy/Piedmont

i) Germany/Mittelmosel

j) Lebanon/Bekaa Valley

ANSWERS PAGE 118

QUIZ 5 – ANAGRAMS – GENERAL

Well-Known Champagnes

1. ogler pro

2. mice err

3. spiced hiker pie

4. rain rut

5. rave loudly

Well-Known Grape Varieties

6. a handy corn

7. onion trip

8. line rigs

9. caning oval buns

10. be calm

ANSWERS PAGE 120

SECTION 2 – THE TOP THREE WINE PRODUCING COUNTRIES IN EUROPE

A total of eighteen quizzes covering questions on all aspects of wine in France (8), Italy (5), and Spain (5).

Questions on each country include wine production, grape varieties, producers, wine regions etc., and are followed by wine-matching quizzes and anagrams.

The 18 Quizzes are:

QUIZ 6 — WINES OF FRANCE – PART 1

QUIZ 7 — WINES OF FRANCE – PART 2

QUIZ 8 — WINES OF FRANCE – PART 3

QUIZ 9 — WINES OF FRANCE – PART 4

QUIZ 10 – WINES OF FRANCE – PART 5

QUIZ 11 – MATCH THESE TOP FRENCH CHATEAUX
        WITH THEIR WINE/VINEYARD AREAS

QUIZ 12 – MATCH THESE FRENCH WINES WITH THEIR WINE/VINEYARD AREAS

QUIZ 13 – ANAGRAMS – WINES OF FRANCE

QUIZ 14 – WINES OF ITALY – PART 1

QUIZ 15 – WINES OF ITALY – PART 2

QUIZ 16 – WINES OF ITALY – PART 3

QUIZ 17 – MATCH FAMOUS ITALIAN WINES WITH THEIR DOC AREAS

QUIZ 18 – ANAGRAMS – WINES OF ITALY

QUIZ 19 – WINES OF SPAIN – PART 1

QUIZ 20 – WINES OF SPAIN – PART 2

QUIZ 21 – WINES OF SPAIN – PART 3

QUIZ 22 – MATCH THESE SPANISH NAMES WITH THEIR CORRESPONDING
        REGIONS/GRAPES/TOWNS/WINE TERMS ETC

QUIZ 23 – ANAGRAMS – WINES OF SPAIN

QUIZ 6 – WINES OF FRANCE – PART 1

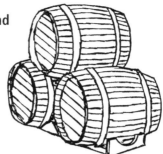

1. In which region would you find the wine Gigondas?
   a) *Burgundy*
   b) *Loire*
   c) *Rhône*

2. From which grape is Cahors principally made?
   a) *Merlot*
   b) *Cabernet Sauvignon*
   c) *Malbec*

3. Near which well-known river is Muscadet made?

4. Chambolle Musigny is from which wine region?

5. In the 1855 Bordeaux Classification which 'Growth' is Château Talbot?
   a) *3rd Growth*
   b) *4th Growth*
   c) *5th Growth*

6. Is Château Cheval Blanc produced in St-Emilion or Pomerol?

7. In which region is Vinsobres produced?
   a) *Southern Rhône*
   b) *Loire Valley*
   c) *Roussillon*

8. The southern Rhône region produces which well-known rosé?
   a) *Anjou*
   b) *Lirac*
   c) *Tavel*

9. Is the champagne house of Taittinger based in Reims or Epernay?

10. Of the ten Beaujolais villages, name the two beginning with the letter 'M'?

ANSWERS PAGE 121

QUIZ 7 – WINES OF FRANCE – PART 2

1. Of the five Bordeaux First Growths, one of them was not in the original 1855 Classification. Which one is it?

2. Name two of the other four First Growths?

3. Château-Chalon is a Vin Jaune style wine from which French region?
   a) *Provence*
   b) *Jura*
   c) *Chablis*

4. Can a Blanc de Noirs champagne be made from white grapes?

5. What is the leading red grape variety in the middle Loire Valley?
   a) *Cabernet Franc*
   b) *Cabernet Sauvignon*
   c) *Merlot*

6. What is the leading white grape variety in the middle Loire Valley?
   a) *Sauvignon Blanc*
   b) *Chenin Blanc*
   c) *Chardonnay*

7. What is the name of the building in which the annual charity wine auction is held in the Burgundian town of Beaune?

8. Hugel is a famous wine producer in which French wine region?
   a) *Burgundy*
   b) *Loire Valley*
   c) *Alsace*

9. Does the wine 'Mercurey' come from Mâconnais or the Côte Chalonnaise wine region?

10. The French town of Troyes is in the southernmost part of which famous wine region?
    a) *Champagne*
    b) *Côte d'Or*
    c) *Rhône Valley*

ANSWERS PAGE 123

CHABLIS
Appellation Contrôlée

75 cle

13% vol.

LOUIS JADOT
F 21200 - FRANCE

QUIZ 8 – WINES OF FRANCE – PART 3

1. What is the prime red grape variety in the Alsace region?
2. Which French wine region is situated east of Burgundy and is close to the Swiss border?
   a) Jura
   b) Alsace
   c) Chablis
3. Condrieu, in the northern Rhône, is famous for one particular white grape variety. What is it?
4. Is the famous Burgundy wine 'Clos de Vougeot' in the Côte de Beaune or Côte de Nuits?
5. What is the well-known Swiss grape variety that's also grown in very small quantities in Alsace?
   a) Grüner Veltliner
   b) Chasselas
   c) Savagnin
6. Which town beginning with the letter 'M', in the eastern Languedoc wine region, has both a university and an airport?
7. Can a Blanc de Blancs champagne be made from red grapes?
8. Which well-known Loire wine is made around the town of Nantes?
9. Which wine region runs along the eastern side of the Vosges Mountains?
   a) Burgundy
   b) Rhône Valley
   c) Alsace
10. What is the name of the wine region that is south of the Jura, and just north of Grenobles?
    a) Beaujolais
    b) Savoie
    c) Rhône

ANSWERS PAGE 124

QUIZ 9 – WINES OF FRANCE – PART 4

1. What are the names of the two well-known white wines, made from Sauvignon Blanc grapes, which are situated on either side of the river in the eastern Loire?

2. The acronym 'GSM' refers to three important grape varieties in the Rhône Valley. What are they?

3. In the Oscar-winning film, 'Sideways', Miles carries around with him a famous wine from St-Emilion which, in a depressed state of mind, he drinks in a burger restaurant. What is the wine?
   a) Château Cheval Blanc
   b) Château Ausone
   c) Château Angélus

4. Which champagne house created their Prestige Cuvée in honour of Sir Winston Churchill?
   a) Taittinger
   b) Ruinart
   c) Pol Roger

5. Weissburgunder is the German name for which grape variety?
   a) Pinot Gris
   b) Pinot Blanc
   c) Pinot Noir

6. What is the principle grape variety used in the Gascon wine of Madiran?
   a) Tannat
   b) Grenache
   c) Syrah

7. From which French wine region is the sweet Grand Cru wine 'Quarts de Chaume'?
   a) Burgundy
   b) Loire Valley
   c) Bordeaux

8. In which French wine region is the aptly-named town of Bouzy?

9. What is the romantic-sounding name of the northernmost Beaujolais Cru?

10. What is the name of the wine area that sits between the Dordogne and Garonne rivers, close to the town of Bordeaux?

ANSWERS PAGE 126

QUIZ 10 – WINES OF FRANCE – PART 5

1. Which French island produces an elegant red wine using the Sciaccarellu grape variety?

2. In which region can the town of Colmar be found?

3. Wines from the adjacent villages of Cornas and St-Péray are made in which wine region?
   a) Provence
   b) Alsace
   c) Rhône Valley

4. Pinot Noir is the prime grape variety in which famous French wine region?

5. From which white grape variety is the Loire wine Quincy made?
   a) Chenin Blanc
   b) Sauvignon Blanc
   c) Chardonnay

6. Which famous champagne house produces the iconic Dom Pérignon?

7. What was the name of the vine-destroying louse that devastated French vineyards from the late 1860's?

8. What are the two famous types of dessert wines produced in an area roughly 30 miles south east of the town of Bordeaux?

9. The Gewürztraminer grape variety is commonly grown in which French wine region?
   a) Loire
   b) Languedoc
   c) Alsace

10. Château de Beaucastel is a top producer in which area of the southern Rhône?
    a) Châteauneuf-du-Pape
    b) Gigondas
    c) Rasteau

ANSWERS PAGE 127

12

QUIZ 11 – MATCH THESE TOP FRENCH CHATEAUX WITH THEIR WINE/ VINEYARD AREAS

1. Château Latour

2. Château Mont-Redon

3. Château-Grillet

4. Château de Riquewihr

5. Château Coutet

6. Château de Meursault

7. Château Ausone

8. Château Cos d'Estournel

9. Château Thivin

10. Château Soucherie

a) Bordeaux/St-Emilion

b) Burgundy/Beaujolais

c) Alsace

d) Loire Valley/Anjou

e) Bordeaux/St-Estephe

f) Rhône/Condrieu

g) Burgundy/Côte de Beaune

h) Bordeaux/Barsac

i) Rhône/Châteauneuf-du-Pape

j) Bordeaux/Pauillac

ANSWERS PAGE 129

'Charles de Gaulle' Corkscrew

QUIZ 12 – MATCH THESE FRENCH WINES WITH THEIR WINE/ VINEYARD AREAS

1. Richebourg

2. Belle Epoque

3. St-Nicolas-de-Bourgueil

4. Le Pin

5. Domaines Schlumberger

6. Chénas

7. Chave Hermitage

8. Domaine de Chevalier

9. La Grande Dame

10. St-Chinian

a) Burgundy/Beaujolais

b) Bordeaux/Pomerol

c) Languedoc/Herault

d) Champagne/Perrier-Jouët, Epernay

e) Rhône/North

f) Burgundy/Côte de Nuits

g) Alsace

h) Champagne/Veuve Clicquot, Reims

i) Bordeaux/Pessac-Léognan

j) Middle Loire Valley

ANSWERS PAGE 130

QUIZ 13 – ANAGRAMS – WINES OF FRANCE

French Grape Varieties

1. a beacon ensuring tv

2. give iron

3. omen ills

4. elm rot

5. rude mover

French Wines

6. made cuts

7. scarab

8. erotic toe

9. glacial

10. barmen itch

ANSWERS PAGE 132

QUIZ 14 – WINES OF ITALY – PART 1

1. Brunello di Montalcino is made from which single grape variety?
2. Which of these Piedmontese wines is not made from the Nebbiolo grape?
    a) *Barolo*
    b) *Barbera*
    c) *Barbaresco*
3. Which town in Umbria is also the name of a well-known white wine?
4. What is the Italian equivalent grape variety to Californian Zinfandel?
    a) *Primitivo*
    b) *Sangiovese*
    c) *Trebbiano*
5. Where is *Primitivo* mainly grown in Italy?
    a) *Sicily*
    b) *Puglia*
    c) *Piedmont*
6. To which small town in Tuscany does the white grape Vernaccia append its name?
    a) *San Gimignano*
    b) *Siena*
    c) *Luca*
7. Is Prosecco produced in north, central, or south Italy?
8. Which white wine has the same name as a well-known Italian cheese?
9. The Nero d'Avola grape variety is widely grown on which Italian island?
10. What is the name of the high quality sparkling wine produced in Lombardy?

ANSWERS PAGE 133

'Screwpull' Corkscrew

QUIZ 15 – WINES OF ITALY – PART 2

1. Near to which Italian lake is Bardolino produced?
   a) Iseo
   b) Como
   c) Garda

2. The producer Antinori is particularly famous in which region of Italy?
   a) Tuscany
   b) Piedmont
   c) Umbria

3. Bisol is a top producer of which type of Italian sparkling wine?

4. Sometimes referred to as the Nebbiolo of the south, what is the name of the grape variety widely grown in Campania and Basilicata?
   a) Nero d'Avola
   b) Glera
   c) Aglianico

5. The top quality wines of Sassicaia, Masseto, and Ornellaia are produced in which tiny DOC region?
   a) Bolgheri
   b) Trentino
   c) Alto Adige

6. What is the Italian word for rosé wine?

7. What is the name of the fifth generation Piedmontese family who are particularly famous in Barbaresco?
   a) Gaja
   b) Giacosa
   c) Felluga

8. In which region of Italy is Soave produced?
   a) Lazio
   b) Campania
   c) Veneto

'Waiter's Friend' Corkscrew

9. What is the name of the top tier of Chianti Classico which came into effect in 2014?
   a) Reserva Superiore
   b) Gran Selezione
   c) Classico Gran Reserva

10. The slopes of which Sicilian volcano are planted with grapes, both red and white, that produce some excellent wines?

ANSWERS PAGE 135

QUIZ 16 – WINES OF ITALY – PART 3

1. In which region is Brunello di Montalcino produced?
   a) *Piedmont*
   b) *Tuscany*
   c) *Veneto*

2. Which of these grape varieties is Italian?
   a) *Glera*
   b) *Torrontés*
   c) *Tempranillo*

3. From which grape variety is Barbaresco made?

4. What is the name of the wine made in Conegliano Valdobbiadene?

'Butler's Thief' Corkscrew

5. In which region is the city of Turin?

6. Which wine region is the most northerly in Italy?
   a) *Piedmont*
   b) *Alto Adige*
   c) *Lombardy*

7. Which wine region is the most southerly in Italy?
   a) *Campania*
   b) *Calabria*
   c) *Basilicata*

8. Close to which major city is Frascati produced?

9. The red grape Montepulciano is best known when it's appended to which region?
   a) *Umbria*
   b) *Abruzzo*
   c) *Alto Adige*

10. Literally meaning 'Tears of Christ' what is the name of this wine, grown on the slopes of Mount Vesuvius?

QUIZ 17 – MATCH FAMOUS ITALIAN WINES WITH THEIR DOC AREAS

1. Barbera d'Alba

2. Brunello di Montalcino

3. Verdicchio dei Castelli di Jesi

4. Marsala

5. Lambrusco

6. Franciacorta

7. Est! Est!! Est!!!

8. Amarone della Valpolicella

9. Primitivo

10. Aglianico del Vulture

a) Emilia-Romagna

b) Lazio

c) Basilicata

d) Puglia

e) Piedmont

f) Veneto

g) Tuscany

h) Lombardy

i) Sicily

j) Marche

'T Bar' Corkscrew

ANSWERS PAGE 138

QUIZ 18 – ANAGRAMS – WINES OF ITALY

Italian Grape Varieties

1. gave noises

2. boob line

3. oregano arm

4. copier on

5. babe intro

Italian Wines

6. adorn boil

'Vintage Propeller' Corkscrew

7. african actor

8. carols bum

9. alas ram

10. eco crops

ANSWERS PAGE 140

QUIZ 19 – WINES OF SPAIN – PART 1

1. Around which town in southern Spain is Manzanilla produced?
   a) *Jerez de la Frontera* b) *Sanlúcar de Barrameda* c) *Cádiz*

2. What is the main red grape variety grown in the Bierzo region of northern Spain?
   a) *Mencía*
   b) *Garnacha*
   c) *Tempranillo*

3. Campo Viejo is one of the biggest brand names in which Spanish wine region?

4. The Spanish sparkling wine, Cava, is mainly produced in which region?
   a) *Penedès*
   b) *Priorat*
   c) *Navarra*

5. What is the Spanish name for a farm or wine estate?
   a) *Casa Farma*
   b) *Vinoteca*
   c) *Finca*

6. On what type of Spanish wine would you find 'flor' during the fermentation process?

7. In which region is Pingus produced?
   a) *Toro*
   b) *Ribera del Duero*
   c) *Rueda*

8. Formerly known as Rioja Baja, what is this sub-region called now?
   a) *Rioja Oriental*
   b) *Rioja Este*
   c) *Rioja Levante*

9. What is the Spanish word for rosé wine?

10. What are the large clay pots, used for winemaking, called in Spain?
    a) *Tinajas*
    b) *Barriles*
    c) *Frascos*

ANSWERS PAGE 141

21

QUIZ 20 – WINES OF SPAIN – PART 2

1. What is the Spanish word for the grape harvest?

2. In which wine region is Valdepeñas produced?
    a) *Rioja*
    b) *La Mancha*
    c) *Extremadura*

3. The small wine region of Toro is in north-west, central, or south-east Spain?

4. Which famous architect designed the Marqués de Riscal luxury hotel in Rioja?
    a) *Frank Gehry*
    b) *Renzo Piano*
    c) *Richard Rogers*

5. What does the word 'Cosecha' mean in relation to Spanish wine?

6. What is a winery or winery cellar called in Spain?

7. If a Spanish wine is 'dulce' is it sweet or dry?

8. Rías Baixas, in Galicia, is particularly famous for which Spanish white wine?
    a) *Albariño*
    b) *Palomino Fino*
    c) *Airén*

9. Which white wine is the Rueda region particularly well-known for producing?
    a) *Godello*
    b) *Viura*
    c) *Verdejo*

10. The character of Montilla wine is similar to what other type of Spanish wine?

ANSWERS PAGE 143

QUIZ 21 – WINES OF SPAIN – PART 3

1. What is the name of the principal grape variety used to make Fino sherry?
2. Empordà is a Spanish wine region. True or False?
3. Which Spanish town, close to the wine region of Priorat, sounds like a type of herb?
4. What is the Garnacha grape called in France?
5. What is the name of the wine region that neighbours Rioja just across the River Ebro?
   a) Navarra
   b) Priorat
   c) Rueda
6. The River Duero, in northern Spain, changes its name to what, when it enters Portugal?
7. What is the sweetest type of sherry called, named after the grape from which it is made?
   a) Palo Cortado
   b) Pedro Ximénez
   c) Oloroso
8. There are three main grape varieties that produce Cava. Macabeo and Xarel-lo are two, what is the other one?
   a) Parellada
   b) Trebbiano
   c) Viura
9. What is the most important grape used to produce white Rioja?
   a) Trebbiano
   b) Viura
   c) Verdejo
10. Sherry butts are popularly used to mature what type of alcoholic spirit?
    a) Brandy
    b) Rum
    c) Scotch Whisky

ANSWERS PAGE 144

QUIZ 22 – MATCH THESE SPANISH NAMES WITH THEIR CORRESPONDING REGIONS/GRAPES/TOWNS/WINE TERMS ETC

1. Vega Sicilia

2. Albariño

3. Jerez

4. Pedro Ximénez

5. Bodega

6. Dulce

7. Toro

8. Garnacha

9. Logroño

10. Ebro

a) *Rueda*

b) *Duero*

c) *Tempranillo*

d) *Seco*

e) *Haro*

f) *Manzanilla*

g) *Pingus*

h) *Sanlúcar de Barrameda*

i) *Finca*

j) *Verdejo*

ANSWERS PAGE 146

QUIZ 23 – ANAGRAMS – WINES OF SPAIN

Spanish Grape Varieties

1. old ogle

2. a blob

3. ghana car

4. main pool

5. premixed zone

Spanish Wine Regions

6. canal ham

7. bi zero

8. aorta jail

9. angora rat

10. mad rope

ANSWERS PAGE 147

SECTION 3 – OTHER EUROPEAN WINE COUNTRIES AND ASIA

Here are sixteen quizzes covering other important European wine-producing countries outside of the top three, starting with Germany, the fourth largest wine producer.

Following that are Portugal, England and countries in Central and Eastern Europe. In addition, there are two wine-matching quizzes on Germany and European countries generally, plus three anagram quizzes covering German, Portuguese, and English wines.

The final two quizzes in this section include questions on countries in the Middle East, and then Asia and the Soviet Bloc Countries.

Again, questions on each country include wine production, grape varieties, producers, and wine regions.

The 16 Quizzes are:

QUIZ 24 – WINES OF GERMANY – PART 1

QUIZ 25 – WINES OF GERMANY – PART 2

QUIZ 26 – WINES OF GERMANY – PART 3

QUIZ 27 – MATCH THESE GERMAN NAMES WITH THEIR CORRESPONDING VINEYARDS/GRAPES/PRODUCERS/REGIONS ETC

QUIZ 28 – ANAGRAMS – WINES OF GERMANY

QUIZ 29 – WINES OF PORTUGAL

QUIZ 30 – ANAGRAMS – WINES OF PORTUGAL

QUIZ 31 – WINES OF ENGLAND

QUIZ 32 – ANAGRAMS – WINES OF ENGLAND

QUIZ 33 – WINES OF AUSTRIA AND SWITZERLAND

QUIZ 34 – WINES OF HUNGARY AND ROMANIA

QUIZ 35 – WINES OF BULGARIA, CROATIA, AND SLOVENIA

QUIZ 36 – WINES OF GREECE AND CYPRUS

QUIZ 37 – MATCH WINES OF EUROPEAN COUNTRIES

QUIZ 38 – WINES OF ISRAEL, LEBANON, EGYPT, AND TURKEY

QUIZ 39 – WINES OF ASIA, AND THE SOVIET BLOC COUNTRIES

QUIZ 24 – WINES OF GERMANY – PART 1

1. What is German sparkling wine called?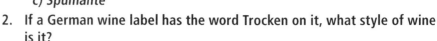
    a) Mousseux
    b) Sekt
    c) Spumante

2. If a German wine label has the word Trocken on it, what style of wine is it?
    a) Dry
    b) Semi-sweet
    c) Sweet

3. What is the name of one of Germany's main red wine producing regions, it has just three letters in its name?
    a) Ahr
    b) Hof
    c) Ulm

4. The Mosel is a major tributary of the Rhine, but what is another important Rhine tributary beginning with the letter 'N' that is also a well-known German wine region?

5. Which region often bottles its wines in the flat belly-shaped bottle called the Bocksbeutel?
    a) Baden
    b) Franken
    c) Pfalz

6. What is the name of the famous wine producer who has a medical title and a name that's synonymous with the word 'slacken' in English?

7. The English term 'Hock' is a name derived from which German town?

8. What is the name of the German term for a higher quality slightly sweeter wine, that sounds like an alternative word for a cupboard?

9. What style of quality German wine is indicated by the letters BA?

10. What is the name of the well-known wine producing town on the River Mosel that sounds like a combination of vegetables and an after-dinner drink?

QUIZ 25 – WINES OF GERMANY – PART 2

1. Finish the name of this famous vineyard, named after a sundial painted on an outcrop of slate – Wehlener–?

2. What is the next step up in quality and sweetness after Kabinett – Auslese or Spätlese?

3. What is the German word meaning castle or mansion that prefixes the name of many vineyards?

4. Two famous wine producing regions are around tributaries of the Mosel. One is Ruwer, what is the name of the other one?
   a) Pfalz
   b) Baden
   c) Saar

5. What is the Pinot Noir grape variety called in Germany?

6. The term 'Steinwein' used to loosely cover all wine from this region in southern Germany, nudging into Bavaria. What is the name of the wine region?
   a) Franken
   b) Baden
   c) Württemberg

7. Two well-known German wine regions start with 'Rhein', one is Rheingau, what is the name of the other one?

8. What is the name of the grape that is widely grown around the world, and is called Grauburgunder in Germany?

9. The Mosel river and wine region joins the Rhine at which town?
   a) Koblenz
   b) Frankfurt
   c) Stuttgart

10. A ferry crosses the Rhine from Rudesheim to Bingen at the mouth of the Nahe river. In which well-known wine region is Rudesheim?
    a) Pfalz
    b) Baden
    c) Rheingau

ANSWERS PAGE 150

QUIZ 26 – WINES OF GERMANY – PART 3

1. Which grape variety is seen as
   the face of Germany?
2. What is the name of the major city, whose
   name is a repetition of its eponymous wine region?
3. The wine region of Ahr, lies very close to which
   leading German city?
   a) Stuttgart
   b) Frankfurt
   c) Bonn
4. What is the name of the river that runs through the town of Würzburg
   in Franken?
   a) Main
   b) Rhine
   c) Kocher
5. Which German wine region is seen as the spiritual home of Riesling?
   a) Rheingau b) Mosel c) Rheinhessen
6. In which year was founded the famous (or infamous) Blue Nun?
   a) 1923
   b) 1933
   c) 1953
7. Until the late 1990s, what style of wine was Blue Nun classified as?
8. Which wine region, other than Baden, sits on the Swiss border?
   a) Pfalz
   b) Württemberg
   c) Franken
9. The River Mosel, from Trier to Koblenz, twists and turns for about 145
   miles. But approximately how long is it in a straight line?
   a) 40 miles
   b) 60 miles
   c) 80 miles
10. What is the name of the river, a tributary of the Rhine, whose
    name begins with a part of the human body, and runs through two
    wine regions?

ANSWERS PAGE 151

QUIZ 27 – MATCH THESE GERMAN NAMES WITH THEIR CORRESPONDING VINEYARDS/GRAPES/PRODUCERS/REGIONS ETC

1. Bernkastel

2. Spätlese

3. Riesling

4. Wehlen

5. Urzig

6. Rheinhessen

7. Paul Weltner

8. Schloss Johannisberg

9. Hock

10. Saar

a) Schloss Vollrads

b) Bocksbeutel

c) JJ Prum

d) Ahr

e) Piesport

f) Ruwer

g) Dornfelder

h) Würzgarten

i) Kabinett

j) Sonnenuhr

ANSWERS PAGE 153

QUIZ 28 – ANAGRAMS – WINES OF GERMANY

German Grape Varieties

1. dustpan burger

2. lethal guru rum

3. urbane drug rug

4. fondled err

5. subdue wringers

German Wine Towns

6. bleak terns

7. car hag

8. arab rugs

9. hide serum

10. entire sin

ANSWERS PAGE 155

QUIZ 29 – WINES OF PORTUGAL

1. Which is the largest wine region in Portugal by vineyard areas planted?
   a) Alentejo
   b) Douro
   c) Minho

2. Cliff Richard's winery making the Vida Nova & Vida Onda ranges of wines is situated in which wine area?
   a) Algarve
   b) Douro
   c) Tejo

3. What does LBV stand for on a bottle of Port?

4. What grape makes the vast majority of modern inexpensive volume Madeira wine?
   a) Malvasia
   b) Tinta Negra Mole
   c) Verdelho

5. Does the Douro wine region nowadays still make more Port in volume terms, or more still unfortified red table wine?
   a) More Port
   b) More red table wine
   c) About 50%/50%

ANSWERS PAGE 156

6. Which of these wine regions is a UNESCO World Heritage Site?
   a) Azores b) Bairrada c) Setúbal

7. Which of these famous Portuguese wine companies does not make Port?
   a) Blandy's
   b) Fonseca
   c) Ramos Pinto

8. What type of wine is the wine region Setúbal famous for producing?
   a) Dry white wines
   b) Sweet dessert wines
   c) Tannic red wines

9. The Colares DOC vineyards, north-west of Lisbon, produce light tannic red wine which is grown in what type of soil?
   a) Clay b) Quartz & Slate c) Sand

10 Which of these is the sweetest style of Madeira fortified wines?
   a) Bual
   b) Malmsey
   c) Sercial

QUIZ 30 – ANAGRAMS – WINES OF PORTUGAL

Portuguese Wine Regions

1. ale tubs

2. arab raid

3. ado

4. a doll voyeur

5. alone jet

Port Wine Houses

6. last roy

7. on faces

8. pine root

9. ham rags

10. nans mead

ANSWERS PAGE 158

34

QUIZ 31 – WINES OF ENGLAND

1. Around what proportion of England's wine production is sparkling wines?
   a) 30% b) 50% c) 70%

2. Which is the famous Cornish vineyard near Bodmin Moor and Padstow which has been producing award-winning wines since 1989?
   a) Camel Valley b) Knightor Winery c) Polmassick Vineyard

3. Which is the largest producer of wine by volume in England?
   a) Chapel Down in Kent
   b) Denbies in Surrey
   c) Nyetimber in Sussex

4. Approximately how many commercial vineyards are there in England?
   a) 250 b) 450 c) 650

5. Which is the most planted grape variety in England?
   a) Chardonnay
   b) Bacchus
   c) Pinot Noir

6. About what proportion of English wine is white, including sparkling wines?
   a) 55% to 60%
   b) 65% to 70%
   c) 75% to 80%

7. Which English winery has gained the first ever Royal Warrant for English sparkling wine?
   a) Camel Valley
   b) Nyetimber
   c) Ridgeview

8. 2018, with its hot and dry weather, became a record year for English wine production. About how much wine was produced?
   a) 9 million bottles
   b) 13 million bottles
   c) 17 million bottles

9. Which of these counties in England has the most wineries and vineyards in commercial production?
   a) Devon
   b) Kent
   c) Sussex

10. Which Grand Marque Champagne House was the first to plant a vineyard in Kent?
    a) Veuve Clicquot b) Moët & Chandon c) Taittinger

ANSWERS PAGE 160

35

QUIZ 32 – ANAGRAMS – WINES OF ENGLAND

English Wine Producers

1. bravely lied

2. sit now

3. steel bayonet

4. reworking art pads

5. calve lamely

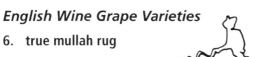

English Wine Grape Varieties

6. true mullah rug

7. to rage

8. hardy canon

9. insincere three

10. in portion

ANSWERS PAGE 162

QUIZ 33 – WINES OF AUSTRIA AND SWITZERLAND

1. In which year did the Austrian 'Antifreeze' wine scandal occur?
    a) 1975
    b) 1985
    c) 1995

2. How many DAC Regions (Districtus Austriae Controllatus) are there in Austria, now the strictest Appellation Control Laws and Rules in Europe?
    a) 10 b) 14 c) 20

3. Approximately what percentage of Swiss wines are exported?
    a) 1%–2% b) 10%–15% c) 25%–30%

4. Which type of wine does both Austria and Switzerland make most of in volume terms?
    a) Red
    b) Sparkling
    c) White

5. What is Switzerland's most planted grape variety?
    a) Chasselas b) Müller-Thurgau c) Riesling Silvaner

6. What is Austria's most planted grape variety?
    a) Grüner Veltliner
    b) Riesling
    c) Traminer

ANSWERS PAGE 164

7. What is Switzerland's largest wine canton (wine region)?
    a) Ticino
    b) Valais
    c) Vaud

8. Which country produces the most wine in volume and value?
    a) Austria
    b) About the same volume and value
    c) Switzerland

9. Austria has a wine estate that is almost 2,000 years old and still producing high quality wines. What is the estate called?
    a) Klosterneuburg Monastery
    b) Nikolaihof Winery
    c) Domane Wachau

10 Austria produces a serious amount of 3 separate quality tiers of sparkling wines from Kamptal and Kremstal. What are these called?
    a) Espumoso
    b) Mousseux
    c) Sekt

QUIZ 34 – WINES OF HUNGARY AND ROMANIA

ANSWERS PAGE 166

1. Which of these countries is the largest volume wine producer in Central & Eastern Europe?
    a) *Austria*
    b) *Hungary*
    c) *Romania*

2. The Royal Tokaji Wine Company, part-owned by the well-known wine writer, Hugh Johnson, is based in which town in Hungary?
    a) *Mad* b) *Tarcal* c) *Tokaj*

3. What was the 1960's and 20th century name for the dark, heavy, strong, red wine from Eger, north-east Hungary?
    a) *Bullamakanka*
    b) *Bull's Blood*
    c) *Strong Arm*

4. Transylvania is a very large mainly white wine region in Romania. What is the dominant grape variety?
    a) *Chardonnay* b) *Feteasca Regala* c) *Sauvignon Blanc*

5. What is the largest wine region in Hungary called; it is famed for white wines grown on pre-phylloxera sandy soils?
    a) *Duna* b) *Kunsag* 3) *Sopron*

6. Which country imports the highest volume of wine from Romania?
    a) *Germany*
    b) *The Netherlands*
    c) *The UK*

7. In Romania what percentage of all wines produced are homemade productions, from family allotments and back gardens used for home consumption and traded with friends?
    a) *25% to 35%* b) *45% to 55%* c) *65% to 75%*

8. Which grape variety is used to make the great and historic Tokaji sweet dessert wines from 3 puttonyos up to Essencia, the sweetest and the most expensive?
    a) *Furmint* b) *Irsai Oliver* c) *Kadarka*

9. Which DOC wine area/region in Romania is the most compact in area, and is best known for its premium red 'Bordeaux like wines' with top Cabernet Sauvignon and Merlot?
    a) *DOC Dealu Mare* b) *DOC Oltina* c) *DOC Tirnave*

10. When did Tokaji in Hungary introduce the first ever classification of the quality of vineyards and wines?
    a) *1600–1630* b) *1700–1730* c) *1800–1830*

QUIZ 35 – WINES OF BULGARIA, CROATIA, AND SLOVENIA

1. In Bulgaria which is the most prolific planted indigenous red grape variety?
   a) Mavrud b) Pamid c) Rubin

2. In Bulgaria, what proportion of wines produced are now made from international grape varieties?
   a) 35% b) 55% c) 75%

3. In which country is the only underwater winery in Europe, where you can dive down 20 metres to select your own bottle from the underwater cellar. The wine is Edivo Vina?
   a) Bulgaria
   b) Croatia
   c) Slovenia

4. Who is the famous 'Croatian' Napa Valley top winemaker, who also owns two of the best wine estates in Croatia?
   a) Miljenko Grgic
   b) Marjan Simcic
   c) Sasa Spiranec

ANSWERS PAGE 168

5. Which European grape variety was originally said to have originated from Austria, but is now attributed to Slovenia?
   a) Blaufränkisch
   b) Grüner Veltliner
   c) St-Laurent

6. Which famous red wine grape is now said to have been born as, or related to, the Plavac Mali grape in Croatia?
   a) Carmenère b) Shiraz c) Zinfandel

7. Which country has more wineries, vineyards and tractors per head of population?
   a) Bulgaria b) Croatia c) Slovenia

8. Which country produces the largest percentage of white wine versus red wine?
   a) Bulgaria b) Croatia c) Slovenia

9. Which of these is not a top 5 Bulgarian wine estate in terms of expensive premium wines?
   a) Bessa Valley b) Borovista c) Klet Brda

10. Slovenia has the oldest wine producing vine in the world, in the Maribor Region. How old is this vine?
    a) 200 years b) 300 years c) 400 years

QUIZ 36 – WINES OF GREECE AND CYPRUS

1. Which is the largest wine producing zone in Greece?
   a) Macedonia b) Peloponnese c) Thessaly

2. With Greece's fast growing wine production over
   the past 10 years, and now with over 1,300 commercial
   wineries, about how many bottles are produced per year?
   a) 150 to 200 million b) 230 to 280 million c) 300 to 350 million

3. Assyrtiko, for dry or sweet white wines, is the iconic white grape
   variety of Greece. It produces the best balanced, complex and most
   expensive white wines in Greece. Which island did it originate from?
   a) Crete b) Rhodes c) Santorini

4. Naoussa region in northern Greece makes top quality red wines which
   are said to closely resemble which classic red wine in terms of
   balance, taste and paleness of colour?
   a) Barolo b) Burgundy c) Chianti

5. In Cyprus, the famous dessert wine Commandaria, made from
   sun-dried Mavro and Xynisteri grapes, has been constantly produced
   there for about how long?
   a) 280 years b) 1,280 years c) 2,800 years

6. Which island has never been invaded by Phylloxera, the grape vine
   killing louse which destroyed much of Europe's vineyards in the 1870s?
   a) Crete b) Cyprus c) Rhodes

7. Which of these islands in Greece makes famous very sweet dessert
   wines and Vino Santo from the Muscat grape?
   a) Samos b) Tinos c) Zante

8. Retsina white and rosé wines are made by adding what
   ingredient to the grape juice must during fermentation?
   a) Mint b) Pine Resin c) Wild Yeast

9. Cyprus Sherry used to be the island's largest exported wine from 1960
   to 1980, and was 60% of all the wine volume produced in Cyprus.
   What was the biggest brand of Cyprus Sherry called?
   a) Croft b) Emva c) Lustau

10. What proportion of wine produced in Greece
    is white wine from white grapes?
    a) 25% to 35%
    b) 40% to 50%
    c) 55% to 65%

QUIZ 37 – MATCH WINES OF EUROPEAN COUNTRIES

Top Wine Estates

1. Michel Boven

2. Davino Winery

3. Domaine Lyrarakis

4. Szepsy Estate

5. Winegut Emmerich Knoll

Their European Country

a) Romania

b) Greece

c) Switzerland

d) Austria

e) Hungary

Country Origin of Grape

6. Greece

7. Hungary

8. Croatia

9. Austria

10. Switzerland

White Grape Varieties

f) Grüner Veltliner

g) Chasselas

h) Furmint

i) Assyrtiko

j) Graševina

ANSWERS PAGE 173

41

QUIZ 38 – WINES OF ISRAEL, LEBANON, EGYPT, AND TURKEY

1. Chateau Belle-Vue, Chateau Ksara and Chateau Musar are all wine estates in which country?
   a) Israel
   b) Lebanon
   c) Turkey

2. Turkey, with 99% of its population being Muslim and wine forbidden to be sold to Turkish citizens within the country, produces wine for export only (or for holidaymakers in Turkish hotels). Where is Turkey in the league of world wine production by value and volume?
   a) 6th largest b) 12th largest c) 22nd largest

3. Which winery in Lebanon, founded in 1857 by the Jesuits Monastery, was the birthplace of modern Lebanese wines and is now the biggest wine producer by volume?
   a) Chateau Belle-Vue b) Chateau Ksara c) Chateau Sanctus

4. What is the average annual vintage production of wine from the vineyards of Israel?
   a) 10 to 15 million bottles
   b) 20 to 30 million bottles
   c) 40 to 50 million bottles

5. About how many wineries are commercially producing wine in Egypt?
   a) 3 to 5 wineries b) 10 to 15 wineries c) 20 to 30 wineries

6. Lebanon has over 50 wineries and produces quality wine mainly for export. On average what is the annual volume production in bottles?
   a) 4 million to 7 million b) 8 million to 14 million
   c) 15 million to 20 million

7. Which of Turkey's 34 or so commercially produced grape varieties is called the Pinot Noir of Turkey, with Burgundian characteristics?
   a) Kalecik Karasi b) Narince c) Okuzgozu

8. Which country or region is by far the largest importer of Israeli wine?
   a) The European Union b) Russia c) USA

HERMON
MOUNT HERMON RED

9. What proportion of grapes grown in Turkey is made into wine?
   a) 2% to 6% b) 10% to 15% c) 20% to 30%

10. Which of these does not produce a top quality and widely exported Israeli Cabernet Sauvignon wine?
    a) Chateau Isaac
    b) Golan Heights Winery
    c) Hevron Heights Winery

QUIZ 39 – WINES OF ASIA AND THE SOVIET BLOC COUNTRIES

1. Which famous Bordeaux First Growth wine Château opened the first European owned winery in China?
   a) *Château Cheval Blanc*
   b) *Château Lafite Rothschild*
   c) *Château Latour*

2. Omar Khayyam wine from Chateau Indage in India, was the first Indian wine to be imported into the UK in 1989. What type of wine is it?
   a) *Red still b) Sparkling white blend c) White still*

3. Near to which famous city in Japan are the ancient historic vineyards of Yamanushi?
   a) *Osaka b) Hiroshima c) Tokyo*

4. What is the most prolific planted red wine grape (in hectares) in Bulgaria?
   a) *Cabernet Sauvignon b) Merlot c) Mavrud*

5. Does Japan make more red, sparkling or white wines in volume terms?
   a) *Red b) Sparkling c) White*

6. Georgian wines have for millennia been fermented and aged in Qvevri, what are they?
   a) *Huge oak barrels*
   b) *Concrete vats*
   c) *Clay amphorae*

7. In Bulgaria, wine estates barely existed 30 years ago; after the collapse of the Soviet Union most wineries were abandoned and closed, along with the large cooperatives. Roughly how many commercial wine estates are there now in Bulgaria?
   a) *100 to 150 b) 200 to 250 c) 300 to 350*

8. Which Englishman (also the owner of Bride Valley Wines of Dorset) partnered up with Piero Masi to import top quality Indian wine into the UK and Europe?
   a) *Hugh Johnson b) Oz Clarke c) Steven Spurrier*

9. Most Russian wine is now produced between the coastal plain of the Black Sea and the Caspian Sea. The quality is improving, and Russians nowadays drink about how many bottles of wine per year?
   a) *10 to 20 bottles b) 40 to 60 bottles c) 70 to 100 bottles.*

10. In China, what is the most popular type of wine consumed by volume share?
    a) *Red wine b) Sparkling wine c) White wine*

ANSWERS PAGE 179

43

SECTION 4 – NORTH AND SOUTH AMERICA

For this section there are fifteen quizzes, starting with USA wines, including the important regions of California, Oregon, and Washington State, followed by a quiz on Canadian wine.

Then we move on to South America, where the quizzes focus mainly on Chile and Argentina, but also include quizzes on other South American wine producing countries.

There are two wine-matching quizzes, and two anagram quizzes, on USA and Chilean wines, as well as a quiz of anagrams on South American wines.

The 15 Quizzes are:

QUIZ 40 – WINES OF CALIFORNIA – PART 1

QUIZ 41 – WINES OF CALIFORNIA – PART 2

QUIZ 42 – WINES OF OREGON AND WASHINGTON STATE

QUIZ 43 – WINES OF OTHER USA WINE AREAS

QUIZ 44 – MATCH FAMOUS CALIFORNIA AND USA WINES

QUIZ 45 – ANAGRAMS – WINES OF USA

QUIZ 46 – WINES OF CANADA

QUIZ 47 – WINES OF CHILE – PART 1

QUIZ 48 – WINES OF CHILE – PART 2

QUIZ 49 – MATCH FAMOUS CHILEAN WINES

QUIZ 50 – ANAGRAMS – WINES OF CHILE

QUIZ 51 – WINES OF ARGENTINA – PART 1

QUIZ 52 – WINES OF ARGENTINA – PART 2

QUIZ 53 – WINES OF SOUTH AMERICA, EXCLUDING CHILE AND ARGENTINA

QUIZ 54 – ANAGRAMS – WINES OF SOUTH AMERICA

QUIZ 40 – WINES OF CALIFORNIA – PART 1

ANSWERS PAGE 181

1. Which is the most northern wine region in California?
    a) *Lake County*
    b) *Mendocino*
    c) *Napa Valley*

2. Which country imports the highest value and volume of Californian wine?
    a) *Canada*
    b) *Germany*
    c) *Hong Kong*

3. What is the name of the film about two friends having adventures on a wine tasting trip around Santa Barbara County?
    a) *Sideways*
    b) *Uncorked*
    c) *Wine Country*

4. What is the most expensive Californian wine, sometimes selling for over $6,000 a bottle?
    a) *Opus One*
    b) *Sine Qua Non*
    c) *Screaming Eagle*

5. Which Californian grape variety is said to be from the same origin as the Primitivo grape from Puglia in southern Italy?

6. Which area produces the highest volume of wine in California (over 70%)?
    a) *Central Valley* b) *Napa Valley* c) *Sonoma*

7. How many active commercial wineries are there in California?
    a) *2,700* b) *3,800* c) *4,900*

8. Which is the most planted white wine grape in California?
    a) *Chardonnay* b) *Sauvignon Blanc* c) *Viognier*

9. Which is the most planted red wine grape in California?
    a) *Cabernet Sauvignon*
    b) *Merlot*
    c) *Pinot Noir*

10. Which is the oldest commercial winery still operating in California?
    a) *Beringer*
    b) *Buena Vista*
    c) *Inglenook*

2016

CALDER WINE COMPANY
PETITE SIRAH
NAPA VALLEY

QUIZ 41 – WINES OF CALIFORNIA – PART 2

1. Which famous Champagne House does NOT produce a Californian sparkling wine?
   a) Krug
   b) Mumm
   c) Louis Roederer

2. Which is the most widely planted wine grape in California?
   a) Cabernet Sauvignon
   b) Chardonnay
   c) Zinfandel

OPUS ONE

3. The area of California with planted vineyards is what percentage of France's vineyards?
   a) 10% b) 20% c) 30%

4. The total area of California is what percentage of the total area of France, the largest country of the 27 in the European Union?
   a) 35% b) 55% c) 75%

5. Which California winery is closest to Hollywood – less than 10 miles away?
   a) San Antonio Winery b) Aqua Dulce c) Seal Beach Winery

6. What is the most planted red grape in the Napa Valley?
   a) Cabernet Sauvignon b) Merlot c) Pinot Noir

7. What is the name of the 2019 film about six women friends travelling to Napa Valley to celebrate a 50th birthday?
   a) A Good Year b) A Walk in the Clouds c) Wine Country

8. Which Californian sparkling wine is the favourite at the White House for State and Presidential Dinners? (used for over 86 State dinners since President Nixon)
   a) Domaine Carneros
   b) Fetzer
   c) Schramsberg

9. What percentage of wine in 2019, from the total of 20 USA States producing commercial wines, comes from California?
   a) 70% b) 80% c) 90%

10 The film Bottle Shock, made in 2008, is about the Judgement of Paris in 1976 when Californian wines beat the top French Bordeaux and Burgundy wines in a blind tasting. Who organised the tasting?
   a) Michael Broadbent
   b) Hugh Johnson
   c) Steven Spurrier

ANSWERS PAGE 183

QUIZ 42 – WINES OF OREGON AND WASHINGTON STATE

1. Which US state is the second largest producer of wine, after California?
    a) *New York*
    b) *Oregon*
    c) *Washington*
2. What is the top wine grape in volume and value that is produced in Oregon?
    a) *Chardonnay*
    b) *Pinot Gris*
    c) *Pinot Noir*
3. What proportion of all USA wine (by volume) is produced in the 3 West Coast States?
    a) *90%* b) *80%* c) *70%*
4. In which state did the top quality Burgundy House Joseph Drouhin establish Domaine Drouhin in 1987?
    a) *Oregon* b) *Washington* c) *In both states*
5. Which of these estates is a top winery in Washington State known for exclusively producing methode champenoise sparkling wines?
    a) *Columbia Winery* b) *The Eyrie Vineyards* c) *Treveri Cellars*
6. Which of these AVA wine areas is not in Washington State?
    a) *Rogue Valley*
    b) *Walla Walla*
    c) *Yakima Valley*
7. Which is the most prolific white grape variety grown in Oregon State, and known as its signature white?
    a) *Chardonnay* b) *Pinot Gris* c) *Riesling*
8. Which of these areas is an AVA wine area in Oregon State?
    a) *Columbia Valley*
    b) *Finger Lakes*
    c) *Willamette Valley*
9. Which of these vineyards became the first ever biodynamic Oregon winery back in 1978?
    a) *Cooper Mountain Vineyards*
    b) *Montinore Estate*
    c) *Wilridge Winery*
10. Which is the most planted grape in Washington State?
    a) *Chardonnay* b) *Merlot* c) *Riesling*

ANSWERS PAGE 184

QUIZ 43 – WINES OF OTHER USA WINE AREAS

1. How many US states have a commercial wine industry of more than 10 wineries currently operating and producing wine (as at 2020)?
   a) 10–19 b) 20–29 c) 30–51

2. What is the most planted grape variety in New York State?
   a) Aurore b) Chardonnay c) Concord

3. The oldest winery in the USA that is still producing wine today was started in 1839 by Christian monks and is called the Brotherhood Winery. Which state is it in?
   a) New York b) Texas c) Virginia

4. Approximately how many commercial wineries does Pennsylvania have, as at 2020?
   a) 50 to 99 b) 100 to 199 c) 200 to 300

5. Which of these wineries is a well-known top quality Texas estate?
   a) Flat Creek b) Ridge Vineyards c) Standing Stone Vineyard

6. New York State, the third largest wine producing state, has four major AVA wine growing regions. Which of the following is the largest wine region in terms of value and volume?
   a) Finger Lakes b) Hudson River c) Lake Erie

7. Which of these 'M' states has the highest number of commercial wineries operating?
   a) Maryland b) Michigan c) Missouri

8. Continental Divide vineyard in Colorado State has the honour of being what, in the USA?
   a) The highest vineyard
   b) The lowest vineyard
   c) The largest biodynamic vineyard

9. Which wine is the favourite and most drunk wine brand in America by a long way?
   a) Barefoot Wines
   b) Sutter Home
   c) Woodbridge Wines

PARADISE SPRINGS
WINERY

10. In which US state is Donald Trump's winery situated?
    a) New York b) New Jersey c) Virginia

ANSWERS PAGE 186

QUIZ 44 – MATCH FAMOUS CALIFORNIA AND USA WINES

Famous Wines

1. Stag's Leap – Cabernet Sauvignon
2. Gallo Thunderbird – Fortified Blend
3. Domaine Drouhin – Pinot Noir
4. Chateau Ste Michelle – Riesling
5. Firestone – Merlot

Regions

a) *Willamette Valley, Oregon*

b) *Santa Barbara, California*

c) *Central Valley, California*

d) *Napa Valley, California*

e) *Columbia Valley,
   Washington State*

Famous Wines

6. Opus One
7. Clos du Bois
8. Cakebread Cellars
9. Domaine Chandon
10. Ravenswood

Grape Varieties

f) *Pinot Noir*

g) *Sparkling Blend*

h) *Zinfandel*

i) *Chardonnay*

j) *Cabernet Sauvignon*

ANSWERS PAGE 188

QUIZ 45 – ANAGRAMS – WINES OF USA

Prime Wine-Producing States

1. african oil

2. hating snow

3. key worn

4. goer no

5. coal door

Californian Wine Regions

6. moan so

7. icon demon

8. enemy rot

9. paella navy

10. czars aunt

ANSWERS PAGE 190

QUIZ 46 – WINES OF CANADA

1. Approximately how much wine does Canada produce based on average production from 2015 to 2020?
    a) Less than New Zealand
    b) More than New Zealand
    c) More than Australia

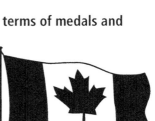

2. Which is the largest wine producing region in terms of volume and vineyard area?
    a) British Columbia b) Ontario c) Nova Scotia

3. What is Canadian Ice Wine?
    a) A dry white wine to drink with ice b) From late picked very ripe grapes producing a dessert wine c) Intensely sweet dessert wine individually picked when grapes are frozen

4. Of which type of wine does Canada produce the most?
    a) Red b) Sparkling c) White

5. Which is the most 'awarded' wine estate, in terms of medals and trophies in the last 15 years?
    a) Mission Hill
    b) Pillitteri Estates
    c) Tawse Winery

6. Which red grape variety is most planted and produced in Ontario wine country?
    a) Cabernet Franc
    b) Cabernet Sauvignon
    c) Merlot

7. Which is the oldest wine region/area in Canada still operating commercially?
    a) Niagara on the Lake b) Pelee Island c) Twenty Valley

8. Which rosé and red sparkling wine at 7% ABV was the biggest selling wine in Canada from 1960 to the end of 1980.
    a) Baby Duck b) Pink Diana c) Whispering Angel

9. British Columbia's wine industry has recently developed very quickly. Up until the 1930s BC grew peaches and apples. In 2020 there were around 380 wineries. How many wineries (approx) were there back in 1980?
    a) 28 b) 58 c) 98

10 From which grape variety is the majority of Canadian Ice Wine made?
    a) Cabernet Franc b) Riesling c) Vidal

QUIZ 47 – WINES OF CHILE – PART 1

1. Vineyards are planted in the Atacama Desert. True or false?
2. Which wine region has the same name as a famous old Hollywood movie?
3. Which huge Chilean wine producer, founded in 1883, has vineyards in all the major regions?
   a) De Martino
   b) Concha y Toro
   c) Caliterra
4. Cono Sur is a famous producer that's particularly well-known for which grape variety?
   a) Pinot Noir
   b) Sémillon
   c) Merlot
5. In Chile, what are Maule, Leyda, and Elqui?
6. Is Maipo the name of a grape variety or a wine region?
7. Is the official Chilean wine map divided north to south, west to east, or both?
8. Is the well-known wine producer Casa Lapostolle French-owned or Spanish-owned?
9. Which local grape variety, still grown today, was the most widely planted in Chile up to the end of the 1990s?
   a) País
   b) Carmenère
   c) Gewürtztraminer
10. In which wine region did the Spanish wine legend, Miguel Torres, invest heavily in 1979?
    a) Colchagua
    b) Maule
    c) Curicó

ANSWERS PAGE 194

QUIZ 48 – WINES OF CHILE – PART 2

1. Which of these wine regions
   is the most northerly?
   a) *Aconcagua*
   b) *Curicó*
   c) *Colchagua*

2. For well over a hundred years the Carmenère grape in Chile was often
   thought to be a different grape variety. Which one was it?
   a) *Pinot Noir*
   b) *Cabernet Sauvignon*
   c) *Merlot*

3. Most Chilean vines are not grafted onto North American rootstock, as
   in the majority of other parts of the world, but are free of which
   louse, or pest, that attacks vine roots?

4. Which well-known producer's name translates literally as
   'southern cone'?

5. Which wine region sounds like a well-known move in rugby?

6. Which wine has a Franco-Chilean ownership between the Rothschild
   family and Concha y Toro?
   a) *Almamater*
   b) *Almaviva*
   c) *Almatoro*

7. Which well-known Spanish wine producer has a substantial holding of
   vineyards in several Chilean regions?
   a) *Martín Códax*
   b) *Miguel Torres*
   c) *Telmo Rodríguez*

8. The main concentration of vineyards in Chile is located near which
   major city?

9. There are three main wine-producing regions in southern Chile. Itata
   and Malleco are two, what is the name of the other one?
   a) *Casablanca*
   b) *San Antonio*
   c) *Bío Bío*

10. Which Chilean region that comprises the southern end of the Andes
    mountain range is shared with Argentina?

ANSWERS PAGE 195

QUIZ 49 – PART 1. MATCH THESE FAMOUS CHILEAN WINE PRODUCERS WITH THEIR PRIME REGION

1. Errazuriz

   a) Casablanca Valley

2. Underraga

   b) Colchagua Valley

3. Casa Marín

   c) Maipo Valley

4. Kingston Family Vineyards

   d) Aconcagua Valley

5. Luis Felipe Edwards

   e) San Antonio Valley

QUIZ 49 – PART 2. FIVE OF THE FOLLOWING REGIONS ARE IN THE NORTHERN PART OF THE MAIN CHILEAN WINEGROWING AREA, BUT WHICH FIVE ARE IN THE SOUTHERN PART?

ANSWERS PAGE 197

6 — 10

f) Maule

g) Bío Bío

h) San Antonio

i) Malleco

j) Leyda

k) Aconcagua

l) Itata

m) Curicó

n) Casablanca

o) Maipo

QUIZ 50 – ANAGRAMS – WINES OF CHILE

Well-Known Chilean Wines

1. met son

2. asian tart

3. dream on

4. adore mint

5. race trial

Chilean Wine Regions

6. mi lair

7. aim op

8. a canal scab

9. satan onion

10. la emu

ANSWERS PAGE 198

CHILE

QUIZ 51 – WINES OF ARGENTINA – PART 1

1. Which wine region in Argentina has a similar name to a well-known region in Spain?
   a) La Navarra
   b) La Rioja
   c) La Rueda

2. Can wine grapes be grown in Patagonia, in the far south of Argentina?

3. What is by far the largest wine-producing region in Argentina?

4. Founded by a British train engineer in the late nineteenth century, what's the name of this English-sounding producer?
   a) Norton
   b) Lindlay
   c) Roberts

5. What is the name of this high-altitude region that's like a map backwards!?

6. Who is this well-known producer that sounds similar to the American word for courgette?

7. What is the name of the grape variety that really put Argentina on the wine map in the early 1990s?

8. What is the name of the mountain range that runs between many of the vineyards of Argentina and Chile?

9. With mountains to the west, desert to the south, and just three letters in its name, what is this wine-producing valley called, that grows over a dozen different wine grapes?

10. The Torrontés grape variety is grown in many regions of Argentina. Is it red or white?

ANSWERS PAE 199

QUIZ 52 – WINES OF ARGENTINA – PART 2

ANSWERS PAGE 201

1. Which country borders Argentina and is well-known for producing wine from the Tannat red grape variety?
    a) Brazil b) Paraguay c) Uruguay

2. One of the main wine areas next to the Mendoza region has the same name as the river that flows through it. What is the name of the wine area/river?
    a) San Conchas b) San Juan c) San Lerma

3. Until about thirty years ago, a famous champagne house was happy to sell their sparkling wine produced in Argentina as 'Champagne'. What was their name?
    a) Moët & Chandon
    b) Veuve Clicquot
    c) Bollinger

4. This lesser-known wine region's first three letters are the name of a domestic animal. What is the name of the region?
    a) Dogalima b) Henerama c) Catamarca

5. With a character similar to Malbec, what is the name of the local red grape variety which is planted extensively in Argentina?

6. It's the same grape variety, and different countries around the world either call it Shiraz or Syrah. Which one of the two names is it in Argentina?

7. This sub-region of Mendoza has been called 'The headquarters of Malbec'. What is its name?
    a) Maipú b) Cruz de Piedra c) Luján de Cuyo

8. What is the name of the grape variety, grown predominantly in the Mendoza wine region, that, apart from one letter, has the same name as a famous sweet Sherry grape?

9. What is the wine region whose name includes Argentina's capital city, that has been producing some high quality wine since the beginning of the 21st century?
    a) Buenos Aires Communes
    b) Buenos Aires Province
    c) Buenos Aires Pueblo

10. Which Argentine wine producer has the same name as a famous motorcycle brand?

QUIZ 53 – WINES OF SOUTH AMERICA, EXCLUDING CHILE AND ARGENTINA

1. This well-known grape variety in Uruguay is often locally called Harriague. But what is it more commonly known as?

2. In Peru, what is Pisco?
   a) Grape Brandy
   b) Cactus Vodka
   c) Pine Whisky

3. In which South American country are the wine areas of Campos de Cima da Serra, and Serra Gaúcha?
   a) Uruguay
   b) Peru
   c) Brazil

4. In Bolivia, what is Singani?
   a) A Pisco-type drink
   b) A wine region
   c) A micro-climate

5. Some of the world's highest vineyards are in Bolivia. What do they rise up to?
   a) 10,500 ft b) 14,500 ft c) 18,500 ft

6. Around 90% of all Uruguayan wine production is in one part of the country. Which part is It?
   a) Northern border with Brazil
   b) Western border with Argentina
   c) Southern coast of Uruguay

7. In Peru, what are Ica and Tacna?
   a) Wine regions
   b) Grape varieties
   c) Wine producers

8. In Brazil, what is Isabel?
   a) Wine region
   b) Grape variety
   c) Wine producer

9. When were wine grapes first grown in Bolivia?
   a) 14th century b) 15th century c) 16th century

10. In Peru, what are Tacama and Santiago Queirolo?
    a) Wine regions
    b) Grape varieties
    c) Wine producers

ANSWERS PAGE 203

QUIZ 54 – ANAGRAMS – WINES OF SOUTH AMERICA

South American Grape Varieties

1. males ran

2. aria nag

3. lilac or

4. a sip

5. arab nod

Argentine and Chilean Wine Regions

6. mad zone

7. a cacao gun

8. delay

9. gore iron

10. pearl

ANSWERS PAGE 204

SECTION 5 – WINES OF AUSTRALIA, NEW ZEALAND AND SOUTH AFRICA

These twelve quizzes are made up of four quizzes each on Australia, New Zealand, and South Africa.

The questions follow the same format for each of the three countries. They begin with two quizzes for each country on wines, grapes, history and regions.

Then a quiz apiece on wine-matching, and finally a quiz each featuring tricky anagrams for you to solve.

The 12 quizzes are:

QUIZ 55 – WINES OF AUSTRALIA – PART 1

1. Which country imports by far the most Australian wine in value and volume?
   a) China b) UK c) USA

2. Langmeil Freedom Vineyard, planted in 1843 and now producing quality Shiraz with some vines over 150 years old, is based in which wine growing region?
   a) Barossa Valley
   b) Coonawarra
   c) McLaren Vale

3. Of which type of wine does Australia produce the most?
   a) Red b) Sparkling c) White

4. Which one of the six Australian States produces well over 50% of all wine in volume?
   a) South Australia
   b) Victoria
   c) Western Australia

5. Which red wine grape is the most planted in Australia?
   a) Cabernet Sauvignon b) Merlot c) Shiraz

6. The wine critic Robert Parker said that this wine 'has replaced Bordeaux's Petrus as the world's most exotic and concentrated wine'?
   a) Clarendon Hills b) Penfolds Grange c) Henschke Hill of Grace

7. Where are the Piper River & Tamar Valley wine regions, producing racy Pinot Noirs and sparkling wines?
   a) New South Wales
   b) Queensland
   c) Tasmania

8. Who is called 'The Father of Australian Wine' as he brought over the first grape vine cuttings from France in 1824?
   a) Jim Barry b) James Busby c) Max Schubert

9. Which one of these wine estates does not produce a Pinot Noir?
   a) Coldstream Hills (Yarra Valley)
   b) Bay of Fires (Tasmania)
   c) Vasse Felix (Margaret River)

10. About what percentage of all wine produced in Australia is consumed within the country, and not exported?
    a) 20% to 30% b) 40% to 50% c) 60% to 70%

ANSWERS PAGE 206

QUIZ 56 – WINES OF AUSTRALIA – PART 2

1. Which grape variety was seen as making Australia's heritage wine and was imported as Syrah from the Rhône Valley in France?

2. Which country does Australia import most wines from in terms of volume?
   a) France
   b) Italy
   c) New Zealand

3. Which white grape variety is the most planted in Australia?
   a) Chardonnay
   b) Sauvignon Blanc
   c) Sémillon

4. Mornington Peninsula and Yarra Valley wine regions, both producing great Pinot Noirs, are closest to which Australian city?
   a) Melbourne b) Perth c) Sydney

5. What is Margaret River's (Western Australia) most planted grape variety?
   a) Cabernet Sauvignon b) Chardonnay c) Sauvignon Blanc

6. Which wine estate was awarded the 'Best Australian Sparkling Wine Trophy' in 2019?
   a) Domaine Chandon
   b) House of Arras
   c) Jansz

7 Grange Hermitage Bin 95 is Australia's most expensive and iconic red wine, stated to be the Southern Hemisphere's only 'First Growth'. It is made by which wine estate founded in 1844?
   a) Hardy's Estate b) Penfolds Estate c) Wynn's Estate

8. All six Australian States have wine regions. How many separate wine regions are there in total?
   a) 35 b) 65 c) 95

9. Which is Australia's oldest vineyard and winery that has continuously produced wines since 1828?
   a) Tyrrell's Wines
   b) Wyndham Estate
   c) Yalumba

10. Which winery near Adelaide in South Australia makes Shiraz today from very old vines planted in the 1860s, vines now over 160 years old?
    a) Henschke Cellars of Eden Valley b) Mount Horrocks Wines of Clare Valley c) Yalumba of Barossa Valley

ANSWERS PAGE 209

QUIZ 57 – MATCH AUSTRALIAN WINES

Both Wine Estates and Grape	*Wine Region or Area*
1. Tamar Ridge & Bay of Fires (Pinot Noir)	*a) Hunter Valley/NSW*
2. Vasse Felix & Leeuwin Estate (Chardonnay)	*b) Barossa Valley*
3. Yalumba & Château Tanunda (Bordeaux blend)	*c) Margaret River*
4. Mount Pleasant & Tyrrell's Wines (Sémillon)	*d) Adelaide/Coonawarra*
5. Chapel Hill & Bird in Hand (Shiraz)	*e) Tasmania*

Wine Estates	*Grape Variety or Type*
6. Domaine Chandon & Jansz	*f) Pinot Noir*
7. Penfolds Grange & Wolf Blass	*g) Chardonnay*
8. Pewsey Vale & Mount Horrocks	*h) Sparkling blend*
9. Coldstream Hills & Yarra Yerring	*i) Shiraz blend*
10. Bannockburn & Cullen	*j) Riesling*

ANSWERS PAGE 211

64

QUIZ 58 – ANAGRAMS – WINES OF AUSTRALIA

Australian Famous 'Valley' Wine Regions

1. boar ass

2. array

3. a tram

4. leap in

5. red newt

6. need

7. woad block

8. the urn

9. clear

10. vicar role

ANSWERS PAGE 214

65

QUIZ 59 – WINES OF NEW ZEALAND – PART 1

NEW ZEALAND

1. Is the wine region of Hawke's Bay on the North Island or the South Island?

2. The well-known wine, Ata Rangi, is produced in which wine region on the North Island?
   a) *Martinborough*
   b) *Hawke's Bay*
   c) *Auckland*

3. Formerly Montana Wines, what name did this brand change to in 2010?
   a) *Babich Wines*
   b) *Brancott Estate*
   c) *Mission Estate*

4. Central Otago is particularly famous for producing high quality wine from which grape variety?

5. Cloudy Bay was originally famous for which grape variety?

6. The brand name, Deutz, is famous in New Zealand for producing which style of wine?
   a) *Dessert Wine*
   b) *Fortified Wine*
   c) *Sparkling Wine*

7. The Gimblett Gravels wine growing district is situated in which region?
   a) *Hawke's Bay*
   b) *Central Otago*
   c) *Nelson*

8. Which wine region lies immediately north of Hawke's Bay?
   a) *Auckland*
   b) *Nelson*
   c) *Gisborne*

9. Which one of the two wine-producing regions of Wairarapa and Waipara lies on the South Island?

10. The wine region of Nelson lies next to which region on the South Island?

CLOUDY BAY

QUIZ 60 – WINES OF NEW ZEALAND – PART 2

1. The Bay of Plenty is on the South Island. True or false?
2. The Waitaki Valley is in which wine growing region?
   a) Central Otago
   b) Marlborough
   c) Martinborough
3. Syrah and Shiraz are the same grape variety. Which one is it in New Zealand?
4. Is the grape variety in question 3 grown in Central Otago?
5. Which wine region has the lion's share of sparkling wine production?
   a) Auckland
   b) Marlborough
   c) Hawke's Bay
6. Over how many years ago were the first planting of grape vines in New Zealand?
   a) 100 years
   b) 200 years
   c) 300 years
7. Waiheke Island is part of which wine region?
   a) Marlborough b) Hawke's Bay c) Auckland
8. Pinot Gris is one of the grape varieties grown in the wine region of Gisborne. True or false?
9. Elephant Hill is a well-known producer in which wine region?
   a) Hawke's Bay
   b) Central Otago
   c) Gisborne
10. Pioneering producers established the modern wine industry in the Nelson wine region in which twentieth century decade?
    a) 1960s
    b) 1970s
    c) 1980s

ANSWERS PAGE 218

QUIZ 61 – MATCH WINES OF NEW ZEALAND

ANSWERS PAGE 219

Famous Wines	*NZ Wine Regions & Grapes*
1. Felton Road & Two Paddocks	a) Auckland Red Blends
2. Church Road & Mission Estate Blancs	b) Marlborough Sauvignon
3. Vavasour & Greywacke	c) Canterbury Rieslings
4. Coopers Creek & Man of War	d) Central Otago Pinot Noirs
5. Giesen & Mud House	e) Hawke's Bay Merlots

Famous Wines	*Grape Variety*
6. Oyster Bay & Cloudy Bay	f) Riesling
7. Elephant Hill & Squawking Magpie	g) Chardonnay
8. Milton & Poverty Bay	h) Sauvignon Blanc
9. Brancott Estate & St Clair	i) Merlot
10. Pegasus Bay & Greystone	j) Pinot Noir

QUIZ 62 – ANAGRAMS – WINES OF NEW ZEALAND

New Zealand Wine Regions

1. trance ruby

2. lens on

3. pat ebony fly

4. armouring both

5. away pale rival

New Zealand Wine Producers

6. daub coyly

7. hellish writ

8. ate mat

9. lethal hen lip

10. racial nits

ANSWERS PAGE 222

QUIZ 63 – WINES OF SOUTH AFRICA – PART 1

1. Which is the most widely planted grape variety in South Africa?
   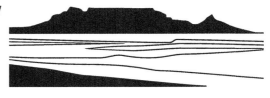
   a) *Chenin Blanc*
   b) *Merlot*
   c) *Sauvignon Blanc*

2. Which nation's immigrants to South Africa were the first to plant vineyards?
   a) *France* b) *Germany* c) *Netherlands*

3. About how many different wine grape varieties are planted commercially in South Africa?
   a) *25 to 50* b) *51 to 100* c) *101 plus*

4. The Rhône type wines Goats do Roam and Goat-Roti are made at which wine estate in Paarl?
   a) *Bon Courage* b) *Fairview* c) *Springfield Estate*

5. What is the most southern of the Wine of Origin Producing Districts of South Africa?
   a) *Elgin* b) *Swartland* c) *Walker Bay*

6. The Big Easy is a top wine range owned and made by which famous sports personality?
   a) *Ernie Els* b) *Retief Goosen* c) *Paul Harris*

7. Which sparkling wine was served at President Nelson Mandela's and President Barack Obama's inauguration ceremonies?
   a) *Graham Beck* b) *Klein Constantia* c) *Thelema*

8. Which wine estate in Stellenbosch, founded in 1692, has a cheetah and eagle sanctuary?
   a) *Boschendal* b) *Meerlust* c) *Spier*

9. How many Wine of Origin Producing Districts (WOPDs) are there in South Africa?
   a) *9* b) *19* c) *29*

10. Which wine did Emperor Napoleon drink every day during his exile on St Helena from 1815 to 1821, and was also his last deathbed drink.
    a) *Boplaas*
    b) *Nederburg*
    c) *Vin de Constance*

QUIZ 64 – WINES OF SOUTH AFRICA – PART 2

1. What is the name of the South African state-run wine company founded in 1918 in Paarl, now with the largest capacity wine cellars in the world?
   a) CWG b) De Krans c) KWV

2. Which beautiful and high quality wine estate is owned by a famous diamond jewellery company?
   a) Delaire Graff Estate
   b) Van Cleef Vineyards
   c) Winston Winery

3. Of which grape variety are these three wine estates – Bouchard Finlayson, Newton Johnson, and Paul Cluver – famous for producing some of South Africa's best quality examples?
   a) Chardonnay b) Pinotage c) Pinot Noir

4. Which South African wine was claimed to be President Mandela's favourite?
   a) Bridge of Hope Pinotage
   b) Magna Carta Chenin Blanc
   c) Vin de Constance Muscat

5. Which wine estate has Queen Elizabeth II stayed at and is still a Royal favourite wine served at Buckingham Palace?
   a) Boschendal Wines b) Constantia Glen c) Vergelegen Wines

6. Which wine area in South Africa pioneered the first 'Burgundian' Chardonnays & Pinot Noirs?
   a) Cederberg b) Swartland c) Walker Bay

7. What is the average annual wine production in South Africa in number of bottles?
   a) 700 million b) 1,000 million c) 1,300 million

8. What does the Southern Right Vineyard, situated in Walker Bay, have on its wine label?
   a) Cheetah b) Elephant c) Whale

9. South Africa's indigenous signature grape is Pinotage, a red grape that is a cross between Pinot Noir and Cinsaut. When was it created and first planted in South Africa?
   a) 1905 b) 1925 c) 1935

10. Which country imports the most South African wine by value and volume?
    a) Germany b) The Netherlands c) United Kingdom

ANSWERS PAGE 226

QUIZ 65 – MATCH WINES OF SOUTH AFRICA

Top Producers

1. Cederberg 'Five Generations'

2. Ken Forrester FMC

3. Hamilton Russell

4. Kanonkop 'Black Label'

5. Warwick 'The White Lady'

Grape Varieties

a) *Pinot Noir*

b) *Pinotage*

c) *Chenin Blanc*

d) *Chardonnay*

e) *Cabernet Sauvignon*

Top Wine Estates

6. Delaire Graff Estate

7. Chamonix Wine Farm

8. Paul Cluver

9. Southern Right

10. KWV

Wine Regions/Areas

f) *Elgin*

g) *Paarl*

h) *Franschhoek*

i) *Stellenbosch*

j) *Walker Bay*

ANSWERS PAGE 230

QUIZ 66 – ANAGRAMS – WINES OF SOUTH AFRICA

South African Wine Regions

1. bakery law

2. leg in

3. action ants

4. blotch lenses

5. drawn last

South African Grape Varieties

6. can belch inn

7. anus tic

8. gape into

9. nacho randy

10. calm brood

ANSWERS PAGE 232

SECTION 6 – A DOZEN LIGHT-HEARTED WINE QUIZZES

Twelve quizzes for you to try which will stretch your wine knowledge in many strange ways.

Some questions are a bit obscure and frivolous, and you may have to guess at either a, b, or c. You have a 33% chance, and the answer could surprise you.

The 12 Wine Trivia Quizzes are:

QUIZ 67 – WINE AND THE HOLLYWOOD MOVIES

QUIZ 68 – WINE AND POLITICS

QUIZ 69 – WINE AND RELIGION

QUIZ 70 – WINE SCANDALS AND FRAUDS

QUIZ 71 – CRAZY AND WEIRD WINES

QUIZ 72 – ODD WINE NAMES AND EVEN ODDER LABELS

QUIZ 73 – THE GUINNESS BOOK OF RECORDS AND WINES

QUIZ 74 – FAMOUS PEOPLE AND THEIR WINES – PART 1

QUIZ 75 – FAMOUS PEOPLE AND THEIR WINES – PART 2

QUIZ 76 – FAMOUS PEOPLE'S WINE QUOTES – PART 1

QUIZ 77 – FAMOUS PEOPLE'S WINE QUOTES – PART 2

QUIZ 78 – WINE DRINKING HEROES AND DRUNKS IN BOOKS & FILMS

So do try these slightly weird and waggish wine quizzes. There are 120 sometimes crazy, hopefully fun, and occasionally wise questions to have a go at. Just dip in and out when you are in need of a dose of wine trivia. Many answers are perplexing and unexpected, but aim to amuse not annoy!

QUIZ 67 – WINE AND THE HOLLYWOOD MOVIES

1. Which champagne does James Bond exclusively drink in 14 Bond Films from 1973?
    a) Bollinger b) Dom Pérignon c) Krug

2. Marilyn Monroe wine brand from the Napa Valley is made from which grape?
    a) Chardonnay b) Merlot c) Pinot Noir

3. Who threw Corellian Wine in Han Solo's face in a Star Wars film?
    a) Chewbacca b) Princess Leia c) Rey

4. In Silence of the Lambs, Hannibal Lecter drinks which wine with liver and fava beans?
    a) Barolo b) Chianti c) Valpolicella

5. Château Latour and Château Cheval Blanc are featured in which animated feature film?
    a) 101 Dalmatians
    b) Lady and the Tramp
    c) Ratatouille

6. Which Hollywood actor paid £30,000 for a bottle of dessert wine at a London Restaurant?
    a) George Clooney
    b) Johnny Depp
    c) Brad Pitt

7. Bottle Shock, a film released in 2008 and starring Alan Rickman, is about what wine related topic or events?
    a) Running a vineyard in Provence
    b) Hiding their wines from the Germans in WWII
    c) 'The Judgement of Paris' in 1976

8. Michael Corleone's favourite red wine in The Godfather films is which of these?
    a) Amarone b) Bardolino c) Nero d'Avola

9. 'We want the finest wines available to humanity. We want them here, and we want them now' is at the end of which film?
    a) The Godfather III b) Goodfellas c) Withnail and I

10. In which film does James Bond say, 'Drinking Dom Pérignon 1953 above a temperature of 38 degrees Fahrenheit. That's as bad as listening to The Beatles without earmuffs'
    a) Dr. No
    b) Goldfinger
    c) Octopussy

ANSWERS PAGE 234

QUIZ 68 – WINE AND POLITICS

1. How many bottles of champagne is
   Winston Churchill said to have drunk
   in his lifetime?
   a) 10,000 bottles
   b) 30,000 bottles
   c) over 50,000 bottles

2. Which President of the USA often drank
   Château Lafite Rothschild, but hid its
   label, and then often offered his guests
   cheap Gallo wines from California.
   a) Thomas Jefferson
   b) Herbert Hoover
   c) Richard Nixon

3. Which of these places has the largest wine cellar in number of bottles
   stored – worth over £3 million?
   a) Elysée Palace
   b) Parliament House of Commons
   c) The USA Government

4. What was Saddam Hussein's favourite wine. His palaces' cellars
   were stuffed with it?
   a) Chateau Musar b) Mateus Rosé c) Tawny Port

5. 60% of all wine drunk from the wine cellar of The House of Commons
   (Government Store) is from which country?
   a) France b) Italy c) UK

6. Which one of these world leaders drank wine –
   the other two are teetotal?
   a) Neville Chamberlain b) Hitler c) President Trump

7. Clos Napoleon (visited by Emperor Napoleon) is a top wine domaine
   in which Burgundy Communal Appellation?
   a) Chambertin b) Fixin c) Vougeot

8. Which American President owns the largest vineyard in Virginia?
   a) Jimmy Carter b) Bill Clinton c) Donald Trump

9. Churchill's favourite racehorse that he owned, was named after his
   favourite champagne. Which one was it?
   a) Bollinger b) Moët & Chandon c) Pol Roger

10. Which of these 'Despotic Dictators' loved fine red wine
    and drank it daily?
    a) Muammar al-Gaddafi b) Kim Jong Il c) Pol Pot

ANSWERS PAGE 236

QUIZ 69 – WINE AND RELIGION

1. When did the Christian Catholic Church first introduce the doctrine of 'transubstantiation' of the belief in the red altar wine changing into the blood of Christ?
   a) 6th century
   b) 10th century
   c) 12th century

2. Who was the Greek God of Wine?

3. Who was the Roman God of Wine?

4. Over 6,000 years ago in Egypt, which Cobra faced 'Goddess of Wine' was worshipped by the Pharaohs and High Priests by ceremonially drinking wine?
   a) Amunet b) Isis c) Renetutet

5. Where does Vin Santo (Holy Wine) originally come from?
   a) Lombardy b) Puglia c) Tuscany

6. Which is the first religion to use wine in religious ceremonies?
   a) Armenian b) Egyptian c) Greek

7. The oldest winery in the USA, still producing wine today, was started by Christian monks and is called the Brotherhood Winery.
   Which State is it in?
   a) California b) New York c) Texas

8. Who planted the first ever vineyard in the world, according to the Bible?
   a) Isaiah b) Lot c) Noah

9. From which European countries do the majority of altar/sacramental wine come, for use in UK churches?
   a) Cyprus & Greece
   b) France & Spain
   c) Germany & Georgia

10. Which civilisation enjoyed and performed a religious once a month 'Day of Intoxication' with singing, dancing & music, but mostly dedicated to drinking copious amounts of wine.
    a) Egyptian
    b) Greek
    c) Mexican

ANSWERS PAGE 238

QUIZ 70 – WINE SCANDALS AND FRAUDS

1. Which country was accused and convicted of wineries adding 'Antifreeze' to their wines to make them sweeter?
    a) Austria b) Bulgaria c) Germany

2. What was the maximum penalty in Medieval Germany for adulterating or diluting wines?
    a) Branding b) Put in the Stocks and beaten c) Death by hanging

3. In 1985 a bottle of 'supposedly' 1787 Château Lafite Bordeaux wine was found in Paris, and auctioned at Christie's London for £105,000. It was claimed to have belonged to which US President?
    a) John Hancock b) Thomas Jefferson c) George Washington

4. In Italy in 2000, over 20,000 bottles of wine were sold off at 100 euros plus each. It was just cheap Sicilian wine, but was passed off as a Super Tuscan. Which one?
    a) Ornellaia b) Sassicaia c) Solaia

5. Red Bicyclette was a French wine brand sold by Gallo of California (the largest wine company in the world), right across the USA. From 2006 to 2008 over 18 million bottles were sold as Pinot Noir, but there was no Pinot Noir in it. What grapes were in it?
    a) Carmenère & Malbec b) Merlot & Syrah c) Grenache & Mourvèdre

ANSWERS PAGE 240

6. Who is currently considered to be the world's biggest wine forger, forging over £100 million of rare wines sold at auction in the USA between 2005 & 2008?
    a) Rudy Kurniawan b) Bill Koch c) Hardy Rodenstock

7. Which wine region in France was found out in 2008 to be adding over 200 tonnes of sugar in a poor vintage to strengthen their ABV/alcoholic strength?
    a) Beaujolais b) Burgundy c) Macon

8. Which prestigious brand of Australian wine was faked in China (in 2018) in very large volumes?
    a) Jacob's Creek b) Penfolds c) Yalumba

9. In 2018 in France, 66 million bottles of wine were seized as fakes, many being passed off as Châteauneuf-du-Pape and other top Rhône wines. Where were they really from?
    a) Languedoc b) La Mancha c) Sicily

10. Which rare fine wine is deemed to be the most counterfeited wine in the world?
    a) Domaine de la Romanée-Conti
    b) Château Lafite Rothschild
    c) Penfolds Grange

QUIZ 71 – CRAZY AND WEIRD WINES

1. The white wine 'Cats Pee on a Gooseberry Bush' is made from which grape?
   a) Chenin Blanc
   b) Catarratto
   c) Sauvignon Blanc

2. Bored Doe (a deer looking bored) and Goats do Roam (a herd of goats) are wines having fun with French Bordeaux and Côtes du Rhône. Which South African Estate makes them?
   a) Bon Courage b) Fairview c) Rustenberg

3. Which famous Italian wine is made from dried grapes left in the sun on straw mats to shrivel and concentrate the juice?
   a) Amarone b) Barolo c) Ripasso

4. Cake Flavoured Wines made by Birthday Cake Vineyards, produce red wines flavoured as Black Forest Gateau and Coffee Cake, and white wines as Strawberry Shortcake etc. They are made in which US state?
   a) California b) New York c) Virginia

5. In which country is Pornfelder wine made, produced by Lukas Krauss as a range of 'sex, wine and rock & roll'?
   a) Austria b) Germany c) Portugal

6. Gallo Wines (the largest wine company in the world) was built on white 'Thunderbird Wines' appealing to the young, and also now the homeless, and is often called 'the bum's wine'. What ABV (Alcohol %) does it have?
   a) 10% b) 15% c) 20%

7. The biggest selling 'blue' naturally coloured wine is made by which wine estate?
   a) Blumond Blue Bubbly from Italy b) Gik from Spain
   c) Vindigo from France

8. Starboard (a Port by any other name), Palomino Fino (like a sherry) and Essensia (top dessert wine) are all made in California by whom?
   a) Frog's Leap b) Quady Wines c) Wente Vineyards

9. Which of these rude wine names is not a real wine. The two real ones sell millions of bottles per year in the USA.
   a) Sassy Bitch b) Sexy Tart c) Stu Pedasso

10. Which Champagne House was the first to age top vintage champagne 50 metres under the sea for 50 years.
    a) Krug b) Moët & Chandon c) Veuve Clicquot

QUIZ 72 – ODD WINE NAMES AND EVEN ODDER LABELS

1. Old Fart and Old Git are two top selling wines in the USA and the UK. They are made in France from which colour grapes?
   a) Red
   b) White

2. Bull's Blood, always with a black bull on a red label, was a popular best-selling red wine from the 1970s to 2000.
   Which European country was it from?
   a) Austria b) Hungary c) Spain

3. A famous 'sex symbol' wine (label with sexy photo of the actress) is made in California, and is now a collector's trophy.
   What is the wine called?
   a) Ursula Andress Chardonnay
   b) Marilyn Monroe Merlot
   c) Mae West Zinfandel

4. Pisse-Dru is an easy drinking red wine from which wine region of France?
   a) Beaujolais b) Macon c) Rhône

5. What is the name of a top quality red Pinotage wine from Flagstone Winery in South Africa?
   a) Cigar Volante b) Spatzendeck c) Writer's Block

6. Blasted Church is a red wine from which Country?
   a) Australia b) Canada c) USA

7. What colour is the best seller wine, 'Sex', which is produced in the USA?
   a) Pink b) Red c) White

8. The brand Naked Grape is now made as a range of white, red and rosé wines. Which grape variety was the first ever Naked Grape wine made from?
   a) Grenache b) Merlot c) Riesling

9. Rude Boy Chardonnay and Rude Girl Shiraz (with an active label), are best-selling wines from which country?
   a) Australia b) New Zealand c) South Africa

10. Wild Cat white wine from the Catarratto grape, and made by 'flying winemakers' from Australia, is from which part of Italy?
    a) Puglia b) Sicily c) Tuscany

QUIZ 73 – THE GUINNESS BOOK OF RECORDS AND WINES

1. The oldest chemical evidence of wine was found, and carbon-dated, from which centuries BC?
   a) 8000 to 7000 BC
   b) 6000 to 5500 BC
   c) 4000 to 3000 BC

2. The longest wine list in a restaurant is of multi vintages of 1,746 different wines. It is over 200 pages long. In which city is this restaurant?
   a) London b) Luxembourg City c) Paris

3. The largest bottle of wine ever filled was almost 14 feet high, and was equivalent to how many full 75cl bottles?
   a) 2,100 bottles b) 3,100 bottles c) 4,100 bottles

4. The oldest wine still produced commercially, and now for over 3,000 years, is named what?
   a) Commandaria, Cyprus
   b) Château de Goulaine, France
   c) Schloss Johannisberg, Germany

5. The most lucrative single wine fraud ever committed was when 400 bottles of Romanée-Conti wine, were faked and sold for over £2 million. In which country did this take place?
   a) France b) Italy c) USA

6. The most expensive bottle of port ever sold at auction was a Niepoort vintage port of 1863. It was sold at Sotheby's in Hong Kong in 2019. What price did it sell for?
   a) £62,000 b) £102,000 c) £152,000

7. The first robot sommelier called 'Wine Bot' was invented to taste, compare, and recommend compatible foods for over 30 different wines. In which country was this?
   a) England b) Japan c) USA

8. The oldest Appellation d'Origine laws and defined areas were first established in which country?
   a) Cyprus b) France c) Greece

9. The largest wine cellar in the world, in volume and area, is in Paarl, South Africa. It has a capacity to store how many bottles?
   a) 65 million b) 125 million c) 185 million

10. What is the world record for 'sabering' the most champagne bottles in 30 seconds (cutting the necks off each bottle with a sword)?
    a) 29 bottles b) 39 bottles c) 49 bottles

ANSWERS PAGE 247

QUIZ 74 – FAMOUS PEOPLE AND THEIR WINES – PART 1

1. Which winemaker was made the first ever Decanter
    Magazine 'Man of the Year' in 1984?
    a) Serge Hochar b) Len Evans c) José Domecq
2. Which famous 'Rapper' makes and sells his own
    very expensive and exclusive champagne brand
    named Ace of Spades?
    a) 50 Cent b) Ice Cube c) Jay Z
3. Which of these famous Roman Emperors in classical times owned large
    vineyards producing the most sought after Falerian white wine?
    a) Emperor Julius Caesar b) Emperor Augustus c) Emperor Sulla
4. Which French actor/actress owns vineyards in three French
    regions, and has stated his/her profession in their passport as
    winemaker/vigneron?
    a) Gerard Depardieu b) Catherine Deneuve c) Roger Vadim
5. Sting, the singer, owns a wine estate where he produces six
    different wines, from six different grape varieties.
    In which wine area is the winery?
    a) Chianti in Italy
    b) Provence in France
    c) Napa Valley in USA
6. What is the name of Brad Pitt and Angelina Jolie's top award-winning
    winery which produces expensive rosé wine from Provence?
    a) Whispering Angel b) Château Miraval c) Maison Saint Aix
7. Which Englishman was made Decanter Magazine 'Man of the Year' in
    2017. He had also just written his Memoir entitled 'Wine. A Way of Life'?
    a) Hugh Johnson b) Oz Clarke c) Steven Spurrier.
8. Madonna's family vineyard and winery named 'Ciccone', the family
    name, produces wines from seven European grape varieties. In which
    US state is it situated?
    a) California b) Michigan c) New York
9. Which year did Sam Neill launch and first produce wines at his multi
    award-winning Pinot Noir estate, called Two Paddocks, situated in
    Central Otago, New Zealand?
    a) 1973 b) 1983 c) 1993
10. Cliff Richard has owned two vineyards producing red,
    white and rosé wines, which sell out under the name of Vida Nova and
    Onda Nova. In which country is Cliff Richard's wine estate situated?
    a) Italy b) Portugal c) Spain.

ANSWERS PAGE 248

QUIZ 75 – FAMOUS PEOPLE AND THEIR WINES – PART 2

1. Which fictional hero declared 'Taittinger Blanc de Blancs Brut 1943, it's probably the finest champagne in the world.' It was in the first book written about this hero?
   a) James Bond b) Harry Palmer c) Jack Reacher

2. The son of John–? one of the top London wine merchants and wine importers, as well as the King's Deputy Royal Butler, was which famous author?
   a) Geoffrey Chaucer b) Samuel Pepys c) William Shakespeare

3. Which supermarket's wines has Queen Elizabeth II given the Royal Warrant to for Wines & Spirits; they are frequently served at Buckingham Palace and Windsor Castle?
   a) Marks & Spencer b) Sainsbury's c) Waitrose

4. Which famous wine was in the cellars of Saddam Hussein's palaces in great quantities. It was his favourite wine?
   a) Mumm Champagne b) Mateus Rosé c) Warre's Port

5. Which famous actress loved and drank lots of this particular champagne (Dom Pérignon by Moët & Chandon), saying 'this is definitely the best champagne in the world'?
   a) Brigitte Bardot b) Judy Garland c) Marilyn Monroe

6. Francis Ford Coppola (the director of the films The Godfather 1, 2 and 3) owns two wine estates in Sonoma, California. One of them is claimed to be the oldest winery in California. What is its name?
   a) Beringer b) Inglenook c) Stag's Leap.

7. Winston Churchill's favourite racehorse was named after a champagne; which one?
   a) Bollinger b) Krug c) Pol Roger

8. What was Emperor Napoleon Bonaparte's favourite 'Grand Cru' red Burgundy wine called?
   a) Chambertin b) Musigny c) Clos de Vougeot

THOMAS JEFFERSON

9. Daisy Fay, the rich socialite girlfriend and later long term lover of 'The Great Gatsby', was found very drunk and sobbing on her wedding day to Tom Buchanan. Which 'favourite' wine had she got plastered on?
   a) Champagne b) Pinot Grigio c) Sauternes

10. Which was President Obama's favourite sparkling wine, served at his Inauguration Ball and numerous White House State Banquets and Official Dinners?
   a) Domaine Carneros (California)   b) Graham Beck (South Africa)
   c) Roederer Estate (California)

ANSWERS PAGE 250

QUIZ 76 – FAMOUS PEOPLE'S WINE QUOTES – PART 1

1. Which great American author said 'always do sober what you said you
   would do when drunk, that will teach you to keep your mouth shut'?
     a) Ernest Hemingway b) F. Scott Fitzgerald c) Mark Twain

2. Who, in Roman times, said 'In wine there is health' (in vino sanitas)?
     a) Emperor Claudius b) Julius Caesar c) Pliny the Elder

3. Who is said to have exclaimed excitedly
   'come quickly, I am tasting the stars', when
   trying their first champagne?
     a) Marilyn Monroe
     b) Dom Pérignon
     c) Oscar Wilde

4. Who said, 'after much sombre contemplation,
   I'm naming my new and finest racehorse Pol Roger.
   Hopefully his running will give me as much pleasure'?
     a) Winston Churchill b) Yves Saint Laurent c) Philip Oppenheimer

5. Robert Parker Jr (of Wine Advocate) said 'this (Bordeaux year) is a
   vintage of legendary proportions, that has produced the most perfect
   wines in the post-World War II era.' Which year in Bordeaux was that?
     a) 1961 b) 1982 c) 1990

6. Who said 'The discovery of a wine is a greater moment than a
   discovery of a constellation. The sky is full of stars'?
     a) Benjamin Franklin b) Samuel Pepys c) William Shakespeare

7. Miles Raymond, in the film Sideways, says 'No, if anyone
   orders Merlot, I'm leaving.' Yet what is his favourite
   wine that he drinks at the end of the film?
     a) Château Cheval Blanc b) Stag's Leap Cask 23.
     c) Petrus

8. Which great war leader said 'In victory you
   deserve champagne, in defeat you need it'?
     a) President de Gaulle b) Napoleon Bonaparte
     c) General George Patton

9. Rick Stein said of which wine grape variety 'This Château has
   produced my House White in all my restaurants for over 18 years. Its
   wine is dry, crisp, elegant with a lemon grass zing'?
     a) Chardonnay b) Riesling c) Sauvignon Blanc

10. 'The connoisseur does not drink wine, but tastes of its secrets.' Which
    wine loving artist said this?
      a) Paul Cezanne b) Salvador Dali c) Pablo Picasso

ANSWERS PAGE 252

QUIZ 77 – FAMOUS PEOPLE'S WINE QUOTES – PART 2

1. Which James Bond actor, when Dr No said 'That's a Dom Pérignon '55, it would be a pity to break it', replied 'I prefer the '53 myself'?
   a) Sean Connery b) Daniel Craig c) Roger Moore

2. Which historic religious leader said in the 16th century, 'Beer is made by men, wine by God'?
   a) John Calvin b) Pope Gregory XIII c) Martin Luther

3. Which comedian/actor, who loved wine, said 'I cook with wine, sometimes I even add it to the food', and 'In Afghanistan we lost our corkscrew, we had to live on food and water for several days'?
   a) W.C. Fields b) Steve Martin c) Robin Williams

4. In which film did Steven Spurrier (played by actor Alan Rickman) say 'Wine is sunlight, held together by water'?
   a) Bottle Shock b) Sideways c) Wine Country

5. Which author and cartoonist wrote 'It's a naive domestic Burgundy without any breeding, but I think you'll be amused by its presumption'?
   a) Charles Adams b) Charles M Schulz c) James Thurber

6. Which famous 'drinking' painter said 'I love all painting. I'm like a drinker who needs a wine, as long as it's wine, it doesn't matter which wine'?
   a) Vincent Van Gogh
   b) Pablo Picasso
   c) Jackson Pollock

7. Which character in an English TV series said 'I can certainly see that you know your wine. Most of the guests who stay here wouldn't know the difference between Bordeaux and Claret'?
   a) Del Boy Trotter b) Basil Fawlty c) Reginald Perrin

8. 'Wine sets the wisest man to sing loudly, laugh like a fool, drives him to dancing. It even tempts him to blurt out stories that should never be told' is a quote from which classical ancient philosopher?
   a) Aristotle b) Homer c) Plato

9. 'Penicillin cures, but wine makes people happy' was said by which scientist?
   a) Alexander Fleming b) Edward Jenner c) Louis Pasteur

10. 'White wine is like electricity. Red wine looks and tastes like liquefied Beefsteak' is a quote by which novelist and poet?
    a) Emily Bronte b) James Joyce c) Jonathan Swift

QUIZ 78 – WINE DRINKING HEROES AND DRUNKS IN BOOKS AND FILMS

1. What is the name of the novel written by Rex Pickett, which in 2004 was made into a very successful comedy-drama film. It is about two good friends enjoying a wine trip holiday, driving across the southern California wine country?
   a) Saving Grapes b) Sideways c) Vertical

2. Which actress, in the film called 'The Seven Year Itch', proclaims her love of dunking potato chips (potato crisps) in her champagne?
   a) Audrey Hepburn b) Shirley MacLaine c) Marilyn Monroe

3. The Sun Also Rises, a book by Ernest Hemingway, has his hero, wine loving Jake Barnes, drinking his expat friends under the table each night on their travels and adventures within which country?
   a) France b) Italy c) Spain

4. Which champagne brand was shown throughout Baz Luhrmann's remake of 'The Great Gatsby' film in 2013?
   a) Bollinger b) Moët & Chandon c) Pommery

5. Who is Shakespeare's most famous drunk, enjoying copious quantities of 'Sack'?
   a) Andrew Aguecheek b) Banquo c) Falstaff

6. In which famous film did the hero Rick Blaine drink champagne in most scenes, and his famous toast to his lady friends was 'Here's looking at you, kid'?
   a) Casablanca b) Notorious c) The Big Sleep

7. Which author used these 'spiffing' phrases when the hero of his novels often had a bit too much wine or champagne to drink – 'tanked to the uvula, oiled, plastered, blotto and sozzled', amongst his many phrases?
   a) Philip Roth b) James Thurber c) P. G. Wodehouse

8. Which actor, when playing James Bond in his film roles, favours Château Cheval Blanc, Château Mouton Rothschild 1934, and Bollinger Champagne?
   a) Sean Connery b) Roger Moore c) Daniel Craig

9. Which novel written by Evelyn Waugh has a leading character called Paul Pennyfeather, a member of the Bollinger Club who, when frequently challenged by friends saying he is drunk, replies 'Well what else is there to do'?
   a) Decline and Fall b) Brideshead Revisited c) Vile Bodies

10. Which film, starring Maurice Chevalier and Leslie Caron, and directed by Vincente Minnelli, features the song 'The night they invented champagne'?
    a) An American in Paris b) Gigi c) High Society

ANSWERS PAGE 257

SECTION 7 – WINE HISTORY, GRAPE VARIETIES, AND FACTS ON MAKING, TASTING, KEEPING AND BUYING WINE

These nine quizzes are all on the practical and factual nature of wine.

The history of winemaking is examined along with 2 quizzes on which grape varieties are used for famous wines worldwide.

Winemaking, opening, keeping, serving and tasting wines along with wine laws and labels are also covered.

Finally there is a quiz on world famous wine brands and wine based drinks.

Hopefully you will enjoy finding out how much you know about types of wine grapes, wine culture and the process and practices of production and consumption.

The 9 Quizzes are:

QUIZ 79 – THE HISTORY OF WINE

QUIZ 80 – WINE GRAPE VARIETIES – PART 1

QUIZ 81 – WINE GRAPE VARIETIES – PART 2

QUIZ 82 – THE WINE YEAR, TERROIR, AND WINEMAKING

QUIZ 83 – WINE LABELS AND WINE LAWS

QUIZ 84 – OPENING, KEEPING AND SERVING WINE

QUIZ 85 – BUYING AND SELLING WINE

QUIZ 86 – WINE TASTING AND FOOD MATCHING

QUIZ 87 – WINE BRANDS AND WINE BASED DRINKS

QUIZ 79 – THE HISTORY OF WINE

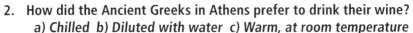

1. In which country is the 'believed to be' oldest winery in the world, which was discovered in a cave in 2012. It dates back to circa 4000 BC?
   a) Armenia b) Georgia c) Israel

2. How did the Ancient Greeks in Athens prefer to drink their wine?
   a) Chilled b) Diluted with water c) Warm, at room temperature

3. In Roman times, how did they keep and store their wines until they were ready to drink them?
   a) In clay amphorae
   b) In large earthenware pots or jars
   c) In goat skins

4. About when, far back in time, were the first vineyards planted in the Burgundy region of France?
   a) Circa 100 to 180 AD b) Circa 300 to 380 AD c) Circa 500 to 580 AD

5. Which Holy Roman Emperor created detailed rules and laws for planting vines and winemaking to improve the quality of the wine in France and Germany, in the 9th century AD?
   a) Emperor Charlemagne b) Emperor Francis c) Emperor Maximilian

6. Which Pope 'who loved wine' was a native of Bordeaux, and from 1305 owned a top rated famous wine-producing Château in the Graves region, which still bears his name today?
   a) Benedict XI b) Clement V c) Celestine V

7. When were vineyards first planted in Madeira by Portuguese explorers and settlers?
   a) 1300s b) 1400s c) 1500s

8. Which holy order of monks were the first to plant and cultivate the finest vineyards in Europe at the time, starting with their Mother Monasteries in Cluny, Burgundy, and in Monte Cassino, Italy?
   a) Benedictines b) Cistercians c) Franciscans

9. Which of these wine estates of Pomerol, on the Bordeaux right bank, made its first ever vintage in 1979 and is now amongst the three most expensive wines in the world?
   a) Le Pin b) Petrus c) Château Lafleur.

10. The 1945 vintage, just at the end of World War II, is now pronounced to be (by many wine experts) 'the single most incredible vintage of the 20th century'. For which type of wine?
    a) Bordeaux in France b) Port in Portugal c) Chianti in Italy.

QUIZ 80 – WINE GRAPE VARIETIES – PART 1

1. Pinot Meunier, the third of the famous champagne grape varieties, after Chardonnay and Pinot Noir, is what colour?
   a) Red b) White

2. What is the most planted red grape variety in Pomerol and St-Emilion, right bank of the Bordeaux Region?
   a) Cabernet Sauvignon b) Merlot c) Pinot Noir

3. The Riesling grape variety is planted in the highest abundance and volume proportion in which country?
   a) Austria b) Germany c) France

4. The noble Nebbiolo grape, produced for long ageing in oak barrels, makes the classic and expensive red Barolo wine, in which wine region of Italy?
   a) Lombardy b) Piedmont c) Puglia

5. The Albariño and Godello grapes from Spain are mainly planted in which wine region?
   a) Galicia b) Navarra c) Rueda

Riesling

6. The Malbec red wine grape used to be called Cot or Auxerrois when made in the French Cahors region. It is now the most prevalent and iconic grape variety in which South American country?
   a) Argentina b) Chile c) Uruguay

7. Which classic grape variety produces the fresh, tense, limpid yet stony white wines of Chablis in France?
   a) Cabernet Sauvignon
   b) Chardonnay
   c) Chenin Blanc

Chardonnay

8. Which of these is not a wine grape variety?
   a) Bonarda b) Brunello c) Bucelas

9. Canada's Ice Wine, a stunning sweet and very expensive dessert wine, was traditionally only made with, and is still now made mostly from, which grape variety?
   a) Chardonnay b) Riesling c) Vidal

Viognier

10. Which grape variety can sometimes smell of petrol, in a nice but strange way. It is often a sign of high quality and intensity as the wine ages?
    a) Gewürztraminer b) Muscat c) Riesling

Chenin Blanc

QUIZ 81 – WINE GRAPE VARIETIES – PART 2

ANSWERS PAGE 264

1. Which famous wine grape is called Spätburgunder in Germany, and in Switzerland it is called Blauburgunder?
   a) Chardonnay b) Gamay c) Pinot Noir

2. Tannat is a thick skinned red grape with a high tannin content. In which country is it now the most prominent grape variety, and also considered to be the country's national grape?
   a) Brazil b) Croatia c) Uruguay

3. Which grape variety can be described as bone dry, sometimes with green gooseberry fruit, and a slightly smoky perfume?
   a) Chenin Blanc b) Gewürztraminer c) Sauvignon Blanc

4. Which of these is not a grape variety?
   a) Carignan b) Franken c) Roditis

5. Which country has the most Syrah vineyards, and produces the most Syrah, or Shiraz, red wine?
   a) Australia b) France c) USA

Zinfandel

6. Does the Bacchus grape variety produce red or white wine?
   a) Red b) White

7. Which grape variety was thought to be Merlot, in Chile, until quite recently?
   a) Cannonau
   b) Carmenère
   c) Monastrell

Pinot Noir

8. Assyrtiko is the native grape, and is mostly produced, in which country?
   a) Austria
   b) Greece
   c) Italy.

9. Which grape variety has all these six different names, dependent on the wine region and country in which it is grown – Aragonês, Cencibel, Tinto del País, Tinto Fino, Tinta Roriz and Ull de Llebre?
   a) Bobal
   b) Garnacha
   c) Tempranillo

Cabernet Sauvignon

10. The Palomino grape variety is the dominant grape used in producing which fortified wine?
    a) Marsala b) Port c) Sherry

Syrah

QUIZ 82 – THE WINE YEAR, TERROIR, AND WINEMAKING

1. When is peak harvest time for wine grapes in the Northern Hemisphere?
    a) July and August
    b) September and October
    c) November and December

2. When is the peak harvest time for wine grapes
    for vineyards planted in the Southern Hemisphere?
    a) January and February
    b) March and April
    c) May and June

3. In which wine growing area of France has it been traditional with white winemaking to put whole bunches of grapes with their stems into the fermentation vats, instead of the normal de-stemming?
    a) Bordeaux b) Burgundy c) Loire Valley

4. Which is the most expensive vineyard region in France, by cost per hectare, for buying vineyards that are classed growths, or premier crus?
    a) Bordeaux b) Burgundy c) Champagne

5. What is the average adaptive life of a wine grape vine?
    a) 10 to 20 years b) 25 to 35 years c) 35 to 45 years

6. What method is used to produce 'Orange' wine, which has lately become a very fashionable trend, especially in Italy, Eastern Europe, Australia and the USA?
    a) Red grapes gently pressed b) White grapes fermented with skins
    c) Red and white grapes fermented with skins

7. Which country in Europe has the largest area
    of land planted with vineyards?
    a) France b) Italy c) Spain

8. About how many 75cl bottles of wine do you
    get from a 'barrique' French oak barrel?
    a) 200 b) 300 c) 400

9. What is 'Botrytis', when applied to a white wine
    and its wine grapes?
    a) Excess tannin that makes the wine too astringent
    b) A fault that occurs when the wine is exposed to oxygen during fermentation
    c) A fungus infection that triggers 'Noble Rot'

Ribera del Duero. Denominación de Origen

10. What does 'fining' mean in winemaking?
    a) A process to remove the sediment b) A method for keeping the temperature low during fermentation c) Chilling to precipitate the formation of tartrate crystals

ANSWERS PAGE 266

QUIZ 83 – WINE LABELS AND WINE LAWS

1. The earliest wine labelling was found on clay wine jars in around 4000 BC. In which country?
   a) Egypt b) Greece c) Turkey

2. The oldest handwritten separate wine labels were produced on parchment and tied onto wine bottles in 1668. In which French wine region?
   a) Burgundy b) Champagne c) Rhône

3. During the late 18th century and early 19th century, metal wine labels of silver or pewter were made popular to hang around the neck of crystal decanters and wine bottles in which country?
   a) England b) France c) Germany

4. The first ever printed modern rectangular paper wine bottle labels were produced in Germany when Senefelder invented the lithography printing process in which year?
   a) 1728 b) 1768 c) 1798

5. Which wines were the first to include bright colours, including gold and silver, onto their printed wine bottle labels in the 1850s?
   a) Barolos b) Champagnes c) Sauternes

6. In which decade did countries first introduce wine label laws stipulating the minimum information required to be printed on the label?
   a) 1920s b) 1930s c) 1950s

7. Which Bordeaux wine estate has a different famous artist paint and design a label for every vintage year; the artists include Chagall, Dalí, Miró, Henry Moore, Picasso, Andy Warhol and many others?
   a) Château Margaux b) Château Mouton Rothschild
   c) Petrus

8. Which Australian winery copied the famous Bordeaux Château and had Australian artists paint and design a label for every vintage of their top wines, from 1980 onwards?
   a) De Bortoli b) Leeuwin Estate c) Penfolds

9. The quality wines with labels 'Big Ass Red' and 'White Trash White' are from which country or region?
   a) Australia b) California c) South Africa

10. What is the name given to collectors of the different, individually designed, top capsules 'caps' from champagne bottles?
    a) Coleopterists b) Placomusophiles
    c) Oenophilliasts

QUIZ 84 – OPENING, KEEPING, AND SERVING WINE

1. In which century were corkscrews invented?
    a) 16th century
    b) 17th century
    c) 18th century

2. What proportion of New Zealand wines now use screw caps?
    a) 60% b) 75% c) 90% Plus

3. Which country produces between 60% to 70% of all the cork used for wine bottles?
    a) Greece b) Portugal c) Spain

4. Which red wines produced from these grapes should be paler in colour, and lighter in body?
    a) Malbec b) Pinot Noir c) Syrah

5. For how long do wine experts suggest that you should keep New Zealand Sauvignon Blanc before drinking it?
    a) Drink youngest available b) 3 to 5 years c) Over 5 years

6. What is the ideal temperature for a top red Bordeaux, Châteauneuf-du-Pape, Barolo or Brunello to be served/drunk at?
    a) 13C to 16C (55F to 60F) b) 18C to 21C (65F to 70F)
    c) 24C to 27C (75F to 80F)

7. If a red wine is very deep in colour, smells peppery with a hint of spice and tobacco, and a taste of blackberries, blueberries, mint and herbs, which wine is it likely to be?
    a) Merlot b) Pinot Noir c) Syrah

8. Which of these professional wine qualifications is the hardest to achieve, or at least there are fewer people in the world currently who have attained it?
    a) Master of Wine b) Master Sommelier

9. The appearance of which of these is a good indication of a mature, well aged fine wine, either red or white?
    a) Lees, a sediment on the bottom b) Legs, tracks left around and down the side of a glass when swirled c) A wide, pale or colourless rim at the top of the glass when swirled

10. For how long is it suggested that you can keep a top red 'classed growth' Bordeaux wine, if it is at proper temperatures (8C to 14C) in a cellar-type environment, for it still to be in top mature condition?
    a) 10 to 12 years b) 18 to 24 years c) 30 to 50 years

ANSWERS PAGE 270

QUIZ 85 – BUYING AND SELLING WINE

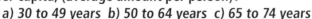

1. Which of these is the oldest Wine Merchant
   in the UK, founded in 1698?
   a) Berry Bros. & Rudd
   b) Justerini & Brooks
   c) Lay & Wheeler

BY APPOINTMENT TO
H.M THE QUEEN
WINE & SPIRIT MERCHANTS
LONDON

2. Which of these age groups in the UK
   drinks the most red wine in volume,
   per capita, (average amount per person)?
   a) 30 to 49 years b) 50 to 64 years c) 65 to 74 years

3. Which auction house sells the most wine worldwide per annum in
   value terms?
   a) Acker Merrall & Condit
   b) Sotheby's
   c) Zachys

4. What percentage of wine by volume is bought at the big eight
   supermarket chains in the UK?
   a) 40% to 50% b) 55% to 65% c) 70% to 80%

5. If you bought a special Rehoboam of champagne or wine for a party
   or wedding, how many normal 75cl bottles would it hold?
   a) 4 b) 6 c) 8

6. What is the most popular wine brand for the past 5 years by volume
   and value in the UK?
   a) Barefoot from California
   b) Blossom Hill from USA
   c) Hardy's from Australia

7. Which country drinks the most Prosecco
   sparkling wine from Italy?
   a) Germany b) UK c) USA

8. Which grape variety is the favourite of the British public by volume in
   an average year?
   a) Chardonnay b) Pinot Grigio c) Sauvignon Blanc

9. Which wine retailer in the UK won, yet again, in 2019 the award for
   'Online Wine Retailer of the Year'?
   a) Lay & Wheeler b) Majestic c) The Wine Society

10. How old is the average red wine when opened and drunk
    at home in the UK?
    a) 1 to 3 years
    b) 4 to 7 years
    c) 8 to 15 years

ANSWERS PAGE 272

QUIZ 86 – WINE TASTING AND FOOD MATCHING

1. If a Bordeaux red wine has the look of a deep bluish purple colour with no pale rim to its edge, about how many years old is it likely to be?
   a) 2 to 5 years
   b) 6 to 10 years
   c) 11 to 20 years

Fruit Aromas
Herb Aromas
Earth Aromas
Other Smells
Intensity

SMELL

2. Which of these white wines of vintage 1990 would be the most amber in colour, and the darkest looking, after being cellared/kept for 30+ years?
   a) Burgundy b) Champagne c) Sauternes

3. Which white wine is said to have these specific flavours and aromas – grassy, nettles, zingy and crisp, lime notes, green apples and passion fruit?
   a) Chardonnay b) Sauvignon Blanc c) Viognier

4. Which red grape produces a wine with this nose and flavours profile – peppery, spicy herbs, bacon, tobacco and smoke, vanilla, and blackberry fruit?
   a) Malbec b) Merlot c) Syrah

5. Which famous wine taster and critic was welcomed into Decanter Magazine's 'Hall of Fame' in 2020?
   a) Gerard Basset b) Hugh Johnson c) Robert Parker

6. Which of these sizes of wine bottle ages and matures red wine at the slowest rate per year?
   a) 75cl bottle b) Magnum c) Jeroboam

7. Which of these wines should, according to wine sommeliers, match and complement best a green Thai curry?
   a) Chenin Blanc b) Gewürtztraminer c) Sauvignon Blanc

8. Which wine has been, traditionally for two centuries, the classic French pairing with foie gras?
   a) Chardonnay b) Pinot Noir c) Sauternes

9. Which would a Master Sommelier say is the best of these three meats to serve with a top quality, mature Argentine Malbec Reserva red wine?
   a) Fillet or rib eye steak b) Grilled pork chops c) Roast leg of lamb

10. Why should you taste wine in a restaurant before it is then fully poured for everyone?
    a) To test that it is at the right temperature b) To test for cork taint and other flaws c) To ensure that you like it

ANSWERS PAGE 274

QUIZ 87 – WINE BRANDS AND WINE BASED DRINKS

1. Which wine brand was launched in the UK in the early 1970s by IDV (now Diageo), as a red wine which looked and sounded special, had a gold label, was in a special shaped bottle, and became an immediate best seller for decades?
    a) Black Tower b) Jacob's Creek c) Le Piat d'Or

2. Which UK supermarket has a wide range of House Wines branded as 'Taste the Difference'?
    a) Morrisons b) Sainsbury's c) Waitrose

3. Lillet is a French wine-based aperitif made in Podensac in the Bordeaux Region in red and white versions. Which two grapes make the white and red Lillet?
    a) Chardonnay & Pinot Noir b) Sémillon & Merlot
    c) Sauvignon Blanc & Cabernet Sauvignon

4. Which is the largest selling wine brand in the world, selling over 20 million cases a year?
    a) Barefoot b) Great Wall c) Sutter Home.

5. Which is the largest selling Australian wine brand, producing 30 different grape variety wines and selling over 8 million cases (100 million bottles) a year in the USA alone?
    a) Hardy's b) Oxford Landing c) Yellow Tail

6. Which large drinks company owns and produces Dubonnet red wine based aperitif in France?
    a) Constellation Brands b) Heaven Hill c) Pernod Ricard

7. Which white wine brand was launched in the UK during 1970 and became the toast of the budget 'wine knowing' elite for decades, costing all of £1.79 in 1979?
    a) Barossa Pearl b) Hirondelle c) Saint Mont

8. Noilly Prat, called the original French vermouth launched by Louis Noilly and Claude Prat in 1856, was and is produced in which region of France?
    a) Burgundy b) Jura c) Provence

9. Which brand of wine has been consistently voted as 'Europe's most admired wine brand' for over nine years in a row?
    a) Antinori b) Calvet c) Torres

10. Which wine brand is from the largest producer of table wine in the whole of Latin America. This single brand exports over 15 million cases of wine a year?
    a) Concha y Toro b) Cono Sur c) Santa Rita

DARK HORSE

BLUE NUN
1987 LIEBFRAUMILCH
RHEINHESSEN QUALITÄTSWEIN
VIN BLANC
WHITE WINE

SECTION 8 – ICONIC WINES AND WINE TYPES OF THE WORLD

The thirteen final selection of quizzes in The World of Wine Quiz Book are all on iconic, famous or critically acclaimed wines of the world.

The first four quizzes are on iconic wines of the Old and New World.

The next six quizzes are all on separate types of wines – white, red, sparkling, sweet, fortified and pinks.

Finally there are three quizzes on general wine knowledge to take you full circle from the introductory quizzes that started the book.

The 13 Wine Quizzes are:

QUIZ 88 – ICONIC WINES OF EUROPE

QUIZ 89 – ICONIC WINES OUTSIDE EUROPE

QUIZ 90 – MATCH ICONIC WINES OF THE WORLD – Part 1

QUIZ 91 – MATCH ICONIC WINES OF THE WORLD – Part 2

QUIZ 92 – WHITE WINES OF THE WORLD

QUIZ 93 – RED WINES OF THE WORLD

QUIZ 94 – SPARKLING WINES OF THE WORLD

QUIZ 95 – SWEET DESSERT WINES OF THE WORLD

QUIZ 96 – FORTIFIED WINES OF THE WORLD

QUIZ 97 – PINK, BLUSH AND ORANGE WINES OF THE WORLD

QUIZ 98 – MATCH REGIONS/COUNTRIES WITH THEIR PRIME GRAPE VARIETIES

QUIZ 99 – FINALE OF GENERAL WINE QUESTIONS – Part 1

QUIZ 100 - FINALE OF GENERAL WINE QUESTIONS – Part 2

QUIZ 88 – ICONIC WINES OF EUROPE

1. Which wine estate is deemed by wine critics to be the pinnacle and essence of Châteauneuf-du-Pape?
   a) Château de Beaucastel b) Château Mont-Redon c) Vieux Telegraphe

2. Which classed growth wine from Margaux in Bordeaux is judged as showing 'complex aromas and perfume with serious elegance and grace, becoming profound as it ages'?
   a) Château Giscours b) Château Palmer c) Château Rauzan-Ségla

3. Which red Burgundy estate is seen as the most prestigious, only producing Grand Cru wines and circa 6,000 bottles a year at a cost of £2k to £10K per bottle, depending on the vintage?
   a) Domaine Leroy b) Domaine de Comtes Lafon
   c) Domaine de la Romanée-Conti

4. Which world-famous sweet dessert Bordeaux wine is made from almost 100% Sémillon grapes, and is often the most prized and expensive sweet wine in the world?
   a) Château Coutet b) Château Suduiraut c) Château d'Yquem

5. Which Pomerol wine from the Bordeaux region only started in 1979, and is often the most expensive wine in the world because it only produces 7k to 8k bottles of 100% Merlot per vintage?
   a) Château Lafleur b) Petrus c) Le Pin

6. Egon Muller Scharzhofberger Riesling Trockenbeerenauslese has always been the most expensive wine in Germany. Which area is it from?
   a) Mosel b) Nahe c) Rheingau

7. Which French wine has, by average vintage prices over time, been the most expensive wine in the world, according to the Guinness Book of Records?
   a) Domaine de la Romanée-Conti b) Petrus c) Château d'Yquem

8. Which is the new iconic, rarest, and most consistently costly red wine in Spain, overtaking Vega Sicilia, which was the flagship iconic wine for over 100 years?
   a) Alvaro Palacios L'Ermita (Priorat)
   b) Dominio de Pingus (Ribera del Duero) c) Teso La Monja (Toro)

9. Which of these is a Super Tuscan wine made from a Bordeaux blend of grapes with Sangiovese added?
   a) Castello di Ama b) Castello di Brolio c) Tignanello

10. Which champagne is only made as a vintage Blanc de Blancs, and only released in 'superlative years'. Only 3 to 4 vintages are ever produced for each decade?
    a) Dom Pérignon b) Krug c) Salon

QUIZ 89 – ICONIC WINES OUTSIDE EUROPE

1. Screaming Eagle Cabernet Sauvignon 1992 sold for $500,000 for an Imperial size bottle at a charity auction in the year 2000. Where is it from?
   a) California b) Oregon c) Washington State

2. Which Bordeaux First Growth Château now also owns iconic wineries in Chile (Los Vascos), Argentina (Domaine Caro), and in China (Domaine de Long Dai)?
   a) Château Lafite Rothschild
   b) Château Latour
   c) Château Margaux

3. The most expensive Ice Wine ever sold was Royal DeMaria Chardonnay vintage 2000 from Canada, which sold as a half-bottle to a Saudi Prince in 2006 for how much?
   a) $30,000 b) $50,000 c) $70,000

4. Cloudy Bay, the first iconic New Zealand wine, was founded by David Hohnen in 1985 and then sold in 2003 to which company?
   a) Moët & Chandon b) LVMH c) Veuve Clicquot

5. Chateau Musar, from the Bekaa Valley in Lebanon, was founded by Gaston Hochar in which decade?
   a) 1930s b) 1950s c) 1970s

6. Penfolds Grange Hermitage Bin 95, the long-time iconic red wine of Australia, is made from 95%+ of which grape variety?
   a) Cabernet Sauvignon b) Merlot c) Shiraz

7. Noemia Malbec from Argentina, which can sell for over £200 a bottle, is grown and produced in which wine region?
   a) Mendoza b) Rio Negro c) Salta

8. Camel Valley Winery in England, which has won many more wine awards than any other English Winery, is situated in which county?
   a) Cornwall b) Kent c) Sussex

9. Groot Constantia Grand Constance dessert wine (a favourite of Napoleon, European Kings and Tzars of Russia), is made from which grape variety?
   a) Muscat b) Sauvignon Blanc c) Sémillon

10. The oldest winery in the New World is situated in the Coahuila region of Mexico, and was founded by the Spanish Conquistadors in 1597. What is the wine estate called?
    a) Casa Madero b) Chateau Camou c) Monte Xanic

ANSWERS PAGE 282

QUIZ 90 – MATCH ICONIC WINES OF THE WORLD – PART 1

Wine Chateaux of the World *Country and Wine Region*

1. Chateau Musar

a) Australia, Barossa Valley

2. Chateau Ste Michelle

b) France, Bordeaux

3. Château Montrose

c) USA, Washington State

4. Château Tanunda

d) Lebanon, Bekaa Valley

5. Chateau Los Boldos

e) Chile, Cachapoal Valley

Wine Country and Wine Type *Grape Variety*

6. Canadian, Ice Wine

f) Chardonnay

7. Italian, Chianti

g) Tempranillo

8. French, Chablis

h) Vidal

9. Spanish, Rioja

i) Touriga Nacional

10. Portuguese, Douro

j) Sangiovese

QUIZ 91 – MATCH ICONIC WINES OF THE WORLD – PART 2

Iconic Wine Brands and Estates   *Grape Variety*

1. Cloudy Bay, New Zealand   *a) White Zinfandel*

2. Blossom Hill, USA   *b) Merlot*

3. Petrus, France   *c) Malbec*

4. Catena Zapata, Argentina   *d) Pinotage*

5. Kanonkop, South Africa   *e) Sauvignon Blanc*

Iconic Winemakers' Wines   *Type of Wine*

6. Adriano Adami   *f) Barbaresco, Red*

7. Nicolas Feuillatte   *g) Burgundy, White*

8. Angelo Gaja   *h) Prosecco, Sparkling*

9. Marqués de Riscal   *i) Champagne, Sparkling*

10. Jean-Marc Brocard   *j) Rioja, Red*

ANSWERS PAGE 288

QUIZ 92 – WHITE WINES OF THE WORLD

1. What is the name of the famous white wine, made from Viognier grapes, that lies within Condrieu's appellation in the northern Rhône?
   a) *Château-Grillet*
   b) *Château de Beaucastel*
   c) *Château d'Yquem*

2. Which well-known grape variety, commonly grown in England, has the name of a famous Roman God?

3. The high quality wine region of Kamptal is in which European country?
   a) *Germany* b) *Luxembourg* c) *Austria*

4. From which Greek island has wine produced from the famous Assyrtiko grape variety won most awards?
   a) *Crete* b) *Santorini* c) *Samos*

5. In the 1976 'Judgement of Paris' when top Californian wines competed with top French wines in a blind tasting in Paris, which Californian wine won the white wine section?
   a) *Chateau Montelena* b) *Stag's Leap* c) *William Hill Estate*

6. The famous Cloudy Bay Sauvignon Blanc is produced in which New Zealand wine region?
   a) *Central Otago* b) *Marlborough* c) *Hawke's Bay*

7. In which wine region in Germany is Silvaner the most planted grape variety?
   a) *Mosel* b) *Baden* c) *Franken*

8. Which Portuguese city is closest to the production region of the famous Vinho Verde?
   a) *Porto* b) *Lisbon* c) *Faro*

9. Which Argentine white grape variety has been enjoying increasing popularity in recent years?
   a) *Torrontés* b) *Muscat of Alexandria* c) *Chenin Blanc*

10. What is the name of the wine region in Mexico that produces about 85% of the country's wine?
    a) *Baja California* b) *Baja Arizona* c) *Baja New Mexico*

ANSWERS PAGE 290

QUIZ 93 – RED WINES OF THE WORLD

1. What is the name of the Beaujolais Cru wine that's named after the local windmill?

2. What are the two grape varieties that were crossed to make the well-known South African grape, Pinotage?
   a) Pinot Noir and Cinsaut
   b) Pinot Noir and Merlot
   c) Pinot Noir and Syrah

3. The famous wine, Penfolds Grange, is produced in which country?
   a) USA b) England c) Australia

4. Which one of the following grape varieties is used in the production of Port?
   a) Tannat
   b) Malmsey
   c) Touriga Nacional

5. Blaufränkisch is the most popular red grape variety grown in the region of Burgenland. Where is Burgenland?
   a) Germany
   b) Austria
   c) Switzerland

6. Oregon is most well-known for producing which red grape variety?
   a) Pinot Noir b) Malbec c) Merlot

7. The famous estate of Château de Beaucastel is in which wine region?
   a) Loire Valley
   b) St-Emilion
   c) Rhône Valley

8. The Italian red Bardolino wine is produced in a region that borders which famous lake?
   a) Lake Garda
   b) Lake Como
   c) Lake Maggiore

9. What is the name of the red grape variety which, since the 1990s, has become synonymous with Argentina?
   a) Tannat b) Malbec c) Merlot

10. The famous Chateau Musar red wine is produced in which country?
    a) Syria
    b) Israel
    c) Lebanon

ANSWERS PAGE 292

QUIZ 94 – SPARKLING WINES OF THE WORLD

1. Which champagne house has a premium marque called Comtes de Champagne?
2. Which sparkling wine's top wine-producing region is Conegliano Valdobbiadene?
3. The well-known sparkling wine brand, Jansz, is produced in which Australian State?
   a) Tasmania b) South Australia c) New South Wales
4. Most Cava sparkling wine is produced in which part of Spain?
   a) La Mancha b) Penedès c) Galicia
5. English sparkling wine produced in Kent and Sussex can be called champagne. True or False?
6. Two of the three main grape varieties used to produce champagne are red. One is Pinot Noir, what is the name of the other one?
   a) Pinot Meunier
   b) Grenache
   c) Merlot
7. The 'Tank Method' is a lower cost system to produce the secondary fermentation in making many sparkling wines. What is the other, French-sounding, name for this method?
   a) Pasteur Method
   b) Carbonaté Method
   c) Charmat Method
8. Franciacorta is a high quality Italian sparkling wine from which region?
   a) Lombardy b) Tuscany c) Piedmont
9. Which famous champagne house owns the Californian sparkling wine, Domaine Carneros?
   a) Mumm b) Taittinger c) Moët & Chandon
10. Which award-winning Argentine sparkling wine from Mendoza has a second name that sounds like a French artist?
    a) Jasmine Manet
    b) Jasmine Degas
    c) Jasmine Monet

QUIZ 95 – SWEET DESSERT WINES OF THE WORLD

1. From which French wine area are Château
   Climens, Château Coutet and Château Suduiraut?
   a) *Bordeaux*
   b) *Loire Valley*
   c) *Provence*

2. What is generally the most expensive
   sweet dessert white wine in the world?
   a) *Scharzhofberger Riesling Trockenbeerenauslese*
   b) *Royal Tokaji Essencia*
   c) *Château d'Yquem*

3. From which grape variety is most of New Zealand's top quality sweet
   dessert wines made?
   a) *Chenin Blanc* b) *Riesling* c) *Sémillon*

4. The famous Italian fortified dessert wine, Marsala, is produced in
   what part of Italy?
   a) *Puglia* b) *Sardinia* c) *Sicily*

5. Which grape variety makes the high quality and expensive sweet wine
   of South Africa's Groot Constantia wine estate?
   a) *Chenin Blanc* b) *Muscat* c) *Sémillon*

6. Which of these wine areas of Germany produces the most quality
   sweet dessert wines in volume and value terms?
   a) *Baden* b) *Mosel* c) *Rheinhessen*

7. Which of these is not a fortified sweet white wine?
   a) *Banyuls* b) *Malaga* c) *Vin Santo.*

8. Which country now makes the most 'Ice Wine' or 'Eiswein' in volume
   and value?
   a) *Canada* b) *Germany* c) *Switzerland*

9. Which grape variety makes the vast majority of sweet 'nectar-like'
   Tokaji Aszú wines in Hungary, the world's oldest sweet wine?
   a) *Furmint* b) *Muscat* c) *Kabar*

10. What is the winemakers' technical name for 'Noble Rot' which before
    harvest time attacks the grape
    bunches and shrivels the berries,
    thus concentrating the sweetness?
    a) *Botrytis Cinerea*
    b) *Plasmopara Viticola*
    c) *Phylloxera*

ANSWERS PAGE 296

QUIZ 96 – FORTIFIED WINES OF THE WORLD

1. Madeira wine produced on the eponymous island, has four main styles. Malmsey, Sercial, and Verdelho are three. What is the name of the other one?
   a) Marsala b) Bual c) Palomino

2. What is the name of the fortified wine produced in the champagne region?
   a) Ratafia b) Pinotia c) Epernay Doux

3. What is the name of this ancient wine from Cyprus that can be both fortified and non-fortified?
   a) Emvadaria b) Commandaria c) Limassoria

4. What is the name of the Canadian winemaker who produces fortified wine from Black Muscat grapes?
   a) Paul Bosc
   b) Andrew Quady
   c) Emma Garner

5. Pineau des Charentes is a fortified wine derived from which well-known French spirit?

6. Which one of the following is one of the main grapes grown to produce Sherry?
   a) Palomino
   b) Garnacha Blanca
   c) Viura

7. What is the name of this South African producer who is famous for making Port-style wines?
   a) De Krans
   b) Hamilton Russell
   c) Paul Sauer

8. What is the name of this grape, that's also known as Aragonês in Portugal, that is one of the three main grapes used to produce Port?
   a) Bastardo b) Baga c) Tinta Roriz

9. The famous aperitif, Dubonnet, is produced in which country?
   a) France b) Switzerland c) Belgium

10. What is the name of this Greek red grape variety that makes a well-known local fortified wine?
    a) Mavrobella
    b) Mavrodaphne
    c) Mavrodoris

QUIZ 97 – PINK, BLUSH, AND ORANGE WINES OF THE WORLD

1. Which country produces the most rosé wine in the world, by volume and value?
   a) France b) Spain c) USA

2. What is Orange wine and how is it made?
   a) Produced by fermenting oranges
   b) Combining red and white grapes and gently pressing
   c) Fermenting with white grape skins included

3. Which grape variety is most frequently used nowadays in the production of rosé wines worldwide?
   a) Grenache
   b) Pinot Noir
   c) Syrah

4. Where were Orange wines first produced in the world?
   a) Australia b) Georgia c) Italy

5. What is the wine called that is produced by lightly pressing red grapes, then fermenting the resulting juice without the skins?
   a) Blush Wines
   b) Pink Wines
   c) Vin Gris

6. Which wine region in France makes the most rosé wine in volume and value?
   a) Bordeaux b) Provence c) Rhône

7. In which decade was the term 'Blush Wine' invented and first used commercially?
   a) 1950s b) 1970s c) 1990s

8. Which of these wines is not a top quality rosé grown in the Provence region of the South of France?
   a) Guigal Tavel
   b) Château Miraval
   c) Whispering Angel

9. Which grape variety produces the most blush wine in the USA?
   a) Cabernet Sauvignon
   b) Pinot Noir
   c) Zinfandel

10. Which is the most expensive rosé 'pink champagne', also awarded the highest points in blind tastings by professional tasters?
    a) Dom Pérignon Rosé
    b) Krug Rosé
    c) Louis Roederer Cristal Rosé

ANSWERS PAGE 300

QUIZ 98 – MATCH REGIONS/COUNTRIES WITH THEIR PRIME GRAPE VARIETIES

1. Barossa Valley

2. Burgundy

3. Tuscany

4. Santorini

5. Argentina

6. New Zealand

7. Médoc

8. Austria

9. Switzerland

10. South Africa

a) Grüner Veltliner

b) Assyrtiko

c) Chasselas

d) Pinot Noir

e) Chenin Blanc

f) Cabernet Sauvignon

g) Sauvignon Blanc

h) Shiraz

i) Sangiovese

j) Malbec

ANSWERS PAGE 302

QUIZ 99 – FINALE OF GENERAL WINE QUESTIONS – PART 1

1. In which French region is the
   wine Pouilly-Fuissé produced?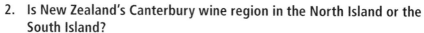
   a) *Loire Valley*
   b) *Côte Chalonnaise*
   c) *Mâconnais*

2. Is New Zealand's Canterbury wine region in the North Island or the
   South Island?

3. In which Italian region is the well-known wine Orvieto produced?
   a) *Umbria*
   b) *Lazio*
   c) *Abruzzo*

4. Which is the driest of these
   Madeira wine styles?
   a) *Bual*
   b) *Sercial*
   c) *Verdelho*

5. In which Californian wine region is
   the famous Stag's Leap produced?
   a) *Napa Valley*
   b) *Santa Barbara*
   c) *Monterey*

ANSWERS PAGE 304

6. The Mosel river flows into the River Rhine at which German town?
   a) *Mainz*
   b) *Bingen*
   c) *Koblenz*

7. In which Australian state is the well-known Yarra Valley wine region?
   a) *Victoria*
   b) *New South Wales*
   c) *South Australia*

8. Which Spanish wine region has the same name as the Spanish word
   for 'bull'?

9. Which South African grape variety is a cross of Pinot Noir and Cinsaut?

10. Which major river runs through many of Austria's prime wine regions?
    a) *River Rhine*
    b) *River Danube*
    c) *River Po*

QUIZ 100 – FINALE OF GENERAL WINE QUESTIONS – PART 2

1. What is the northernmost wine region on New Zealand's North Island?
   a) Northland
   b) Hawke's Bay
   c) Auckland

2. Around which Spanish town is the very dry Manzanilla sherry produced?
   a) Jerez de la Frontera
   b) Cádiz
   c) Sanlúcar de Barrameda

3. The wine region of Bourgueil in the Loire Valley has a neighbouring region which includes the same name. What is it called?
   a) St-Cristóbal-de-Bourgueil
   b) St-Denis-de-Bourgueil
   c) St-Nicolas-de-Bourgueil

4. The tiny country of San Marino produces wine? True or False?

5. Which region produces by far the most Ice Wine in Canada?
   a) Quebec
   b) Ontario
   c) British Columbia

6. What is the northernmost Beaujolais Cru?
   a) Chénas
   b) Juliénas
   c) St-Amour

7. Which mountain range borders both Chilean and Argentine wine growing areas?

8. What is the name of the main city of Piedmont?
   a) Milan
   b) Turin
   c) Verona

9. What is the name of the famous wine region that's about a 3 hour drive south of Perth?

10. In the Champagne region, there is the 'Perching Bar' near the town of Verzy. What is it?
    a) A treetop champagne bar
    b) A bar overlooking Crane nesting sites
    c) A bar with stools in the shape of champagne corks

THE AMPLIFIED ANSWERS

ANSWERS TO QUIZ 1 – GENERAL WINE QUESTIONS – PART 1

1. *b. Spain.* Produced in the Ribera del Duero region in the north of the country, Vega Sicilia Unico is one of the highest quality, most expensive, and prestigious wines in Spain. It was founded in 1864 by Don Eloy Lecanda y Chaves, who brought local grapes from Bordeaux – Cabernet Sauvignon, Merlot and Malbec, and planted them along with the local Spanish grape Tinto Fino (Tempranillo). Today, a typical Vega Sicilia blend comprises Tinto Fino and Cabernet Sauvignon. It is known as Spain's 'First Growth', referring to the top classed growth clarets from Bordeaux.

2. *Alcohol By Volume.* A standard measure of how much alcohol is contained in a given volume of an alcoholic drink. For example, spirits are often 40% ABV, and wine is usually between 12% and 15% ABV. However, international wine labelling laws vary, and the ABV stated on the label in some countries is not always exactly what's in the bottle. A small variance, up or down, in the alcohol content is sometimes legally allowed.

3. *a. Cabernet Sauvignon.* Generally seen as the noblest of all red grape varieties, and now grown all around the world. It is the anchor in the 'Bordeaux Blends' behind such famous classed growth clarets as Château Lafite and Château Latour. It is very often unblended, as a single varietal, and the tasting characteristics of cedarwood or blackcurrants are a common occurrence in this famous grape variety.

4. *True.* Even though Chenin Blanc is the main white grape variety in the central Loire Valley, Sauvignon Blanc is the main one in eastern Loire, producing such wine as Sancerre, Pouilly-Fumé, and Quincy. Comparing the bouquet and taste of a Sancerre Sauvignon Blanc with a New Zealand Sauvignon Blanc shows the huge difference in character that this grape can achieve, with the vastly different terroirs of not just those two wine areas, but also in different terroirs in other countries around the world.

5. *a. Shiraz.* Also known as Syrah in different parts of the world. The terroir of the Barossa Valley, and the subsequent wine-making techniques, are perfect for producing rich and powerful Shiraz wines. The Barossa Valley is one of the world's leading wine regions for producing top quality Shiraz, capturing the distinctive elegant and vibrant flavours of this highly prized grape variety.

6. *b. Madeira.* Most notably famous for producing four different styles of Madeira wine. The sweetest traditional style is from the Malmsey grape. Bual

is slightly less sweet than Malmsey, and Verdelho is less sweet again, and softer, than Bual. Finally, Sercial is the driest variety and a delicious aperitif.

7. **c. South Africa.** Pinotage is a cross between Pinot Noir and Cinsaut. Historically, the Cinsaut grape was called Hermitage in South Africa, hence the name Pinotage. This grape variety is increasingly being grown in other parts of the world, but its origins lie in South Africa, where it is still a much-loved grape, producing quality wine.

8. **True.** The grape variety is now called Glera. Producers changed the name to Glera, and registered the original name as a geographical area, in order to protect Prosecco wine from imitation. The sparkle in Prosecco is usually produced by the less expensive Tank, or Charmat, Method of carbonation, rather than the more expensive champagne method, where the sparkle is produced by a lengthy, and more complicated, secondary fermentation in bottle.

9. **France.** For about 400 years, from the Thirty Years War to the Second World War, the region's ownership has been heavily contested between France and Germany and, indeed, changed hands on several occasions, as has the local language. However, since 1945 most Alsatians primarily speak French. It is easy to see how the architecture of Alsace regional towns and cities reflects the change of French and German ownership over the years.

10. **No.** Wine made from grapes grown in Britain is called English Wine or Welsh Wine. British Wine is usually made by fermenting imported grape juice from elsewhere in the world, and then fortifying it with a distilled spirit, which most commonly results in a 'sherry' type wine that used to be called British Sherry. Now, of course, it has to be labelled British Wine as, legally, Sherry has to come from a delimited region in Andalucía, Spain.

ANSWERS TO QUIZ 2 – GENERAL WINE QUESTIONS – PART 2

1. **True.** Grauburgunder, Pinot Gris, and Pinot Grigio are different names for the same white grape variety depending on the country where it's grown. The grapes normally have a greyish-blue tint to them, hence the name, but colours do vary, as does the character of the wine, according to wine region and terroir.

2. **a. Fermentation/Storage Vessel.** A qvevri is a large egg-shaped earthenware vessel, often sunk into the ground,

used for the fermentation, storage, and ageing of wine. Common in Georgia, they're also increasingly being used in other countries around the world, including England.

3. **b. Port.** There are several grape varieties used in the production of Port, but Touriga Nacional and Tinta Roriz are two of the main ones, along with Touriga Franca. The grapes are grown in the Douro Valley, but a large proportion of the wine is aged in the throng of shippers' lodges in Vila Nova de Gaia, just across the River Douro from Porto.

4. **b. Austria.** In 2020 the wine region of Wachau joined Kremstal and Kamptal as an official DAC (Districtus Austriae Controllatus), which is the high quality controlled appellation under Austrian wine laws. All three regions specialise in Riesling and Grüner Veltliner wines.

5. **River Loire.** The Loire vineyards begin just south-east of Orléans, at Pouilly-sur-Loire and Sancerre, where main grapes include Sauvignon Blanc and Pinot Noir. Then, as the river turns west at Orléans and flows through the middle Loire, Chenin Blanc and Cabernet Franc become the main grape varieties, finishing at the Atlantic Ocean at Nantes, where Muscadet is produced from the Melon de Bourgogne grape.

6. **b. Chasselas.** Easily the most planted grape in Switzerland, Chasselas is particularly prevalent in the western, French-speaking, part of the country. Chasselas is grown in some other countries in the world, but Switzerland is its true home. Its exuberant and powerful nature is well suited to the cool mountainous weather of Switzerland's alpine slopes.

7. **c. Camel Valley.** The award-winning Camel Valley vineyard at Bodmin in Cornwall produces red and white wines, as well as their more famous sparkling wines. Their Pinot Noir Rosé Brut has been a particular triumph, once described by a wine writer as not only one of the finest sparkling rosés in the UK, but also the world!

8. **Vinho Verde.** Produced in Portugal's northernmost province of Minho, Vinho Verde is made right up to the banks of the River Minho, which separates Portugal from the province of Galicia in Spain. 'Verde', meaning 'Green' refers to the fact that these are young wines, meant for drinking early, and are fresh, crisp, and lively.

9. **a. Australia.** Penfolds Grange is Australia's 'First Growth' and arguably its most celebrated wine. It is made almost entirely from Shiraz grapes, and usually with a very small proportion of Cabernet Sauvignon. The vineyards are predominantly in the Barossa Valley, Australia's most important wine region for producing Shiraz.

10. **b. Rhône Valley.** This famous appellation of Côte-Rôtie is located in the northern Rhône, just south of Vienne, and just north of Condrieu. Vineyards are on steep slopes, facing the Rhône river. Produced from the Syrah grape, and usually blended with a small amount of Viognier, the wines are powerful and elegant. The wine from the small appellation of Condrieu is produced from the Viognier grape variety, which has a very recognisable aroma of peaches, dried fruit, and white flowers, resulting in a rich and full-bodied wine. Château-Grillet is the most iconic estate within Condrieu's Appellation territory.

ANSWERS TO QUIZ 3 – MATCH THESE FAMOUS WINES OF THE NEW WORLD WITH THEIR COUNTRY/WINE AREA

1. **e. USA/California.** Established in 1876, Beringer is California's oldest continually operating winery. They're based in St. Helena in the famous Napa Valley region. Direct descendant, Mark Beringer, is the winemaker, and the main grape varieties are Cabernet Sauvignon, Merlot, Zinfandel, Pinot Noir, and Chardonnay.

2. **h. Australia/Victoria.** Established in the 1880s, Brown Brothers is a family run company based in Milawa, in the King Valley of north-east Victoria, producing a total of more than 60 varieties of red, white, sparkling and dessert wine. They also own vineyards in Tasmania.

3. **a. Canada/British Columbia.** Located in the town of Oliver in the South Okanagan region of British Columbia, Burrowing Owl Estate Winery is a relatively young producer, with its first vintage being in 1997. A wide variety of grapes are grown, including Cabernet Sauvignon, Merlot, Cabernet Franc, Syrah, Pinot Noir, Pinot Gris, and Chardonnay, all producing high quality wine.

4. **i. Mexico/Guadalupe Valley.** Founded in 1987, Monte Xanic winery is situated in the Valle de Guadalupe and was Mexico's first boutique winery. Winners of hundreds of medals in international wine competitions across the world, the company continues to produce top quality wines.

5. **b. Chile/Maipo.** Founded in 1880, the Santa Rita winery is located in Alto Jahuel in the beautiful Maipo Valley. It's one of the most prestigious and traditional wineries in Chile. They have an extensive range of wines and,

over the years, have won countless awards for their products. For Santa Rita, quality is key.

6. *d. Argentina/Mendoza.* Founded in 1963 by Alberto Zuccardi, this family-owned wine producer is now on its third generation. Zuccardi is one of Argentina's leading wine producing companies. Its hugely impressive winery is set against a backdrop of the Andes Mountains, and offers fantastic views of Mendoza's Uco Valley.

7. *j. USA/Oregon.* Producing excellent award-winning wines, Willamette Valley Vineyards is one of the top producers of Pinot Noir In the USA. Jim Bernau founded the company in 1983, and in 1988 carried out a 'crowd-funding' campaign as he believed that being owned by a community would be healthier for the business. It's now owned by over 16,000 wine enthusiast shareholders.

8. *c. New Zealand/Martinborough.* A highly respected family business, ranking amongst the top wine producers in New Zealand. The first Ata Rangi vines were planted in 1980. Their wines now feature on wine lists of some of the best restaurants in the world.

9. *f. South Africa/Stellenbosch.* A world-class wine estate, founded in the year 1700, Vergelegen is now one of the top wine-producers in South Africa, selling wines made from a wide range of grape varieties. Situated only about 30 miles from Cape Town, Vergelegen enjoys a mild climate due to its close proximity to the Atlantic Ocean at False Bay.

10. *g. Argentina/Salta.* Situated in the Cafayate Valley in the wine region of Salta, Bodegas Etchart was founded in 1850. At over 1,750 metres above sea level, it is one of the highest vinicultures in the world. A highly respected company, Etchart is one of Argentina's leading wine producers.

ANSWERS TO QUIZ 4 – MATCH THESE FAMOUS WINES OF EUROPE AND THE MIDDLE EAST WITH THEIR COUNTRY/WINE AREA

1. *e. France/Beaujolais.* The eponymous Georges Duboeuf, who died in January 2020 at the age of 86, was the founder of Les Vins Georges Duboeuf, one of the biggest wine merchants in France. He was particularly famous for his range of

wines from the Beaujolais region, and was hugely responsible for the success of Beaujolais Nouveau in its heyday.

2. **h. Italy/Piedmont.** The Gaja winery was founded in 1859 by Giovanni Gaja and is still family owned today, led by Angelo Gaja and his son and two daughters. They are chiefly known for their Barbaresco and Barolo wines and, indeed, Angelo Gaja is known as the 'King of Barbaresco'.

3. **i. Germany/Mittelmosel.** Dr. Loosen is one of Germany's great wine estates, and has been run by the same family for over 200 years. Currently owned by Ernst Loosen, the vineyards lie on the banks of the Mosel river. Dr. Loosen wines continue to receive glowing reviews in the wine press, and no doubt will carry on doing so.

4. **g. Spain/Priorat.** The small region of Priorat, lying close to Barcelona, is one of Spain's stand-out wine regions, and Scala Dei is one of the top producers in that region. Their vineyards are mainly planted with Garnacha and Cariñena grape varieties. Wine writers have consistently given high scores to the wines of Scala Dei.

5. **a. Austria/Wagram.** The high quality wine region of Wagram is approximately 70 miles west of Vienna. Bernard Ott is the eponymous owner of his company, and has been in charge for over 25 years. He is particularly famous for his excellent Grüner Veltliner, which is by far the largest planted grape variety in his vineyards.

6. **j. Lebanon/Bekaa Valley.** The Bekaa Valley is the main wine-growing region in Lebanon. Chateau Ksara was founded in 1857 by Jesuit priests, and is the oldest and largest winery in the country. Their wines are consistent award-winners every year.

7. **c. Israel/Galilee.** The Carmel winery was founded in 1882 by Baron Edmond de Rothschild, owner of Château Lafite in Bordeaux. Its wines are exported to countries all around the world. Most of Carmel's most recent vineyards are planted in the Upper Galilee region, where the majority of the company's finest wines are produced.

8. **b. Slovenia/Goriska Brda.** Krasno is the leading producer in Slovenia, and is a co-op, consisting of over 400 individual growers. They have built up their vineyard area over the last 50 years, and now cultivate over 1,000 hectares (approx. 2,500 acres).

9. **d. Hungary/Tokaj.** In 1994 the Count Degenfeld family successfully revived its wine estate, close to the town of Tokaj in the Tokaji wine region. Since then Grof Degenfeld, which also includes a luxury hotel, have produced high quality wines, chiefly from the leading grape varieties of Furmint,

Hárslevelü, and Yellow Muscat, and making the sweet Tokaji wine, including the famous Aszú.

10. **f. Greece/Santorini.** Founded in 1997, the Hatzidakis Winery is situated just outside the village of Pyrgos in Santorini. Known by many as 'The wizard of wine' Haridimos Hatzidakis was the considerably talented winemaker until, sadly, he died in 2017. His eldest daughter, Stella, has since taken over, and the company's wine, produced from grapes grown in organic vineyards, has continued to be of the highest quality

ANSWERS TO QUIZ 5 – ANAGRAMS – GENERAL

Well-Known Champagnes

1. **Pol Roger.** Founded in 1849, Pol Roger are based in Epernay. It was Winston Churchill's favourite champagne; indeed he was reputed to have drunk two bottles a day! They have a top-end champagne in his honour – Cuvée Sir Winston Churchill.

2. **Mercier.** Also based in Epernay, Mercier was established in 1858. A visit to their premises includes a tour on a small train, which takes people around some of their 18km of cellars. They are owned by the prestigious LVMH Group.

3. **Piper-Heidsieck.** Based in Reims, Piper Heidsieck is one of the oldest champagne houses, established in 1785. Their basic Cuvée Brut is dominated by the two red grapes, Pinot Noir and Pinot Meunier. Chardonnay is a much smaller player in the blend.

4. **Ruinart.** Based in Reims, Ruinart is the oldest champagne house, founded by Nicolas Ruinart in 1729. Now owned by the LVMH Group, the house style of Ruinart champagne is a pre-eminence of Chardonnay over Pinot Noir and Pinot Meunier.

5. **Duval-Leroy.** Founded in 1859 by Jules Duval and Edouard Leroy, Duval-Leroy are based in Vertus, a village in the Côte des Blancs region of champagne, about 13 miles south of Epernay. Still a private company, run by Carol Duval-Leroy and her three sons Julien, Charles, and Louis.

Well-Known Grape Varieties

6. **Chardonnay.** The most famous white wine grape in the world. It can take on various characters, depending on the viticulture and vinification. Rich and

buttery, or crisp and steely, oaked or unoaked and, of course, it's one of the vital grapes in producing champagne.

7. **Pinot Noir.** Famous for producing red burgundy, but also grown around the world. Particularly successful in New Zealand and Oregon, and in Germany where it is known as Spätburgunder. Also one of the important grapes for champagne production.

8. **Riesling.** Aristocratic white grape variety, and the most noble grape in Germany, Alsace, and Austria. It's usually unoaked and has a fresh and aromatic nose. It can make dry, semi-sweet, sweet, and sparkling wines.

9. **Sauvignon Blanc.** For most people, New Zealand, especially Marlborough, is the country that immediately comes to mind when the white grape of Sauvignon Blanc is mentioned. But it is also grown successfully around the world, and is best drunk relatively young.

10. **Malbec.** Particularly famous in Argentina. Until relatively recently, Malbec had long been a blending red grape and, indeed, it still is to a large extent. But Argentine producers have taken it in a different direction, producing hugely successful single varietal wine.

ANSWERS TO QUIZ 6 – WINES OF FRANCE – PART 1

1. **c. Rhône.** The red wine of Gigondas is produced from the Grenache, Syrah, and Mourvèdre grape varieties. Situated only about 15 miles north-east of Châteauneuf-du-Pape, the pretty village of Gigondas is dominated by the jagged limestone landmark of the Dentelles de Montmirail.

2. **c. Malbec.** The Small town of Cahors is around 100 miles east of Bordeaux, and the grapes grown in and around the town, to make the deep red coloured Cahors wine, are predominantly Malbec (locally known as both Côt and Auxerrois).

3. **River Loire.** Muscadet is produced around the mouth of the Loire river, in the Pays Nantais, at the western edge of the Loire wine region. It's made from the white Melon de Bourgogne grape variety. The best known Muscadet region is Sèvre et Maine, just east of Nantes, which has the majority of Muscadet vineyards.

4. **Burgundy/Côte de Nuits.** Chambolle Musigny is situated in the northern part of the Côte d'Or's Côte de Nuit. The wine is made from Burgundy's famous red grape, Pinot Noir. With the capacity to age easily for 10 to 20 years, Chambolle Musigny is a very high quality (and expensive) wine.

5. **b. 4th Growth.** There were five 'Growths' in the original 1855 Classification of Bordeaux. All wines included in the Classification are of high quality, so Château Talbot, even lying in the 4th Growth, is nevertheless a very fine claret. It is located in the Bordeaux commune of St-Julien, just south of the commune of Pauillac, which is home to the famous 1st Growths of Château Lafite, Latour, and Mouton Rothschild.

6. **St-Emilion.** A UNESCO World Heritage Site since 1999, St-Emilion is home to the four famous Premier Grand Cru Classé (A) wines of Châteaux Cheval Blanc, Ausone, Angélus and Pavie. Grapes are primarily a blend of Cabernet Franc and Merlot.

7. **a. Southern Rhône.** The town of Vinsobres is part of the district of Nyons in the southern Rhône wine region, lying about 20 miles north-east of the town of Orange. It was promoted to a stand-alone appellation in 2006. The Mediterranean-type climate is perfect for ripening the Grenache, Syrah, and Mourvèdre grapes used in the production of Vinsobres.

8. **c. Tavel.** Lirac was formerly also well-known for rosé wine in the southern Rhône, but it is increasingly being produced today as a soft, fruity red wine. So Tavel continues to be the stand-out rosé in the region. It is one of the finest food-friendly rosés in France, produced primarily from Grenache and Cinsault grapes.

9. **Reims.** Taittinger is a family-owned champagne house, based in Reims. Pierre-Emmanuel Taittinger stepped down from heading the company in 2019, since when his daughter, Vitalie, has taken over the reins, aided by her brother Clovis. Taittinger is one of the top 'Grandes Marques' champagnes.

10. **Morgon and Moulin-à-Vent.** Morgon is the second largest Beaujolais Cru after Brouilly. It is garnet red in colour, and relatively full-bodied for a Beaujolais wine. Probably the most prestigious of the ten Beaujolais Crus, Moulin-à-Vent is centred on the eponymous windmill, which is now a listed Historic Monument. Both wines are produced from the Gamay grape.

ANSWERS TO QUIZ 7 – WINES OF FRANCE – PART 2

1. ***Château Mouton Rothschild.*** They had to wait until 1973 before being elevated to First Growth status, after decades of lobbying. Even though Château Mouton Rothschild met the required conditions in 1855 for First Growth status, it is believed that they were omitted because the vineyard had recently been bought by an Englishman, and so was no longer under French ownership!

2. ***Château Lafite/Château Latour/Château Margaux/Château Haut-Brion.*** Château Lafite and Château Latour are in the Bordeaux commune of Pauillac, Château Margaux is in the commune of Margaux, and Château Haut-Brion is the only First Growth not in the Medoc, but in the commune of Pessac-Léognan, just off the southern borders of the city of Bordeaux.

3. ***b. Jura.*** This region is east of Burgundy, on the Swiss border. Château-Chalon is the most well-known 'Vin Jaune' style wine for which the Jura is famous. Made from the Savagnin grape variety, this style is achieved by picking the grapes when they are very ripe, fermenting, and then leaving them untopped-up in barrels for at least six years. A thin film of yeast forms on the surface and oxidation is very much a part of the process. It is an acquired taste!

4. ***No.*** A Blanc de Noirs champagne can only be made from one or both of the red champagne grapes – Pinot Noir and Pinot Meunier. Conversely, a Blanc de Blancs champagne can only be made from the white grape of Chardonnay.

5. ***a. Cabernet Franc.*** This grape ripens earlier than its more famous cousin Cabernet Sauvignon, which makes it more suitable for the cooler climate of the Loire wine region. Cabernet Franc is the red grape variety in the well-known middle Loire wines of Chinon, Bourgueil, and Saumur.

6. ***b. Chenin Blanc.*** The famous white grape of South Africa is also the prime white of the middle Loire. Here the Chenin Blanc grape has honeyed and floral aromas, with good fruit flavours and balanced acidity. In the Loire it is also known as the Pineau de la Loire. It is a versatile grape variety that can produce dry, sweet or sparkling wine.

7. ***Hospices de Beaune.*** The charity auction is held in the Hospices de Beaune annually in November. It's the most famous wine auction in the world. The Hospices was founded in 1443 by Nicolas Rolin, Chancellor of Burgundy, as a hospital for the poor. Profits from the sale are used for heritage conservation and hospitals.

8. *c. Alsace.* Other top producers in Alsace include Dopff, Humbrecht, and Trimbach. Hugel are based in the pretty Alsatian town of Riquewihr. The Hugel family have been making wine in Alsace since 1639, and still run the company today. They have been a major force in developing the Alsatian wine industry, particularly during the second half of the twentieth century, and continue to do so today.

9. *Côte Chalonnaise.* Mercurey is the best known of the four most important wine-producing towns in the Côte Chalonnaise. The other three being Montagny, Givry, and Rully. The Côte Chalonnaise region lies between Burgundy's Côte d'Or to the north and Mâconnais to the south. Mercurey wine can be both red and white, from Pinot Noir and Chardonnay grapes, but is most famous for its red.

10. *a. Champagne.* The prime Champagne region runs from the city of Reims in the north to the Côte des Blancs, below Epernay in the south. However, officially it continues further south, through Côte de Sézanne and right down to Côte des Bar, not far short of Chablis. The town of Troyes lies between the Côtes of Sézanne and Bar.

ANSWERS TO QUIZ 8 – WINES OF FRANCE – PART 3

1. *Pinot Noir.* The Alsace wine region is mostly known today for its famous white wines, usually named after their grape varieties. However, the red Pinot Noir is equally successful. Indeed, in the fifteenth and sixteenth centuries Pinot Noir had a higher standing in the region than any of the Alsace whites. It's light and fruity, and goes particularly well with poultry, pork, and even fish.

2. *a. Jura.* The region is famous for its 'Vin Jaune'. Probably an acquired taste, it has similar characteristics to a dry fino sherry, though it's not fortified. Its character comes from being matured in open-topped barrels under a film of yeast, which gives it its unusual oxidative flavour.

3. *Viognier.* The wine from the small appellation of Condrieu is produced from the Viognier grape variety, which has a very recognisable aroma of peaches, dried fruit, and white flowers, resulting in a rich and full-bodied wine. Outside of the Rhône, Viognier grapes are also grown in all the major wine producing countries around the world.

4. **Côte de Nuits.** Situated in the southern half of the Côte de Nuits, between Chambolle Musigny and Vosne-Romanée. Clos de Vougeot is the largest grand cru site in the Côte de Nuits region, covering around 50 hectares (about 125 acres).

5. **b. Chasselas.** This grape is usually vinified to a full, dry, and fruity white wine. In Switzerland it's the most important white grape variety, and is particularly prevalent in the Vaud region. It tends to ripen early, which makes it very suitable for Switzerland's cool alpine slopes. Fifty years ago it was also very much part of the Alsatian wine scene, but has since declined to very small levels.

6. **Montpelier.** Situated in the eastern Languedoc between Sète and Nîmes, and very near to the Mediterranean coast. A large proportion of the town's population is university students. There is also a significant presence of Spanish, Moroccan, Algerian, and Italian communities. A little-known wine appellation around the town is called Grés de Montpelier.

7. **No.** Blanc de Blancs champagne can only be made from white grapes, those of Chardonnay. Other types of champagne can either be made from red grapes, or a blend of red and white grapes. Except Blanc de Noirs champagne, which can only be made from red grapes.

8. **Muscadet.** Produced from the little-known Melon de Bourgogne grape variety, the Muscadet wine production area lies around the mouth of the Loire river, in the Pays Nantais, at the extreme western end of the Loire wine region. Muscadet has several sub-regions, the most important of which is Sèvre et Maine.

9. **c. Alsace.** The vineyards run for over sixty miles along a narrow strip, running north to south, on the eastern side of the Vosges Mountains. The region has changed hands several times over the centuries between France and Germany, and this is reflected in the types of different grape varieties grown there. Protected by the mountains, Alsace has one of the driest climates in France.

10. **b. Savoie.** The wine production area in Savoie is small, but increasing in size. Vineyards are dispersed amongst the mountainous countryside, and the wines generally tend to be light and fresh. Red and rosé wines are produced, but white wines dominate, mostly produced from the Jacquère grape variety, which is almost unique to the Savoie region.

ANSWERS TO QUIZ 9 – WINES OF FRANCE – PART 4

1. *Sancerre and Pouilly-Fumé.* Whereas Chenin Blanc is the prime white wine grape in the middle Loire, Sauvignon Blanc is the main one in the eastern Loire. Both Sancerre and Pouilly-Fumé are similar in taste, and not easy to tell apart. Pouilly-Fumé is perhaps more perfumed, and Sancerre is a little fuller on the palate. Both wines tend to be more complex, and of a very different character, to the Sauvignon Blanc wines of, say, New Zealand.

2. *Grenache/Syrah/Mourvèdre.* These three grape varieties are the mainstay of red wines produced in the southern Rhône. Even in the production of the famous southern Rhône wines of Châteauneuf-du-Pape, which allow up to eighteen different grape varieties in the blend, Grenache, Syrah and Mourvèdre dominate, and particularly Grenache.

3. *a. Château Cheval Blanc.* The 2004 low budget film 'Sideways' won an Oscar for Best Adapted Screenplay, and was nominated in four other categories. One surprising aspect of the film was that the character Miles, who was a depressed wine buff, was a huge Pinot Noir fan; he adored that grape, and absolutely hated Merlot. So it didn't make sense that he was carrying Château Cheval Blanc around with him, which has no Pinot Noir in it. Indeed it contains some Merlot in the blend. It would have made much more sense for him to be carrying a top red Burgundy, made of 100% Pinot Noir.

4. *c. Pol Roger.* This was Churchill's favourite champagne. He was reputed to have drunk an average of two bottles per day, and that in his lifetime would have drunk around 50,000 bottles! Pol Roger created their top end Prestige Cuvée in homage to Sir Winston.

5. *b. Pinot Blanc.* In Germany this grape is called Weissburgunder, Pinot Noir is called Spätburgunder, and Pinot Gris is Grauburgunder. Weissburgunder grapes ripen fairly late, and the wine has a relatively neutral bouquet, but with good acidity on the palate.

6. *a. Tannat.* Madiran is Gascony's famous red wine. Produced from the Tannat grape variety, a grape that has come to the fore in Uruguay, the wine is dark and quite tannic, and is often blended with one or two other grape varieties. It certainly benefits from lengthy maturation, using different degrees of new oak.

7. *b. Loire Valley.* Quarts de Chaume was the Loire's first official Grand Cru. A highly respected sweet wine produced from the Chenin Blanc grape (also known here as Pineau de la Loire), it is situated in the Coteaux du Layon appellation, close to the Layon river, and not far from the town of Angers.

8. **Champagne.** Situated about ten miles north-east of Epernay, in the south-east of Montagne de Reims, the vast majority of grapes grown around the town of Bouzy are Pinot Noir, and are some of the highest quality in the Champagne region. The vineyards are classified as Grand Cru. The still red wine, Bouzy Rouge, is also produced.

9. **St-Amour.** As well as being the northernmost Beaujolais Cru, just south of the Mâconnais, it is also one of the smallest. Produced from the Beaujolais grape variety, Gamay, St-Amour has one of the lightest styles out of all the Beaujolais Crus. Character, though, can vary due to the variety of soils in the region, which include clay, granite, limestone and slate.

10. **Entre-Deux-Mers.** A less alluring wine region, Entre-Deux-Mers produces a large proportion of Bordeaux AOC wine. The fairly ordinary dry white wine produced in the region, and actually called Entre-Deux-Mers, is made from the Sauvignon Blanc, Sémillon, and Muscadelle grape varieties.

ANSWERS TO QUIZ 10 – WINES OF FRANCE – PART 5

1. **Corsica.** Known as Mammolo in Tuscany, but in Corsica the Sciaccarellu red grape variety is mainly grown in the island's oldest wine region, which is around the capital, Ajaccio. It's also important in two other west coast regions, those around Calvi, north of Ajaccio, and Sartene to the south of the capital. It has a relatively high alcohol content, but is soft and spicy.

2. **Alsace.** The medieval city of Colmar is about 45 miles south of Strasbourg, at the northern end of Alsace, and around 25 miles north of Mulhouse, at the southern end of the region. Colmar is seen as the capital of the Alsatian wine region.

3. **c. Rhône Valley.** Cornas and St-Péray are situated just across the Rhône river, on the western side of the town of Valence in the northern Rhône. Cornas wine is made from the Syrah grape variety, and is rich, powerful, and can be long-lived. Marsanne and Roussanne are the main grapes for the production of the white St-Péray wines, which can be either still or sparkling, and have a fresh and floral character.

4. **Burgundy.** Pinot Noir is the famous red Burgundy grape variety, particularly throughout the Côte d'Or, composed of Côte de Nuits in the north, and Côte de Beaune in the south. It is also grown all around the world, and is highly successful in regions such as New Zealand's Central Otago, and USA's Oregon. But its ancestral home is Burgundy.

5. **b. Sauvignon Blanc.** Chenin Blanc is the main white grape variety in the central Loire Valley, but in the eastern Loire, Sauvignon Blanc is king, producing the white wines of Quincy, as well as the more famous Sancerre and Pouilly-Fumé. Quincy wine is dry, aromatic, floral and citrussy.

6. **Moët & Chandon.** Founded in 1743, Moët & Chandon is now part of the luxury goods company, LVMH, Louis Vuitton Moët Hennessy. More simply known as 'Moët', this famous champagne house is based in Epernay. Dom Pérignon is Moët's Prestige Cuvée, and named after the Benedictine monk who made important contributions to the quality of champagne wine, though, contrary to popular belief, did not invent sparkling champagne!

7. **Phylloxera.** Phylloxera is a microscopic louse or aphid that lives on, and eats, the roots and leaves of grape vines, thereby destroying them. From the late nineteenth century, indeed from the late 1860s in France, vast swathes of vineyards in Europe, and elsewhere in the world, were totally devastated by Phylloxera. Since then, vines have generally been grafted onto certain species of American rootstocks, which are resistant to the aphid.

8. **Sauternes and Barsac.** In Sauternes, the most famous dessert wine in the world is produced, Château d'Yquem. It's another luxury product that's now owned by the LVMH Group. Other well-known Sauternes wines are Châteaux Rieussec and Suduiraut. Châteaux Coutet and Climens are famous Barsacs. Many of the Sauternes and Barsac owners also produce dry white wines, but the fame lies in the dessert wines, normally made by blending Sémillon and Sauvignon Blanc grapes.

9. **c. Alsace.** Gewürztraminer is one of the three leading grape varieties grown in Alsace, along with Riesling and Pinot Blanc. The bouquet is relatively easy to identify, being particularly reminiscent of apricots, mangos and lychees. Gewürztraminer vines like mineral-rich, well-drained soils, and Alsace has them in abundance.

10. **a. Châteauneuf-du-Pape.** The legendary Château de Beaucastel is the most famous wine from the Châteauneuf-du-Pape region in the southern Rhône Valley. It was one of the first domaines to practice organic viticulture. Up to eighteen different grape varieties can now legally be used in the making of Châteauneuf-du-Pape wines, and Beaucastel uses most or all of them in their blends. However, Mourvèdre is the dominant grape and can make up about a third of the final blend.

ANSWERS TO QUIZ 11 – MATCH THESE TOP FRENCH CHATEAUX WITH THEIR WINE/VINEYARD AREAS

1. *j. Bordeaux/Pauillac.* Château Latour is one of the five First Growths. They also produce a second wine called Les Forts de Latour, which prices itself easily as a Second Growth. A third wine is also produced, called Pauillac de Château Latour. Obviously, only the best wine goes into their First Growth, but the basic character runs through all three wines.

2. *i. Rhône/Châteauneuf-du-Pape.* Château Mont-Redon is a large estate in the Châteauneuf-du-Pape region in the southern Rhône. The first vines found there date back to Roman times. Today, all the allowed grape varieties in the region are used in the blend to produce Château Mont-Redon, though Grenache is king. The region enjoys a Mediterranean climate, with July the driest month and October the wettest. Though that might alter with climate change!

3. *f. Rhône/Condrieu.* Since 1936, Château-Grillet has had its own appellation, and is the stand-out wine produced in the well-known Condrieu territory in the northern Rhône, and is made from 100% Viognier grapes. Viognier is now grown in many countries around the world, but the northern Rhône is its spiritual home and, in particular, Condrieu and Château-Grillet.

4. *c. Alsace.* Owned by Dopff & Irion, Château de Riquewihr is situated in the beautiful medieval town of Riquewihr, just north of Colmar in the Alsace wine region. The Château itself was built nearly 500 years ago, and was the residence of the Princes of Württemberg. Today, five wines are produced from different grape varieties – Riesling, Gewürztraminer, Muscat, Pinot Gris, and Pinot Noir.

5. *h. Bordeaux/Barsac.* Obtaining organic certification in 2012, Château Coutet is a top class Barsac dessert wine. Grapes are Sémillon and Sauvignon Blanc, with a tiny percentage of Muscadelle. Barsac wine can be designated as a Sauternes and, indeed, Château Coutet is classified as a Sauternes Premier Cru.

6. *g. Burgundy/Côte de Beaune.* Château de Meursault is located in the heart of Burgundy, in the Côte de Beaune, and is one of the most prestigious estates in the Côte d'Or. Producing a range of white wines from Chardonnay grapes and red wines from Pinot Noir, both Grand Cru and Premier Cru Classé.

7. *a. Bordeaux/St-Emilion.* Château Ausone is one of just a few wines in St-Emilion which is ranked Premier Grand Cru Classé (A) in the classification of St-Emilion wine. It is named after the Roman poet, Ausonius, who owned over

40 hectares (100 acres) of vineyard around the town. St-Emilion, today, is a UNESCO World Heritage Site.

8. *e. Bordeaux/St-Estephe.* A famous Second Growth Bordeaux wine from the St-Estephe commune, Château Cos d'Estournel is only a few hundred yards from Château Lafite, which is situated just across the border in Pauillac. The exterior of the Château is probably the most distinctive, and easily recognisable, of all the Bordeaux Châteaux. Château Cos d'Estournel, along with Château Montrose, is at the top of the tree for producing the best quality wine in the commune.

9. *b. Burgundy/Beaujolais.* Château Thivin is the oldest wine-growing estate in the Beaujolais Cru of Côte de Brouilly, at the southernmost end of the region. The Geoffray family have owned the estate since 1877, and critics have rated this wine as the best in the Côte de Brouilly. Today's sixth generation of Geoffrays produce several different cuvées of the wine, as they have vines planted on all four sides of Mont-Brouilly.

10. *d. Loire Valley/Anjou.* Château Soucherie is situated just south of the town of Angers, towards the western end of the Loire Valley. Chenin Blanc grapes represent the majority of their plantings, with Cabernet Franc for the red wines. The 28 hectares (70 acres) wine estate produces top quality Savennières, Anjou, Chaume, and Coteaux du Layon wines.

ANSWERS TO QUIZ 12 – MATCH THESE FRENCH WINES WITH THEIR WINE/VINEYARD AREAS

1. *f. Burgundy/Côte de Nuits.* The large vineyard of Richebourg is located close to the little village of Vosne-Romanée. The wine is highly prized and one of the most expensive in the world, along with its neighbouring cousins, La Tâche, Romanée-St-Vivant, Echézeaux, Grands Echézeaux, and the most famous of all, Domaine de la Romanée-Conti (often abbreviated to DRC).

2. *d. Champagne/Perrier-Jouët, Epernay.* Belle Epoque Vintage Cuvée first appeared in 1964, and is Perrier-Jouët's iconic marque of champagne. It has one of the most recognisable bottle designs in the champagne industry, originally created in 1902. The bottle is adorned with a distinctive spray of Japanese White Anemones. Belle Epoque is only produced in excellent vintage years.

3. *j. Middle Loire Valley.* St-Nicolas-de-Bourgueil lies just north of the Loire river, not far from the town of Saumur. It is a lighter red wine than some of the other reds made in this part of the Loire, and is produced primarily from the Cabernet Franc grape, as with most red wines in the middle Loire. It is the name of the village as well as the red wine it produces.

4. *b. Bordeaux/Pomerol.* Le Pin is one of the most expensive red wines in the world. Cases sell for tens of thousands of pounds each. As well as producing absolutely top quality wine, Le Pin is very scarce, as the vineyard is tiny at only about 2 hectares (5 acres). Its name derives from a solitary pine tree that used to shade the property.

5. *g. Alsace.* Domaines Schlumberger is a vast, top quality Alsatian wine producer, based in Guebwiller, just north of Mulhouse, at the southern end of Alsace. Founded in 1810 by Nicholas Schlumberger, the estate is still owned and run today by the Schlumberger family. The Domaines have four Grand Crus, and all the important Alsace grape varieties are grown on the estate.

6. *a. Burgundy/Beaujolais.* The tiny appellation of Chénas is situated between Juliénas and Moulin-à-Vent, at the northern end of the Beaujolais region. Ironically, the actual town of Chénas lies in the Moulin-à-Vent appellation. Chénas is one of the ten Beaujolais Cru. It got its name from 'Chêne', the French for oak, after the trees that used to occupy the area. The wine is relatively full and rich for a Beaujolais, and is generally perceived to be the second best appellation, after Moulin-à-Vent, out of all the Beaujolais Cru.

7. *e. Rhône/North.* Jean-Louis Chave's Hermitage is among the top ten producers of that appellation. Both red and white Hermitage are produced. The red is mainly from the Syrah grape, and the white is mostly from the Marsanne grape, with a much smaller amount of Roussanne. The Chave vineyards are spread across many parts of the famous hill of Hermitage, which facilitates an ideal blend made from the different terroirs.

8. *i. Bordeaux/Pessac-Léognan.* Domaine de Chevalier is the outstanding property in the commune of Léognan, part of the Pessac-Léognan appellation. The Domaine doesn't have a château, it is situated in a clearing in the middle of a forest, which protects the vines from temperature extremes. The red wine is a blend of mostly Cabernet Sauvignon and Merlot.

9. *h. Champagne/Veuve Clicquot, Reims.* La Grande Dame champagne is made up of various blends of grapes from Grand Cru vineyards, depending on the vintage. It is Veuve Clicquot's Prestige Cuvée, launched in 1972 to commemorate their bicentenary, and to pay tribute to Madame Clicquot, and the role she played in the formative years of the champagne house. The

elegant, refined, and delicate style of La Grande Dame represents the pinnacle of Veuve Clicquot champagne.

10. **c. Languedoc/Herault.** One of the Languedoc's most reputable and reliable appellations, St-Chinian consistently delivers quality wine, red, white, and rosé, using a range of grape varieties. Vineyards are situated around both the village of St-Chinian, and high up in spectacular mountainous country.

ANSWERS TO QUIZ 13 – ANAGRAMS – WINES OF FRANCE

French Grape Varieties

1. **Cabernet Sauvignon.** One of the world's most well-known grape varieties. A progeny of Cabernet Franc and Sauvignon Blanc, it's grown in almost every major wine producing country. It's the main grape variety used to produce the famous left-bank Bordeaux wines in communes such as Pauillac, St-Julien, Margaux, and St-Estephe.

2. **Viognier.** This white wine grape variety, famous in the French appellation of Condrieu in the northern Rhône, is now widely grown around the world. It has a very aromatic bouquet of apricots and peaches, and can also have herbal, pine and lavender notes. It's not an easy grape to grow, but well worth the effort!

3. **Sémillon.** The golden skinned Sémillon grape can produce either dry or sweet wine. It's particularly famous in the Sauternes and Barsac appellations of Bordeaux, where its thin skin facilitates Botrytis, resulting in the delicious dessert wines of those areas. It has been successfully grown in various countries, and especially in Australia's Hunter Valley.

4. **Merlot.** This red wine grape is increasingly used to produce single varietal wine, as well as being part of a blend. It's the predominant variety in Bordeaux's St-Emilion and Pomerol appellations. It ripens earlier than Cabernet Sauvignon, and its popularity has expanded around the world. In France, as well as Bordeaux it finds particular favour in Bergerac and the Languedoc.

5. **Mourvèdre.** This red wine grape variety is grown in many regions around the world, and is particularly important in the Rhône and Provence regions of France. Mourvèdre is not as well-known as many other grape varieties, such

as Cabernet Sauvignon, Merlot etc, and is also not used as much as a stand-alone varietal. But it holds its own in many high quality blends.

French Wines

6. **Muscadet.** Produced at the western end of the Loire Valley, around the town of Nantes, Muscadet is made using the Melon de Bourgogne grape variety. It's a dry, light-bodied white wine, and is one of the classic wines for accompanying fish dishes. The largest, and best-known, sub-region of the Muscadet appellation is Sèvre et Maine.

7. **Barsac.** Along with Sauternes, Barsac is one of the two classic Bordeaux dessert wines. The actual town of Barsac is about 30 miles south of Bordeaux, close to the Garonne river. Blends of grape varieties can include Sémillon, Sauvignon Blanc, and Muscadelle. Château Coutet and Château Climens are the two most famous Barsac wines.

8. **Côte-Rôtie.** This famous appellation is located in the northern Rhône, just south of Vienne, and just north of Condrieu. Vineyards are on steep slopes, facing the Rhône river. Produced from the Syrah grape, and usually blended with a small amount of Viognier, the wines are powerful and elegant.

9. **Gaillac.** Situated just north-east of Toulouse in the south-west of France. It's an historic wine-producing region dating back to Roman times, or even earlier. The multitude of communes around the small town of Gaillac produce red, white, rosé, and sparkling wines. As well as using some of the well-known international grape varieties, a host of little-known local grapes are also used in the various blends.

10. **Chambertin.** A famous Grand Cru vineyard in the Côte de Nuits in northern Burgundy. The wine is exclusively red, and produced from the Pinot Noir grape variety. Gevrey-Chambertin is the largest wine-producing village in the Côte d'Or, and Chambertin is its greatest Grand Cru vineyard. Napoleon was a great admirer of this wine!

ANSWERS TO QUIZ 14 – WINES OF ITALY – PART 1

1. **Sangiovese.** Under Italian wine law, Sangiovese is the only grape variety allowed to make Brunello di Montalcino, one of Italy's most famous, and expensive red wines. Brunello is a local collection of Sangiovese clones. The town of Montalcino is in Tuscany, about

30 miles south of Siena. A lighter, and more affordable, version of Brunello di Montalcino is Rosso di Montalcino.

2. **b. Barbera.** A red wine made from the grape variety of the same name, Barbera. It is a deep coloured, full bodied wine, with good acidity. Barbera wine itself is produced in Piedmont, where both Barolo and Barbaresco, made from the Nebbiolo grape, are generally considered to be superior to Barbera. The Barbera grape variety is grown in many other parts of Italy, including Sicily and Sardinia and, indeed, in many other parts of the world.

3. **Orvieto.** Undoubtedly the best-known wine in Umbria, the white wine of Orvieto is made from a blend of mostly Grechetto and Trebbiano grapes, centred around the town of Orvieto. Until relatively recently, Orvieto lost its way somewhat and became rather unfashionable, but today there is renewed interest, particularly in the Orvieto Classico Secco.

4. **a. Primitivo.** Producing a deeply coloured red wine, usually high in alcohol and tannins, with an intense flavour. It is one of the leading red grape varieties in southern Italy. It is the same grape as Zinfandel, a red wine favourite in California.

5. **b. Puglia.** Primitivo is grown across the region of Puglia, where it also produces the highly regarded Primitivo di Manduria. Puglia is considered to be Primitivo's home, but it is also grown all over the south of Italy.

6. **a. San Gimignano.** Vernaccia di San Gimignano is produced from 100% Vernaccia grapes, grown on the hillsides around the historic town of San Gimignano, a UNESCO World Heritage Site. It's considered to be one of Italy's finest white wines, and has the highly respected DOCG status (Denominazione di Origine Controllata e Garantita).

7. **North Italy.** Prosecco, produced from the Glera grape variety, is made in north-east Italy, in the Veneto and Friuli Venezia Giulia regions. The sparkle is usually achieved by using the Tank, or Charmat, Method of secondary fermentation, which is quicker and cheaper than the traditional champagne method where the secondary fermentation takes place in bottle over a much longer period. The finest, and more expensive, versions of Prosecco usually come from the top quality DOCG region of Conegliano Valdobbiadene.

8. **Pecorino.** A white wine made from the Pecorino grape variety, and produced particularly in the east coast of Italy regions of Marche and Abruzzo, but can also be found in several other Italian wine regions. A typical Pecorino wine has a floral bouquet, and is dry and minerally. Pecorino is a lesser-known indigenous Italian grape variety.

9. **Sicily.** The red Nero d'Avola grape variety is indigenous to Sicily, and named after its historic birthplace around the town of Avola in the south-east of the island. A hearty full-bodied red wine, it's made from the most important grape in Sicily, and is widely planted on the island.

10. **Franciacorta.** Produced by the traditional, or champagne, method of secondary fermentation in bottle, Franciacorta is a high quality sparkling wine made in Lombardy, between the shores of Lake Iseo and the city of Brescia. Grape varieties used are two of the classic champagne grapes of Pinot Noir and Chardonnay, plus Pinot Blanc. It has the top Italian wine status of DOCG (Denominazione di Origine Controllata e Garantita).

ANSWERS TO QUIZ 15 – WINES OF ITALY – PART 2

1. **c. Lake Garda.** Bardolino is produced in the Veneto region of north-east Italy, next to the eastern shores of Lake Garda. Some of the vineyards, close to the town of Bardolino itself, are designated Bardolino Classico. It's a light red wine made from Corvina grapes, with a smaller percentage of Molinara and Rondinella.

2. **a. Tuscany.** Probably the most famous name in Italian wine, Antinori has been producing wine in Tuscany since 1385. Controversy followed Antinori's launch of the iconic Tignanello in the 1970s, and Solaia a few years later, because they contravened the Chianti Classico DOCG wine laws by including Bordeaux grape varieties in the blend. At the time, they were called 'Super Tuscans'. The laws have since changed and they are now accepted into the DOCG regulations. Antinori have invested in many other wine areas in Italy and overseas.

3. **Prosecco.** The Bisol family have been making wine in the Prosecco region for 500 years. Their Prosecco Superiore is produced in the highest quality Prosecco region of Conegliano Valdobbiadene, in the hills nestling between the Adriatic Sea and the Dolomites. The Glera grape variety, which makes Prosecco, is more at home in this area than anywhere else.

4. **c. Aglianico.** This red grape variety achieves its best results in the south of Italy, and particularly in Campania and Basilicata. It buds early and ripens late, and can result in very long-lived wines of great finesse. The famous oenologist Denis Dubourdieu once said that 'Aglianico is probably the grape with the

longest consumer history of all,' claiming that it used to make Falernian wine famed during Roman times.

5. ***a. Bolgheri.*** The Maremma Toscana, a stretch of land on Tuscany's west coast, contains the DOC region of Bolgheri, which produces the iconic wines of Sassicaia, Masseto, and Ornellaia. Cabernet Sauvignon and Merlot are the two main grapes grown in the region for these famous wines.

6. ***Rosato.*** Called rosado in Portugal and Spain, rosé is rosato in Italy. However, different Italian regions often call their rosato wines by a different name. For example, it can be called chiaretto in Lombardy and Veneto, ramato in Friuli Venezia Giulia, and cerasuolo in Abruzzo. But rosato is the classic Italian name for rosé.

7. ***a. Gaja.*** Angelo Gaja is one of Italy's most renowned wine personalities. The Gaja name is well-known throughout the Italian wine fraternity, but nowhere more so than in Piedmont's Barbaresco, where the business is based. Born in 1940, Angelo still overseas the business, along with his two daughters Gaia and Rossana.

8. ***c. Veneto.*** Lying next to the Valpolicella wine region, Soave is a highly important wine appellation in the Veneto, producing Soave, Soave Classico, and Soave Superiore, as well as a sweet Recioto di Soave made from dried grapes. Principal grape varieties are Garganega and Verdicchio, which here is called Trebbiano di Soave.

9. ***b. Gran Selezione.*** Since 2014 Chianti Classico Gran Selezione is the top grade of Chianti, above Chianti Classico Reserva and Chianti Classico. Under the new classification, grapes must be harvested only from the winery's own vineyards, along with increased requirements for minimum alcohol and ageing levels.

10. ***Mount Etna.*** It seems an unlikely prospect, growing vines on the slopes of this rumbling volcano. But grown they are, and often produce very fine wines. The Etna DOC was the very first in Sicily, followed soon after by perhaps Sicily's most famous wine, Marsala. There are many less well-known grape varieties grown on the slopes of Etna, but a better-known one is Nerello Mascalese, which produces an important indigenous volcanic red wine.

ANSWERS TO QUIZ 16 – WINES OF ITALY – PART 3

1. **b. Tuscany.** Brunello di Montalcino is produced from
   100% Sangiovese grapes. It's a high quality, elegant red
   wine, made from vineyards surrounding the town of Montalcino,
   about 70 miles south of Florence. It is Tuscany's answer to
   Piedmont's Barolo.

2. **a. Glera.** This is the grape that's used to produce Prosecco, and it's very
   much at home in this sparkling wine's homeland of north-east Italy, in the
   Veneto and Friuli Venezia Giulia regions. It's a highly productive grape that
   ripens late in the season. Its high acidity and quite neutral palate makes it
   ideal for producing sparkling wine.

3. **Nebbiolo.** The most important red grape variety in Piedmont, particularly
   for Barolo and Barbaresco. The name comes from the Italian word 'Nebbia',
   meaning 'fog', a feature of the hills in Piedmont where the grapes grow. On
   a similar quality level as its close neighbour Barolo, Barbaresco is one of the
   great wines of Italy, produced from one of the great Italian grapes.

4. **Prosecco.** The finest, and more expensive, versions of Prosecco usually come
   from the top quality DOCG region of Conegliano Valdobbiadene in the hills
   nestling between the Adriatic Sea and the Dolomites. The Glera grape variety,
   which makes Prosecco, is more at home in this area than anywhere else.

5. **Piedmont.** Close to Italy's north-west border, Turin is the capital city of
   Piedmont, the region that's home to the three famous Bs of Piedmontese
   wines – Barolo, Barbaresco, and Barbera. Known as the 'King' and 'Queen' of
   Italian wines, Barolo and Barbaresco are produced from the Nebbiolo grape
   variety, and Barbera from its eponymous grape name. Turin is one of Italy's
   most important business and cultural centres.

6. **b. Alto Adige.** Situated at the southern tip of Austria's Tyrol, Alto Adige is
   the most northerly wine region in Italy. It is also one of the country's top white
   wine producing regions, using both international and local grape varieties.

7. **b. Calabria.** Located right into the toe of Italy, Calabria is a wine region
   that lies between the Ionian Sea and the Tyrrhenian Sea. It's separated from
   Sicily by the narrow Strait of Messina. Wines from this region are generally
   not particularly well-known. Probably the two best-known are Ciro and
   Greco di Bianco.

8. **Rome.** Produced around the small town of Frascati, only about 15 miles
   south-east of Rome, Frascati is one of Italy's most well-known white wines.
   Archaeological discoveries have revealed that grapes have been grown here to

make wine since the fifth century BC. Light and fresh in character, Frascati is made from several grape varieties, in particular Malvasia and Trebbiano.

9. **b. Abruzzo.** Montepulciano d'Abruzzo is well-known around the world, and omnipresent in Italian restaurants! It's an easily-quaffed red wine, juicy, fresh and appetising. It's well-rounded with a bouquet and flavour of dark fruits and spice.

10. **Lacryma Christi.** Producing both red and white wines, Lacryma Christi is made from grapes indigenous to the slopes of Mount Vesuvius, just south of Naples. The literal translation of 'Tears of Christ' is said, according to legend, to come from the tears shed by Jesus when Lucifer stole a piece of paradise and forged the Gulf of Naples. Jesus's tears made the land precious and perfect for growing noble vines.

ANSWERS TO QUIZ 17 – MATCH FAMOUS ITALIAN WINES WITH THEIR DOC AREAS

1. **e. Piedmont.** Produced from the eponymous grape variety, Barbera, which is now Piedmont's second most stylish grape after Nebbiolo, Barbera d'Alba is made in and around the town of Alba on steep slopes, the soil of which is often shared with Nebbiolo and Dolcetto grapes. Barbera is an ancient grape which has thrived in the region for centuries. The wine is dark red and full-bodied.

2. **g. Tuscany.** Brunello is also the name of a local selection of Sangiovese clones, and Brunello di Montalcino is produced from 100% Sangiovese grapes. It's a high quality, elegant red wine, made from vineyards surrounding the town of Montalcino, about 70 miles south of Florence. It is Tuscany's answer to Piedmont's Barolo.

3. **j. Marche.** Verdicchio dei Castelli di Jesi is produced in the Marche region on central Italy's east coast. It's a crisp, dry white wine with ripe pear and tropical fruit flavours. The wine-producing zone encompasses the hilly territory around the town of Jesi in the province of Ancona. The Verdicchio grape variety dominates the blend, and Trebbiano and Malvasia can be added.

4. **i. Sicily.** Grown in the far west of the island around the towns of Marsala and Trapani, Marsala is Sicily's classic fortified wine. Akin to a sweet sherry, it is

often used in cooking, or drunk as a dessert wine. Grillo is the most important grape variety used in its production, along with Catarratto and Inzolia.

5. *a. Emilia-Romagna.* The slightly sparkling red Lambrusco is made around the town of Modena, on the borders of Emilia-Romagna. It used to be viewed as a bit of a joke in this country, a kind of cherryade. But all that has changed in recent times. It's now of much higher quality, is drier, and has a higher alcohol content, albeit still only around 11%. It's deeper in colour and more complex than it used to be, and goes very well with food, particularly Italian dishes like lasagne.

6. *h. Lombardy.* Produced from grapes grown on the hills located between Lake Iseo and the city of Brescia, in northern Italy's Lombardy region. Franciacorta does not have a particularly high profile elsewhere in the world, but is a high quality sparkling wine, made by the traditional (champagne) method of secondary fermentation in bottle. Grape varieties are primarily Chardonnay, Pinot Noir (Pinot Nero), and Pinot Blanc (Pinot Bianco).

7. *b. Lazio.* Produced in the commune of Montefiascone in the province of Viterbo in Lazio, close to Lake Bolsena, north of Rome. The two main grape varieties are Trebbiano and Malvasia. The name Est! Est!! Est!!! comes from the legend that, in the twelfth century, a bishop was sent to Rome by the Holy Roman Emperor and, being very much into drinking good wine, he sent his servant ahead of him, and told him to mark the word 'Est!' on any door of an inn serving good wine, so that the bishop would know where to stay. When the servant got to an inn in Montefiascone and drank the wine there, he was so impressed with it that he marked 'Est! Est!! Est!!!' on the door.

8. *f. Veneto.* Amarone della Valpolicella is made in the Veneto region of north-east Italy, and is one of the region's most prestigious red wines. It's made primarily from Corvina, Rondinella, and Molinara grape varieties, and is produced by using partially shrivelled grapes that have been left to dry, which produces a rich, full bodied dry red wine.

9. *d. Puglia.* Primitivo is one of the leading red wines in southern Italy, made from the eponymous grape variety. It is the same grape as California's Zinfandel. It is a full-bodied fruit-driven red wine, and even though it is grown in different parts of the south, Puglia is its heartland.

10. *c. Basilicata.* Aglianico is the only permitted red grape variety, and it's produced in the Vulture area of Basilicata. The grapes are grown on the volcanic soils of nearby Monte Vulture. The wine is full-bodied, and has a rich and tannic structure.

ANSWERS TO QUIZ 18 – ANAGRAMS – WINES OF ITALY

Italian Grape Varieties

1. **Sangiovese.** Widely planted in Italy, but native to Tuscany, where it is the base grape for Chianti, and the only permissible grape for the famous Brunello di Montalcino. The name Sangiovese means 'Blood of Jove', Jove being a Roman name for Zeus. Pockets of Sangiovese plantings can be found elsewhere in the world, such as Australia and the Americas.

2. **Nebbiolo.** The most important red grape variety in Piedmont, particularly for Barolo and Barbaresco. The name comes from the Italian word 'Nebbia', meaning 'fog', a feature of the hills in Piedmont where the grapes grow. Nebbiolo plantings are not easy to find outside of Italy, though they can be found in some parts of Australia and North America, but not many other countries as yet.

3. **Negroamaro.** A red grape variety, native to southern Italy, and in particular, Puglia, along with the Primitivo grape. It is often blended with another grape or grapes to make the wines of Copertino, Salice Salentino, and Squinzano. The name Negroamaro means literally 'Black Bitter'. The wines are certainly a deep red colour, but with medium-full tannins with dark berryfruit flavours.

4. **Pecorino.** A white grape variety, principally grown in central Italy, in the regions of Marche, Abruzzo, Tuscany, Umbria, and Lazio, though it is particularly native to Marche and Abruzzo. It is a lesser known Italian grape variety, and can be confused with an Italian cheese also called Pecorino. The wine, though, has plenty of style and character. It's fresh, delicate, and floral, with minerality on the finish.

5. **Trebbiano.** The white Trebbiano grape variety was originally from Italy, but is now widely grown around the world. In France, it is known as Ugni Blanc, one of the important grapes for making Armagnac and Cognac. Trebbiano has a rich history, and there are even references to it in Roman times. It's a refreshing, light-bodied, dry and crisp wine with fruity flavours.

Italian Wines

6. **Bardolino.** A light red wine produced around the town of Bardolino on the eastern shores of Lake Garda in the Veneto region of northern Italy. It is a lighter cousin to the nearby Valpolicella, and is made by similar grape varieties, those of Corvina, Molinara, and Rondinella.

7. **Franciacorta.** Produced from grapes grown on the hills located between Lake Iseo and the city of Brescia, in northern Italy's Lombardy region. Franciacorta does not have a particularly high profile elsewhere in the world, but is a high quality sparkling wine, made by the traditional (champagne) method of secondary fermentation in bottle. Grape varieties are primarily Chardonnay, Pinot Noir (Pinot Nero), and Pinot Blanc (Pinot Bianco).

8. **Lambrusco.** The slightly sparkling red Lambrusco is made around the town of Modena, on the borders of Emilia-Romagna. It used to be viewed as a bit of a joke in this country, a kind of cherryade. But all that has changed in recent times. It's now of much higher quality, is drier, and has a higher alcohol content, albeit still only around 11%. It's deeper in colour and more complex than it used to be, and goes very well with food, particularly Italian dishes like lasagne.

9. **Marsala.** Grown in the far west of the island of Sicily, around the towns of Marsala and Trapani, Marsala is Sicily's classic fortified wine. Akin to a sweet sherry, it is often used in cooking, or drunk as a dessert wine. Grillo is the most important grape variety used in its production.

10. **Prosecco.** Produced from the Glera grape variety, Prosecco is made in northeast Italy, in the Veneto and Friuli Venezia Giulia regions. The sparkle is usually achieved by using the Tank, or Charmat, Method of secondary fermentation, which is quicker and cheaper than the traditional champagne method where the secondary fermentation takes place in bottle over a much longer period. The finest, and more expensive, versions of Prosecco usually come from the top quality DOCG region of Conegliano Valdobbiadene.

ANSWERS TO QUIZ 19 – WINES OF SPAIN – PART 1

1. **b. Sanlúcar de Barrameda.** Manzanilla sherry, along with fino, is the lightest and driest of all sherries. It tends to have a slightly salty tang, owing to the sea air carried from the nearby Atlantic Ocean. The town of Sanlúcar 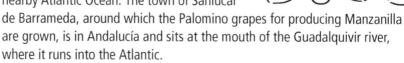 de Barrameda, around which the Palomino grapes for producing Manzanilla are grown, is in Andalucía and sits at the mouth of the Guadalquivir river, where it runs into the Atlantic.

2. **a. Mencía.** Most of the Mencía vines in Bierzo are over 60 years old. This red wine is medium-bodied, aromatic, refreshing and fruity. The grapes ripen

early, and are well suited to the maritime climate of Bierzo. Elsewhere in Spain, Mencía is often blended with, say, Cabernet Sauvignon or Merlot, but in Bierzo it produces high quality wine as a single varietal.

3. *Rioja.* Campo Viejo, with its distinctive yellow label, is produced in the Rioja wine region in northern Spain, mainly from Tempranillo and Garnacha grapes. It is made using the most advanced Rioja wine-making techniques.

4. *a. Penedès.* Cava is mainly produced in Penedès in Catalunya, and the three most important grapes are Macabeo, Parellada, and Xarel-lo. Two producers dominate production, Codorníu and Freixenet. Cava is closer to champagne than, say, Prosecco, because it's usually made using the traditional method of secondary fermentation in bottle, as opposed to Prosecco being mainly produced by the cheaper carbonated Tank, or Charmat, method.

5. *c. Finca.* The Spanish farm or wine estate is called a Finca, but is often also called a bodega. However, the term 'Bodega' can also refer to the warehouse where the wine is stored, or indeed can just be a wine bar.

6. *Sherry.* Flor is a thin layer of indigenous yeast cells that forms on top of dry sherries, Manzanilla, Fino, and Amontillado, during the ageing process, and protects the wine from oxygen. This occurs under what is called 'The Solera System,' which allows biological ageing by adding new wine at the top of the Solera, then renewing each time down through the Solera, emerging eventually at the bottom ready for fining and bottling.

7. *b. Ribera del Duero.* This region in northern Spain, about 100 miles north of Madrid, is the home of two of the most highly respected, and highly priced wines in Spain – Pingus and Vega Sicilia. Dominio de Pingus produces this red wine from Tempranillo grapes, known locally as Tinto Fino. Grapes are hand-selected at optimum ripeness, and the wine is only allowed to be called Pingus in the best possible vintages. Consequently, it is very scarce, and highly sought-after, even at the extremely high prices.

8. *a. Rioja Oriental.* Unsurprisingly, Rioja Oriental is the easternmost zone in the Rioja region in northern Spain. When it was called Rioja Baja, before the name change in 2018, it was seen as the poor relation to the other two Rioja zones, Rioja Alta and Rioja Alavesa. However, nowadays things have changed and Rioja Oriental's image has a much higher standing, borne out by the quality wine being produced there.

9. *Rosado.* Called rosato in Italy, and rosé in France (and most other countries), it is rosado in Spain and, indeed, Portugal.

10. *a. Tinajas*. Often known elsewhere in the world as amphoras or qvevris, these large clay or earthenware pots are called tinajas in Spain. Winemakers

decide whether to ferment or store their wine in tinajas, oak barrels, stainless steel etc. Their decision is a personal one, based on what they think works best in their particular micro-climate, overall terroir, and the style of wine that they intend to achieve.

ANSWERS TO QUIZ 20 – WINES OF SPAIN – PART 2

1. *Vendimia.* In Spain, wine harvests are often followed by festivals – 'Fiestas de la Vendimia'. They can be on the feast of St. Matthew, 21 September, or in Jerez they can be on the feast of the Nativity of our Lady, 8 September. But, of course, wine vintages and festivals in Spain will vary in different parts of the country, depending on weather conditions, grape varieties, decisions made by the producers etc.

2. *b. La Mancha.* Or to be more precise, Castilla-La Mancha. Valdepeñas is an ancient city lying in a sun-baked river valley sprinkled with small rocky formations, hence 'Val de peñas' meaning Valley of Rocks. Some white wines are produced here, but red wine dominates. 'Tinajas', the large clay pots, used to be used for fermentation and storage, but today it's usually stainless steel tanks and oak barrels.

3. *North-West Spain.* The Toro wine region is in the far west of Castilla y León in north-west Spain. The town of Toro itself is only about 40 miles east of the Portuguese border, and lies close to the Duero river, which becomes the Douro when it enters Portugal. Toro is mainly a red wine appellation, and the main grape variety is Tempranillo, known here as Tinta de Toro.

4. *a. Frank Gehry.* The phenomenally successful Guggenheim Museum in Bilbao was also designed by Frank Gehry, and his incredibly distinctive design for the Marqués de Riscal luxury hotel, on the eponymous wine estate, is equally mesmerising. It's a City of Wine complex with, as well as the 5-star luxury hotel and spa, a museum of viticulture, and a wine shop.

5. *Vintage Year.* Cosecha literally means harvest in English, but with regard to Spanish wine it usually translates the harvest as meaning the vintage year.

6. *Bodega.* In Spain, the bodega has various meanings. It can refer to a wine estate as a whole, or a warehouse where wine is stored, a winery or a winery cellar or, indeed, a wine bar.

7. **Sweet.** With Spanish wine, dulce is sweet, seco is dry, semi-seco is medium dry, and brut is very dry.

8. **a. Albariño.** The most important white grape variety in Galicia's Rías Baixas, Albariño, called Alvarinho just across the border in Portugal, is now grown in many countries around the world. In Bordeaux, this grape has been added to the list of authorised grape varieties, as an added measure to combat climate change. In Spain, Albariño wine has rich stonefruit flavours with a lively acidity.

9. **c. Verdejo.** Rueda white wine is dominated by the region's principal grape variety, Verdejo, which has been grown here for hundreds of years. The grapes are usually picked later than the Sauvignon Blanc grapes, which are also grown in this region. The wines are refreshing, aromatic, crisp, and hold their acidity well.

10. **Sherry.** The town of Montilla is about 80 miles north of Malaga in Andalucía, southern Spain. The Pedro Ximénez vines in the surrounding area produce wine that is similar in character to sherry but, unlike sherry, is not fortified. The similarity with sherry continues with the corresponding types of wine styles produced in Montilla, particularly finos and amontillados.

ANSWERS TO QUIZ 21 – WINES OF SPAIN – PART 3

1. **Palomino.** Grown on the chalk soils (called Albarizas) of the sherry region, Palomino, full name Palomino Fino, is the prime grape variety for many styles of sherry, including Fino. This grape withstands drought well, and produces a reliable crop of neutral flavoured, slightly low acid, low sugar grapes, whose wine is prone to oxidation, which all-in-all makes it the perfect raw material to produce sherry. It is also grown in other parts of the world, and often called by a different name.

2. **True.** The wine region of Empordà is in the far north-east corner of Spain, at the top end of Catalunya. It's an attractive region tucked between the mountains of the Pyrenees and the Mediterranean Sea. Wine has been produced in Empordà since around the sixth century BC.

3. **Tarragona.** This town, and its surrounding wine region in north-east Spain, used to be famous for producing intense sweet wines. Nowadays it has mostly moved on to more modern tastes, and modern wines, producing red, white and rosés (rosados).

4. **Grenache.** Garnacha is widely grown around the world, and is known, depending on the country, as either Garnacha or Grenache. In France, it is called Grenache, and is especially prominent in the southern Rhône wine region.

5. **a. Navarra.** The vineyards of Navarra are on the lower slopes of the Pyrenees, descending down to the River Ebro. Rioja is just across the other side of the river. Tempranillo, Garnacha, Cabernet Sauvignon, and Merlot are the main red grapes here. Chardonnay and Viura the predominant whites.

6. **River Douro.** The River Duero is the same river as the famous Douro in Portugal. The Ribera del Duero wine region in Spain produces two of the country's iconic wines, Vega Sicilia and Pingus. Grapes grown along the River Douro in Portugal are well-known for producing particularly excellent red wines and, of course, the fortified wine that's produced by all the famous Port houses.

7. **b. Pedro Ximénez.** Also known as PX, this grape variety is primarily grown in the Sherry region of Andalucía in south-west Spain. It produces a sherry of the same name which is intensely sweet, made by sunning the grapes so that they are reduced to a raisin-like consistency, producing a high concentration of sugars.

8. **a. Parellada.** This is one of the three traditional grape varieties used to produce the sparkling wine Cava, along with Macabeo and Xarel-lo. Cava is mostly made in the Catalonian province of Penedès in north-east Spain. Parellada is a white grape that's also blended with other grapes to produce still dry white wine in the Penedès region.

9. **b. Viura.** Most Rioja wine is red, but the relatively small amount of Rioja white wine that is made is mostly produced from Viura grapes, along with some Malvasia (Malvasia Riojana) and Garnacha Blanca. Viura is also gaining popularity in the French Roussillon wine region.

10. **c. Scotch Whisky.** Sherry butts, usually holding approximately 132 gallons (600 litres), are widely used in the Scotch whisky industry. The Scots have a long history with sherry and, indeed, have been maturing their whisky in sherry butts for well over 200 years. The character of Sherry casks makes an important contribution to the flavour of whisky.

ANSWERS TO QUIZ 22 – MATCH THESE SPANISH NAMES WITH THEIR CORRESPONDING REGIONS/GRAPES/TOWNS/WINE TERMS ETC

1. *g. Pingus.* Vega Sicilia and Pingus are both situated in the Ribera del Duero wine region, and are two of the highest quality, and most expensive, wines in Spain. Dominio de Pingus produces this red wine from Tempranillo grapes, known locally as Tinto Fino. Grapes are hand-selected at optimum ripeness, and the wine is only allowed to be called Pingus in the best possible vintages. Consequently, it is very scarce, and highly sought-after, even at the extremely high prices.

2. *j. Verdejo.* Both Albariño and Verdejo are white grape varieties. Albariño is mainly grown in the Rías Baixas region of Galicia in north-west Spain, and Verdejo is chiefly produced in the Rueda region in northern Spain.

3. *h. Sanlúcar de Barrameda.* Jerez and Sanlúcar de Barrameda, along with Puerto de Santa Maria, are the three capital towns of the sherry region in Andalucía in southern Spain. Sanlúcar is home to the very dry Manzanilla sherry, which tends to have a slightly salty tang, owing to the sea air carried from the nearby Atlantic Ocean. The town of Sanlúcar de Barrameda, around which the Palomino grapes for producing Manzanilla are grown, sits at the mouth of the Guadalquivir river, where it runs into the Atlantic Ocean.

4. *f. Manzanilla.* Pedro Ximénez and Manzanilla are two styles of sherry. Pedro Ximénez is very sweet, smooth, rich, and full of raisin and fig aromas. Manzanilla is the absolute opposite and, along with fino, is the lightest and driest of all sherries.

5. *i. Finca.* In Spain, a bodega and a finca have similar meanings. The Spanish farm or wine estate is called a finca, but can also be called a bodega. They both refer to a wine estate as a whole, or a warehouse where wine is stored, or a winery generally.

6. *d. Seco.* Simply, dulce means sweet in Spanish, and seco means dry. These two terms can often be seen on Spanish wine labels.

7. *a. Rueda.* Both Toro and Rueda are wine regions in northern Spain. Toro is a small region in the far west of Castilla y León in north-west Spain. It's mainly a red wine appellation, and the main grape variety is Tempranillo, known there as Tinta de Toro. Rueda is a larger wine region just to the east of Toro, and in particular is famous for producing the white Verdejo wine made from the eponymous grape variety.

8. **c. Tempranillo.** Garnacha and Tempranillo are both important red grape
    varieties, grown in many parts of Spain. Garnacha is the same as the Grenache
    grape, and is widely planted around the world. Tempranillo is the grape that's
    most associated with Spanish wine.

9. **e. Haro.** Logroño and Haro are two of the most important towns in the Rioja
    wine region in northern Spain. Surrounded by vineyards, both towns are in the
    western part of the region, in the key Rioja Alta zone.

10. **b. Duero.** Both the Ebro and the Duero are important rivers running through
    wine regions in northern Spain. The Ebro river runs through Rioja, and the
    Duero runs through the Ribera del Duero region, which produces some of the
    highest quality wine in all of Spain. The Duero river eventually enters Portugal,
    where its name becomes the River Douro.

ANSWERS TO QUIZ 23 – ANAGRAMS – WINES OF SPAIN

Spanish Grape Varieties

1. **Godello.** A white grape variety that's mainly found in
    north-west Spain, particularly in Valdeorras, and northern
    Portugal. It produces quality wine which combines citrus
    and subtle stone fruit aromas. Its lovely minerality has
    been said to have all the structure of a white Burgundy.

2. **Bobal.** Not a particularly well-known red grape variety, but it's actually
    widely planted in Spain and, indeed, has been cultivated in the Utiel-Requena
    region of Valencia province since the fifteenth century. Bobal has been used
    frequently for blending, but more and more nowadays it's also used to
    produce single varietal wines.

3. **Garnacha.** One of the most widely planted red grapes in the world,
    Garnacha is usually called Grenache outside of Spain. Although
    mainly red, there is also a white Garnacha grown in some parts
    of Spain. A real crowd-pleaser, the red Garnacha is soft and
    fruity, and equally popular drunk on its own or with food.

4. **Palomino.** Grown in some other parts of the world, but primarily famous for
    producing various styles of sherry in the Andalucía region of south-west Spain,
    around the towns of Jerez, Puerto de Santa Maria, and Sanlúcar

de Barrameda. It produces the dry and medium dry sherries, including Manzanilla, Fino, Amontillado, Oloroso, and Palo Cortado.

5. **Pedro Ximénez.** Also known as PX, this grape variety is primarily grown in the Sherry region of Andalucía in south-west Spain. It produces a sherry of the same name which is intensely sweet, made by sunning the grapes so that they are reduced to a raisin-like consistency, producing a high concentration of sugars.

Spanish Wine Regions

6. **La Mancha.** Also home of the famous Manchego cheese (and Don Quixote!). La Mancha is the largest wine region in Spain, situated just south of Madrid. Traditionally, it has produced well-priced table wines of average quality, but nowadays an increasing number of high quality wines are being made in the region.

7. **Bierzo.** Located in north-west Spain in the province of Castilla y León, bordering the wine region of Galicia. A variety of grapes are grown in Bierzo, but it is most well-known for the red grape Mencía (known as Jaen in Portugal). The region has been one of the rising stars in Spain, along with the likes of Rueda, Jumilla and Rías Baixas.

8. **Rioja Alta.** Situated in the western part of the Rioja wine region in northern Spain, the other two Rioja sub-regions being Rioja Alavesa and Rioja Oriental (formerly Rioja Baja). Rioja Alta is home to many top producers. The majority of its vineyards lie south of the Ebro river, which winds its way through the whole Rioja region.

9. **Tarragona.** Located around the coastal city of Tarragona in Catalunya, north-east Spain, just south of Penedès and east of Priorat. In Roman times the great sweet wines of Tarragona were highly praised. Today, some classic sweet wine is still produced, but the region is also home to innovative wine-making techniques, producing a wide variety of grapes and wine styles.

10. **Empordà.** This wine region is in the far north-east corner of Spain, at the top end of Catalunya. It's an attractive region tucked between the mountains of the Pyrenees and the Mediterranean Sea. Wine has been produced in Empordà since around the sixth century BC.

ANSWERS TO QUIZ 24 – WINES OF GERMANY – PART 1

1. **b. Sekt.** Most of the sales of Sekt are in Germany itself. As with Italy's Prosecco, German Sekt is mostly produced by the Tank (or Charmat) Method of secondary fermentation, as opposed to the more expensive traditional (or champagne) method of secondary fermentation in bottle. Sekt is usually sweeter and lower in alcohol than other sparkling wines.

2. **a. Dry.** In the past, German wines were mostly medium dry, medium sweet, or sweet, but in recent years wine producers have responded to world demand, and now around two-thirds of German wine is dry. This can be indicated on the label by the addition of the word 'Trocken' meaning dry.

3. **a. Ahr.** One of Germany's northernmost wine regions, Ahr is centred around the little River Ahr, which runs from the Eifel Mountains to the Rhine. It is one of the smallest wine regions in Germany, and is mostly known for red wine production and, in particular, Spätburgunder (Pinot Noir). Baden and Pfalz, situated in the south of Germany, are two other regions well-known for red wine production.

4. **Nahe.** Close to the Rheingau, Rheinhessen, and Mosel wine regions, the surroundings of the Nahe river, before it runs into the Rhine at Bingen, produce plenty of high quality wine and, indeed, some of the best dry Rieslings in Germany.

5. **b. Franken.** Situated in the north-west of Bavaria in southern Germany, leading grape varieties here are Silvaner and Müller-Thurgau rather than the more famous Riesling. It is home to the distinctive flat-belly, ellipsoidal shaped bottle called the Bocksbeutel. Some local people say that it's shaped that way to stop it rolling away from its owner!

6. **Dr Loosen.** Owned by the same family for over two hundred years, Ernst Loosen currently runs the business. Situated on the banks of the Mosel river, Dr Loosen is one of Germany's great wine estates. Ernst Loosen is a great ambassador for Riesling, and produces one of the best Rieslings in Germany.

7. **Hochheim.** The English term 'Hock' is derived from the town of Hochheim, and is a generic term for Rhine wine, though the word is not often used these days. Riesling is the most important grape here. The Hochheim Wine Festival is one of the biggest wine festivals in the Rheingau wine region, attended by vintners, restaurant owners, artists, and many others.

8. **Kabinett.** Certain quality standards are laid down by German wine laws in order for a wine to carry the term 'Kabinett'. It is the first rung on the higher

quality ladder, ascending as Kabinett, Spätlese, Auslese, Beerenauslese, and Trockenbeerenauslese.

9. **Beerenauslese.** One of the highest quality terms for German wine, with only Trockenbeerenauslese above it. Often referred to as BA, the wines are honey yellow to golden in colour, with intense and full-bodied aromas, and lusciously sweet on the palate but with good acidity.

10. **Piesport.** Situated on a sharp bend on the River Mosel, and only about a dozen miles from Bernkastel, another well-known Mosel wine town. Wine has been produced here since Roman times, evidenced by the fact that a fourth-century Roman wine press was discovered in Piesport in the 1980s.

ANSWERS TO QUIZ 25 – WINES OF GERMANY – PART 2

1. **Sonnenuhr.** The village of Wehlen is located in the middle Mosel, not far from both Bernkastel and Graach. The Famous Wehlener Sonnenuhr vineyard translates as 'Wehlen's Sundial' which refers to an old sundial seen on a rocky vine-draped mount at the heart of the vineyard. Wehlener Sonnenuhr yields some of the most elegant and sophisticated white wines in Germany.

2. **Spätlese.** Meaning 'late harvest', Spätlese wines are riper than Kabinett wines as the grapes have been picked at a later stage in the harvest. They tend to be more intense in flavour and concentration, and are usually sweet, though dry versions are available as Spätlese Trocken.

3. **Schloss.** Meaning castle, mansion, stately home, or château, there are many Schloss wines in Germany, including the famous Schloss Vollrads, and Schloss Johannisberg, both in the Rheingau region.

4. **c. Saar.** The vine-growing area in the Saar Valley follows the river for about 11 miles before reaching the Mosel river at the town of Konz. Producing predominantly Riesling wines, well-known villages in the Saar wine region include Ockfen, Saarburg, and Wiltingen, with its famous Scharzhofberg vineyard.

5. **Spätburgunder.** Germany is one of the world's top producers of Pinot Noir, called Spätburgunder there. The word literally means 'late Burgundian', hence the Pinot Noir connection. Other 'Burgundian' grape names in Germany include Grauburgunder (Pinot Gris), and Weissburgunder (Pinot Blanc).

6. **a. Franken.** Situated in the north-west of Bavaria in southern Germany, leading grape varieties here are Silvaner and Müller-Thurgau rather than the more famous Riesling. It is home to the distinctive flat-belly, ellipsoidal shaped bottle called the Bocksbeutel. Its wines used to be generically called Steinwein. This was because Franken's wine capital, Würzburg, was famous for its top quality vineyard called 'Stein', which had a reputation for making very long-lived wines.

7. **Rheinhessen.** Germany's largest wine-growing region with around 150 villages producing wine. It's bordered top and bottom by Mainz in the north and Worms in the south. Rheinhessen used to be best-known as the home of Liebfraumilch, but that's in the past. These days the region is still making mostly white wine, but from good quality grapes, including Riesling, Pinot Blanc (Weissburgunder), and Silvaner.

8. **Pinot Gris/Pinot Grigio.** Grauburgunder, Pinot Gris, Pinot Grigio are all the same grape variety with different names, depending on the country where it's grown. Grapes normally have a greyish-blue tint to them, hence the name, but colours do vary, as does the character of the wine, according to wine region and terroir.

9. **a. Koblenz.** The source of the Mosel river is in the Vosges Mountains, across the border in France, and the river is lined with vines all the way to meeting the Rhine at Koblenz. All the best Mosel wines are produced from the Riesling grape, and on the steep slopes down towards the river.

10. **c. Rheingau.** The town of Rudesheim is on the northern banks of the Rhine river in the Rheingau wine region. Riesling is the main grape variety grown around the town, producing high quality wines.

ANSWERS TO QUIZ 26 – WINES OF GERMANY – PART 3

1. **Riesling.** The first grape variety that comes to mind when one thinks of Germany is Riesling. Reference to this grape in Germany dates back to 1435. Since then, it has varied in its dryness and sweetness. The new quality 'Prädikat' system was introduced in 1971, when one of the important aspects of top wines was sweetness. However, from the mid-1980s the gradually changing world demand for dry wine meant that German Riesling producers started to make dry versions

of their wine, usually labelled as 'Trocken', and now the majority of German wine, not just Riesling, is dry.

2. **Baden-Baden.** Located roughly in the middle of the Baden wine region in south-west Germany. The region produces several grape varieties, including Riesling, Spätburgunder (Pinot Noir), and Müller-Thurgau. The Baden wine region is primarily a long slim strip of vineyards nestled between the hills of the Black Forest and the River Rhine. Baden-Baden itself is a spa town with a population of about 55,000.

3. **c. Bonn.** Situated only about 25 miles from Germany's city of Bonn, the Ahr region is one of the northernmost wine regions in the country, and is located in the valley of the River Ahr, a tributary of the Rhine. It's one of the smallest wine regions in Germany, and is particularly well-known for making red wine, which makes up the majority of its production. Spätburgunder (Pinot Noir) is the prime red grape variety here.

4. **a. River Main.** The longest tributary on the right bank of the Rhine, and the longest river lying entirely in Germany. The town of Würzburg straddles the river, and is a popular tourist spot. It's located in the eastern wine region of Franken, which features the round flat-shaped wine bottles called Bocksbeutels. Franken wines are predominantly full-bodied and dry.

5. **b. Mosel.** Riesling is, of course, grown all over Germany, but the Mosel wine region is seen as its spiritual home. Its terroir and topography, with its slate soil, is unique and ideal for producing Riesling grapes. Vines here thrive on the precipitous terraces that border the Mosel river. Indeed the region boasts one of the steepest vineyards in the world, the Bremmer Calmont, which has a gradient of up to 68%!

6. **a. 1923.** The famous wine family, the Sichels, founded the Blue Nun brand in 1923. The 1970s were the glory days of Blue Nun when it was a respected favourite of fans worldwide. By the 1980s it was selling over two million cases globally. Today, sophisticated people of a certain age tend to look back on it with amusement, and disbelief that they actually used to drink it! But that's probably unfair, in that the brand has improved its wine according to changing tastes, and is still sold around the world.

7. **Liebfraumilch.** Blue Nun Liebfraumilch was a relatively low alcohol white wine aimed at the international mass market. Its simple brand name was popular, compared with the long, difficult German wine names of the time. It was also marketed as being able to match with any type of food, which again garnered success. After the late 1990s, the brand was repositioned away from the name Liebfraumilch, which had connotations of a semi-

sweet unfashionable product, to a middle-of-the road drier German wine of acceptable taste and quality.

8. *b. Württemberg.* This wine region is well-known in Germany, but not so familiar outside of the country. In recent years the local red Lemberger grape variety has been very successful and rivals the quality of Spätburgunder. The other main red grape is Trollinger, which produces a simple everyday wine. Some decent Riesling wine is also produced here.

9. *b. 60 miles.* When one thinks of a meandering river, one thinks of a gently turning configuration. But when that term is applied to the River Mosel, it means something much more brutal. It loops, turns sharply, and twists its way for about 145 miles from Trier to Koblenz, and its 60 miles straight line distance shows how dramatic the route is!

10. *River Neckar.* This river meets the Rhine at Mannheim, after running through the two wine regions of Württemberg and Baden. Rising in the Black Forest, it travels for about 230 miles before reaching the Rhine.

ANSWERS TO QUIZ 27 – MATCH THESE GERMAN NAMES WITH THEIR CORRESPONDING VINEYARDS/GRAPES/PRODUCERS/REGIONS ETC

1. *e. Piesport.* (Both are villages in the Mosel region). Situated on a sharp bend of the River Mosel, and only about a dozen miles from Bernkastel, another well-known Mosel wine village. Wine has been produced here since Roman times, evidenced by the fact that a fourth-century Roman wine press was discovered in Piesport in the 1980s.

2. *i. Kabinett.* (Both are quality designations). Certain quality standards are laid down by German wine laws in order for a wine to carry the term 'Kabinett'. It is the first rung on the higher quality ladder, ascending as Kabinett, Spätlese, Auslese, Beerenauslese, and Trockenbeerenauslese.

3. *g. Dornfelder.* (Both are grape varieties). Riesling is universally famous, but Dornfelder, a high yielding red grape variety, is far less known. It's grown particularly in the German Pfalz and Rheinhessen regions. Created in 1955, Dornfelder is a cross between Helfensteiner and Heroldrebe grapes, the latter of which bears the name of the creator, August Herold. It's also one of the red grape varieties grown in England.

4. ***j. Sonnenuhr.*** (Both constitute village and associated vineyard). The village of Wehlen is located in the middle Mosel, not far from both Bernkastel and Graach. The Famous Wehlener Sonnenuhr vineyard translates as 'Wehlen's Sundial' which refers to an old sundial seen on a rocky vine-draped mount at the heart of the vineyard. Wehlener Sonnenuhr yields some of the most elegant and sophisticated white wines in Germany.

5. ***h. Würzgarten.*** (Both constitute village and associated vineyard). The village of Urzig is located in the middle Mosel, close to the villages of Wehlen and Bernkastel. Urziger Würzgarten is one of the top vineyards in the Mosel region. It's also one of the steepest!

6. ***d. Ahr.*** (Both are German wine regions). One of Germany's northernmost wine regions, Ahr is centred around the little River Ahr, which runs from the Eifel Mountains to the Rhine. It is one of the smallest wine regions in Germany, and is mostly known for red wine production and, in particular, Spätburgunder (Pinot Noir). Rheinhessen is Germany's largest wine-growing region with around 150 villages producing wine. It's bordered top and bottom by Mainz in the north and Worms in the south. Rheinhessen used to be best-known as the home of Liebfraumilch, but that's in the past. These days the region is still making mostly white wine, but from good quality grapes, including Riesling, Pinot Blanc (Weissburgunder), and Silvaner.

7. ***c. JJ Prum.*** (Both are names of producers). JJ Prum is one of the finest wine estates in the Mosel, particularly for making excellent Riesling wine. It was founded in 1911 by Johann Josef Prum. Paul Weltner is a family-run estate, and is based in the Steigerwald district of the Franken wine region. They are particularly well-known for their Silvaner wine.

8. ***a. Schloss Vollrads.*** (Both are Schloss wine estates). Schloss Johannisberg and Schloss Vollrads are historic wine estates in the Rheingau region. Meaning castle, mansion, stately home, or château, there are many Schloss wines in Germany, but these two are probably the most famous.

9. ***b. Bocksbeutel.*** (Both are types of German wine bottles). The Franken wine region is home to the distinctive flat-belly, ellipsoidal shaped bottle called the Bocksbeutel. Some local people say that it's shaped that way to stop it rolling away from its owner! The Hock bottle is the classic German wine bottle shape, tall and slender with a delicate neck.

10. ***f. Ruwer.*** (Both are the names of rivers). The Saar and Ruwer are the two most famous wine growing tributaries of the Mosel river. The vine-growing area in the Saar Valley follows the river for about 11 miles before reaching the Mosel river at the town of Konz. Both the Saar and Ruwer regions produce predominantly Riesling wines. The Ruwer is a tiny river and a tiny wine region,

but it does have some famous estates, especially that of Maximin Grünhaus who make particularly elegant and fine Rieslings.

ANSWERS TO QUIZ 28 – ANAGRAMS – WINES OF GERMANY

German Grape Varieties

1. **Spätburgunder.** Germany is one of the world's top producers of Pinot Noir, called Spätburgunder there. The word literally means 'late Burgundian', hence the Pinot Noir connection.

2. **Müller-Thurgau.** This grape variety is predominantly grown in Germany, and is a cross between Riesling and Madeleine Royale. It was created in 1882 in Geisenheim by Professor Hermann Müller, from Thurgau in Switzerland.

3. **Grauburgunder.** Grauburgunder, Pinot Gris, and Pinot Grigio are different names for the same grape variety depending on the country where it's grown. The grapes normally have a greyish-blue tint to them, hence the name, but colours do vary, as does the character of the wine, according to wine region and terroir.

4. **Dornfelder.** Riesling is universally famous, but Dornfelder, a high yielding red grape variety, is far less known. It's grown particularly in the German Pfalz and Rheinhessen regions. Created in 1955, Dornfelder is a cross between Helfensteiner and Heroldrebe grapes, the latter of which bears the name of the creator, August Herold. It's also one of the red grape varieties grown in England.

5. **Weissburgunder.** Synonymous with Pinot Blanc, this grape variety thrives in fertile or chalky soils and ripens late. Character can vary but, generally, Weissburgunder has a delicate bouquet, with a light to medium body, and soft acidity.

German Wine Towns

6. **Bernkastel.** A small town in the middle Mosel, Bernkastel is an important wine area, and produces some of Germany's finest Rieslings. The green wall of vines on the valley slopes run for over five miles.

7. **Graach.** Situated very close to Bernkastel in the middle Mosel, the Graach vineyards are part of an extensive slate hillside that ascends above the right bank of the river from Bernkastel to Zeltingen.

8. **Saarburg.** A village in the Saar wine region, Saarburg grows predominantly Riesling grapes. The vine-growing area in the Saar Valley follows the river for about 11 miles before reaching the Mosel river at the town of Konz.

9. **Rudesheim.** Situated in the Rheingau wine region, which is one of the smallest in Germany. Dry Rieslings predominate here. The town of Rudesheim is a tourist magnet, as well as a famous wine producing district. It is part of the UNESCO World Heritage Site in this region.

10. **Nierstein.** Located in the Rheinhessen, which is Germany's largest wine-growing region with around 150 villages producing wine. The village of Nierstein, on the banks of the Rhine, is bordered by some well-known vineyards, such as Pettenthal, and Hipping, producing very high quality wines.

ANSWERS TO QUIZ 29 – WINES OF PORTUGAL

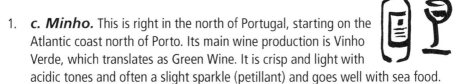

1. **c. Minho.** This is right in the north of Portugal, starting on the Atlantic coast north of Porto. Its main wine production is Vinho Verde, which translates as Green Wine. It is crisp and light with acidic tones and often a slight sparkle (petillant) and goes well with sea food.

2. **a. Algarve.** Sir Cliff Richard's two wine estates Vida Nova & Vida Onda are situated in the Algarve just inland from Albufeira. Cliff's estate is called 'Adega do Cantor' and translates as, 'the house of the singer'. Both estates make red, white and rosé wines each year and they sell mainly in the UK to Cliff Richard's large fan base. They sell out almost immediately!

3. **LBV on a bottle of port stands for Late Bottled Vintage.** It is fortified Port wine from a single vintage year and made in the Douro Valley. Traditionally they age for 4 to 6 years in barrels and are then transferred to bottles. From 2002 LBV can also be sold as 'Bottle Matured.' These wines are not aged in oak barrels but are aged in bottle for a minimum of 3 years before release. Not surprisingly these are cheaper than the traditionally aged LBVs.

4. **b. Tinta Negra Mole.** Nowadays, almost 85% of all Madeiras are made from the Negra Mole red variety of grape. It is the workhorse grape producing very high yields of sweet pale red wines, which are then aged in the Estufagem process (of cooking the young fermenting wine) before ageing them in barrels for 3 years and making the cheaper high volume Madeiras. The 4 traditional grape varieties used for making the top quality and vintage

Madeira fortified wines (listed from sweetest to driest) are – Malvasia (Malmsey), Bual, Verdelho and Sercial.

5. **c. About 50%/50%.** The Douro revolution of producing top quality non fortified red wine (and some whites) started about 25 years ago. Port consumption worldwide had fallen, through lifestyle changes, so that the port houses in the upper Douro Valley had spare vineyard capacity. They had very old high quality vines, some over 100 years old. Thus Quinta do Noval, Niepoort, Crasto, Ramos Pinto, Symington Estates and others created 'The table wine revolution' of mainly red ageworthy wines made largely from blends of indigenous varieties; Touriga Nacional, Touriga Franca, Tinta Barocca, Alicante Bouschet and others. Good whites are also produced. No other classic wine region in the world has changed as much as the Douro in modern times.

6. **a. Azores.** The Pico Island vineyard culture is a UNESCO World Heritage Site. It is the 2nd largest island in the Azores chain of 9 islands and has vineyards dating back to the 15th century. They are walled in to protect them from the winds and seawater on the volcanic slopes; also separated into small rectangular plots of a few vines each (Currais). Centuries ago the wine was so prized that it went directly to the tables of the Russian Tsars. Mainly Verdelho grapes grow on this basaltic rock base, and produces crisp fruity dry whites, perfect with seafood.

7. **a. Blandy's.** They make very fine Madeira fortified wines and are based in the capital city Funchal. They were founded by John Blandy in 1811 and is still owned, run and managed by the family, which is unique on Madeira. John Blandy first arrived in Madeira from London to recuperate from his ill health and all the family stayed there for over 200 years. Other Madeira wineries were founded by English families in the 18th & 19th centuries; these include Cossart Gordon, Leacock, and Miles which are now all part of the Madeira Wine Company run by Blandy's.

8. **b. Sweet Dessert Wines.** Setúbal wines are sited on a peninsular just south of Lisbon, and the sweet and fortified dessert wines are mainly produced using the Muscat of Alexandria grape variety. Their most famous wine is 'Moscatel de Setúbal,' which is a white fortified Muscat wine. It is home to the first grape vines planted on the Iberian Peninsular, circa 4,000 years ago. Moscatel de Setúbal was famous in medieval times especially in the 14th century when England's King Richard II imported large quantities as the English Royal Court Wine.

9. **c. Sand.** Colares vineyards are just north of Lisbon on the Atlantic Coast, planted in sand dunes, as the vineyards are fewer than 300 metres from the

sea. Colares escaped the vine disease Phylloxera in the late 19th century, which laid waste to most of Europe's vineyards. All because the vines are planted in sand and the Phylloxera louse couldn't stand sand. The wines are now hard to find as it is a very small DOC and getting smaller due to suburban expansion of seaside homes; only some 50 acres (20 hectares) are left. It produces light red, quite tannic wines from Ramisco grapes, which age well. They are usually released 10 years after the vintage.

10. **b. Malmsey.** Also known as Malvasia (a white grape variety) it is the sweetest Madeira made. Although a sweet fortified dessert wine, it has a zingy acidity, so is never cloyingly sweet. Its colour is light golden and the wine has notes of figs and marmalade. The other three top Madeiras in order of sweetness, named from the white grapes they are made from are Bual, Verdelho and the driest, often drunk as an aperitif is Sercial. Negra Mole red grapes make around 85% of all Madeiras nowadays; as a grape it is very productive and easy to grow; the sweetness level desired is controlled during the fermentation. All Madeiras are heat aged using the 'Estufagem' process.

ANSWERS TO QUIZ 30 – ANAGRAMS – WINES OF PORTUGAL

Portuguese Wine Regions

1. **Setúbal.** Situated on the peninsula to the south of Lisbon, just across the estuary of the River Tagus, Setúbal is famous for its fortified dessert wines produced mainly from Moscatel grapes. However, this region also produces a wide range of wine from an array of grape varieties, including red wine from Aragonês, Bastardo, Touriga Nacional, and many others, and white wine from Antão Vaz, Arinto, Verdelho, and many more.

2. **Bairrada.** Located in northern Portugal, just south of Porto, and not far from the Atlantic Coast. Baga is the main grape variety for the red wines produced here. Castelão and Rufete grapes are also popular, with all three grapes making deep, richly-coloured reds. The prime white grape varieties are Bical, Maria Gomes, and Cerceal. Sometimes the white blends can include Chardonnay and Sauvignon Blanc. The white wines can be flowery and aromatic, or taste of mineral and citrus.

3. **Dão.** The Dão wine region is situated in northern Portugal, immediately inland from the Bairrada region. It's named after the river that runs through

it. The region's capital, Viseu, is one of the prettiest towns in Portugal. A wide variety of grapes are grown here. The prime reds are Touriga Nacional, Jaen (Mencía in Spain), and Tinta Roriz (Tempranillo in Spain). Easily the best white grape here is Encruzado, now making crisp, fresh and citrus wines.

4. **Douro Valley.** Located in the very north of Portugal, the River Douro starts its journey in Spain, where it is called the River Duero, and finally flows into the Atlantic Ocean at Porto. The Douro Valley is famous for growing the grapes to make Port, but further inland, mainly in the upper Douro along the valley beyond the town of Pinhão, excellent red and white wines are also made.

5. **Alentejo.** Lying in the south of Portugal, east of Lisbon, Alentejo is the country's most extensive wine region. It's best known for its red wines, made from these local grapes, Aragonês, Trincadeira, and Alicante Bouschet, and often in a blend of the three making rich, dense, ripe and fruity wines. Alentejo is also now using more international grapes, especially Syrah and Cabernet Sauvignon making less fruity reds with finesse, full of soft tannins. White wines, which are generally mild, and slightly acidic, with aromas of tropical fruits, are produced mainly from Arinto, Roupeiro, and Antão Vaz grapes.

Port Wine Houses

6. **Taylors.** Taylor Fladgate, owners of Taylor's Port, founded the company in 1692, making it one of the oldest port houses. Taylor's is a top name in the Douro Valley, and one of the most well-respected port houses. Quinta de Vargellas is their leading port wine estate. In 2017 Taylor's celebrated their 325th anniversary by producing a limited edition of a commemorative port, the bottle shape of which was based on the one first used in 1692.

7. **Fonseca.** Another highly respected name in port, owned by The Fladgate Partnership, who also own Taylor's Port. First trading in 1815, their leading wine estates today are Quinta do Cruzeiro and Quinta de Santo António. Fonseca are particularly famous for their outstanding vintage ports.

8. **Niepoort.** Several port houses were founded by British families moving to the Douro, but Niepoort, a leading name in port wine, was established in the nineteenth century by a family who moved from the Netherlands. It is still owned today by the Niepoort family and is a small Port House with a huge reputation. A magnum decanter by Lalique containing Niepoort's Port wine from 1863 has been auctioned in Hong Kong in November 2018 for 100,000 euros, a Guinness World Record for Port.

9. **Grahams.** Founded in 1820 by Scottish brothers William and John Graham. Graham's Port is one of the most highly respected houses in the Douro. The company is owned by Symington Family Estates, who also own Warre's, Dow's

and Cockburn's ports amongst others. Graham's finest port wine estate in the Douro is Quinta Dos Malvedos, undoubtedly one of the region's best estates.

10. ***Sandeman.*** Founded by George Sandeman in 1790. Its famous logo features a caped man, known as 'The Don', wearing a wide Spanish hat (the company is also well-known for sherry production). Sandeman is owned by Sogrape, a group of companies founded in 1942, who own wine estates in many countries other than Portugal, including Spain, Chile, Argentina and New Zealand.

ANSWERS TO QUIZ 31 – WINES OF ENGLAND

1. ***c. Approximately 70%*** of English wines are sparkling, produced predominantly from the same blend of grapes as champagne is made. This is Chardonnay, Pinot Noir, and Pinot Meunier. They have become England's most prestigious wines selling for champagne prices of £25 to £40 plus a bottle and have won many international awards.

2. ***a. Camel Valley in Cornwall.*** This wine estate was planted in 1989 by an ex RAF pilot Bob Lindo and his wife Annie. The sparkling wines from Camel Valley have won more wine awards than any other English vineyard, including Best Sparkling Wine in the World in 2010, beating Bollinger and Louis Roederer champagnes. It has an average annual production of circa 140,000 bottles.

3. ***a. Chapel Down in Kent.*** This is the largest producer of English wines at about 1 million bottles. Second largest is Nyetimber, with over 630 acres (252 hectares) of vineyards spread over three counties (Sussex, Kent & Hampshire), and has the largest area of vineyards in the UK. Denbies in Surrey has 265 acres (106 hectares) and is the third largest. The average vineyard size in England is only 9 acres (3.6 hectares).

4. ***b. About 450 commercial vineyards in England.*** But these vineyards are owned by just over 200 commercial wineries. This is because in England, some of the larger wine estates have multiple vineyards sometimes spread across more than one county.

5. ***a&c. Chardonnay and Pinot Noir.*** Both a and c are correct, as each year they vie for the most planted grape variety in England. Depending on the harvest, the wine production varies by 5% to 10% each vintage. Currently they both account for 35 to 40% each of all vines planted in England. Third most planted is Pinot Meunier, with 10 to 15%. The dominance of these three

varieties is because they're used in the blend producing high quality English sparkling wines.

6. *c. 75% to 80%.* If only still table wine was included then whites would be around 80 to 85%. The amount of still red wine being produced is diminishing each year; red grapes are mainly used in English sparkling wine. The only still red wine expanding in volume is Pinot Noir, as it likes cooler climates and easily commands and obtains premium prices, so is now not only used as part of the Chardonnay and Pinot Noir English sparklers.

7. *a. Camel Valley* gained the first ever Royal Warrant for English wines in 2018. To gain a royal warrant the wines have to be served consistently in UK palaces for over 7 years. Camel Valley sparkling wine is served at many State banquets, as are Nyetimber and Ridgeview, the Queen's three favourite English sparkling wines.

8. *b. 13 million bottles.* Wine production volume in England is growing quickly, but from a small base. Volumes are also very weather dependent. Good vintages from 2025 onwards are predicted to achieve 20 million+ bottles per annum. England is still a very small wine producer in world terms; New Zealand, for example, produces around 400 million bottles of wine, about 30 times the average annual English wine volume.

9. *b. Kent* has the most commercial wineries in England, and also has the largest acreage of vines. There are around 25 commercial wineries in Kent and over 50 vineyards. The biggest three wine estates are Chapel Down, Gusbourne Estate and Lamberhurst. The second highest number of wineries is Devon county with 19 wineries, which are mainly smaller vineyards in area than the Kent estates.

10. *c. Taittinger.* This famous French Champagne House from Reims bought around 175 acres (70 hectares) of Kent land in 2015 that had previously been apple orchards and then planted vineyards with the 3 champagne grapes (Pinot Noir, Pinot Meunier and Chardonnay). This top quality vineyard site for sparkling wine is located very close to Chilham village in East Kent and near to Canterbury. Taittinger's President at that time, Pierre-Emmanuel Taittinger, planted the first grapes in 2017, and Taittinger's new estate is called 'Domaine Evremond' which will be selling its first vintage sparklers in 2023 or 2024. It is planned to produce 300,000 to 400,000 bottles of high quality sparkling wines when the estate is fully mature.

ANSWERS TO QUIZ 32 – ANAGRAMS – WINES OF ENGLAND

English Wine Producers

1. **Bride Valley.** This vineyard is sited in Litton Cheney, Dorset. It was started by Steven Spurrier in 2008, who after 50 years in the wine trade joined the English sparkling wine revolution. Steven was inspired by his wife Bella's sheep farm with south facing chalky slopes. He went to Burgundy and sourced the finest vines of Chardonnay, Pinot Noir, and Pinot Meunier. In 2011 the first Bride Valley harvest was picked, and it sold out on release in 2014. There are now 10 hectares producing 3 elegantly sparkling wines. Back in May 1976 Steven Spurrier changed the world of wine forever, by being responsible for organising the 'Judgement of Paris' blind tasting event, when California wines defeated the best French Bordeaux and Burgundy wines. Sadly Steven died in early 2021.

2. **Wiston.** Wiston Estate Winery is situated in Washington village, West Sussex. The Goring family has owned the Wiston Estate since 1743. The vineyards make up 6.5 hectares on selected chalk slopes and were not planted until 2006. It is now owned and run by Harry & Pip Goring. The wines are made from the traditional blend of champagne grapes for the non-vintage and the vintage; there is also a Rosé, a Blanc de Noirs and a Blanc de Blancs. Wiston was awarded English Winery of the Year in 2018.

3. **Bolney Estate.** The estate is located on the edge of the South Downs, about 14 miles from the south coast. It is one of the English wine pioneers starting with 3 acres (1.2 hectares) of vines in 1972. At that time there were only five other commercial wineries in England. As well as award-winning 'champagne style' wines, a top still Pinot Noir is also produced. Bolney Estate has won Producer of the Year in 2012 and Winery of the Year in 2017, and produces around 150K bottles, with a planned new winery to expand to 500K bottles coming on stream soon.

4. **Windsor Great Park.** This winery was planted in 2010 in Windsor Great Park with a 3 hectare vineyard. The tradition of wine grape-growing in Windsor first started in the reign of Henry II and then ceased for over 1,000 years. Tony Laithwaite, owner of Laithwaite's Wines & Sunday Times Wine Club and much more, chose the vineyard site (Mezel Hill overlooking a small lake) and oversees the winemaking. The first early vintage in 2013 produced only 2,000 bottles and sold out on launch for £35 a bottle. The Queen now produces about 3K to 4K of sparkling wine bottles per annum.

5. **Camel Valley.** In 1989 ex RAF pilot Bob Lindo and his wife Annie bought some land between Bodmin and Padstow in Cornwall and planted their first

8,000 vines. The site was in the Camel Valley and over 30 years later they have achieved much more than their original dreams. Camel Valley has won more wine awards than any other English Winery, has been English Winery of the Year, Producer of the Year, and even won the Best Sparkling Wine in the World, beating Bollinger and Louis Roederer Champagnes.

English Wine Grape Varieties

6. **Müller-Thurgau.** This white grape variety is a cross made way back in 1882 in the Swiss Canton of Thurgau by Hermann Müller – thus the name. It is Riesling crossed with Madeleine Royale. It became very popular first in Germany and was the widest planted white grape from the 1960s to 1980s. It was also one of the first planted grape varieties in England and was the most widely grown grape variety for many years. Its production has reduced a lot in the past 20 years as it is seen as less modern and a bit bland in taste and flavour. It is being largely replaced with plantings of Chardonnay and Bacchus.

7. **Ortega.** It is a white wine grape variety created in 1948 in Germany (cross between Müller-Thurgau & Siegerrebe) and was used mainly to produce sweet dessert wines. Denbies in Surrey produce a top Botrytis Ortega which is honeyed with stone fruit flavours, and at £60+ for a half bottle this is probably the most expensive English wine around. It is often now also used in the production of dry whites, adding fruity aromatic notes to complement acidity. Other English vineyards making dry and sweet Ortega wines are Biddenden, Westwell, New Hall Vineyards, and Woodchester Valley.

8. **Chardonnay.** This is now the most widely planted grape in England, with about 25% to 30% of all vines planted. It is the key component of English sparkling wine, along with Pinot Noir, but is becoming even more popular with more wineries producing Blanc de Blancs sparkling wines, using only Chardonnay. The Chardonnay vine is so adaptable to different climates, easy to grow, and produces a wide variety of styles from an austere Chablis to a fruit salad Australian style; it has become the world's most widely spread grape, found in more countries than any other variety. It is also the world's most planted white grape used for wine, while the most planted white grape variety is Airén, but it is used extensively for brandy, as well as sherry and wine. Airén is almost exclusively grown in Spain.

9. **Reichensteiner.** It is a white grape variety that is mainly grown in Germany, New Zealand and England. It was created in Berlin in 1939, and is a cross between Müller-Thurgau and Madeleine Angevine. It is a high yielding variety with low acidity and some fruit flavours, but is seen as a bit bland. It is thus used in many blends to balance out more high acidity grapes. Some of

the many English estates that use Reichensteiner are Denbies, New Hall, Three Choirs, Lamberhurst and Chapel Down.

10. **Pinot Noir.** It is one of the older grape varieties and has been used in Burgundy since the 1st century AD. France is the largest producer followed by the USA, and surprisingly Germany is the 3rd largest producer. Pinot Noir is thin skinned, producing light red wines; it is also notoriously difficult to grow and is susceptible to many diseases and pests. It produces wines which start out as simple fruity ones, with cherry and strawberry flavours. They age well and add complexity and finesse to the overall taste. Most of England's second most planted grape veriety, Pinot Noir, goes into sparkling wine blends; but an increasing number are making still wine Pinot Noirs. Bolney Estate in Hampshire is one of the pioneers since the mid 1990s.

ANSWERS TO QUIZ 33 – WINES OF AUSTRIA AND SWITZERLAND

1. **b. 1985.** Several Austrian wineries illegally adulterated their wines with diethylene glycol (anti-freeze) to make the wine taste sweeter and seem more full-bodied in the style of late harvest wines. It led to the almost complete collapse of the Austrian wine industry. Longer-term the recovery was led by a change to mainly dry white wines of high quality, and the strictest wine laws in the world.

2. **b. 14.** Since 2002 the DAC of Austria, (their Appellation Control Rules) have introduced the strictest laws on the quality of grapes and their origin, and winemaking techniques are analysed to try to stop a wine scandal ever happening again.

3. **a. 1% to 2%.** The Swiss drink almost all the wine they produce, and fewer than 1 million bottles are exported. Thus they tend to be expensive although they are high quality. Switzerland has one of the highest per capita wine consumption, so also imports 66% of the wines they drink. Most of the wines they do export go to Germany.

4. **c. White.** Both Austria and Switzerland are dominated by the production of white wines. In Austria almost 40% of all grapes grown are Grüner Veltliner, and Switzerland is dominated by the Chasselas grape. For both countries white wine accounts for 60% to 65%.

5. **a. Chasselas.** It is a grape variety only produced in high volumes for wine making in Switzerland. It produces a dry, fruity and full flavoured white wine

especially in the wine regions of Vaud and Valais. Chasselas is used extensively in Turkey and Hungary for table grapes to eat.

6. **a. Grüner Veltliner.** This one grape variety accounts for well over 50% of all white grapes planted in Austria. It is quite unique and has flavours of green pepper and lime and is often seen as an exotic alternative to Sauvignon Blanc. Most of the 26 white grapes used commercially in Austria are also indigenous, and mainly only found in Austria.

7. **b. Valais.** It flanks the Rhône river valley and creates an alpine sun trap for vines. It accounts for almost 50% of all the wines produced in Switzerland. The dramatic steep terraces of vines produce elegant wines especially from Pinot Noir, Syrah, Gamay, and Cornalin for reds and Chasselas, and Petite Arvine for whites.

8. **a. Austria.** It makes 2.5 times more wine in volume than Switzerland. Austria produces on average about 250 million litres compared to Switzerland's average of 100 million litres. Most of the wines produced are white with Grüner Veltliner at almost 50%. Austria exports around 25% of wines produced per year, compared to 1% by Switzerland. Germany imports 47% of all Austrian wines, and second is Switzerland with 11%.

9. **b. Nikolaihof Winery.** It is by far the oldest wine estate in Austria, growing grape vines from 63 AD. This site in Wachau produced wines from the time of the Celts and Romans. The St Nikola Monastery was founded there in 1075. The cellars for Nikolaihof Winery were constructed in a Roman crypt. It also has the distinction of becoming the first biodynamic estate in Europe. Nikolaihof cultivates primarily Riesling, Grüner Veltliner & Neuberger grapes, on 40 to 50+ year old vines, producing many award-winning wines. The 1995 Riesling Vinothek was the first Austrian wine to score a perfect 100 with Robert Parker's Wine Advocate. Klosterneuburg Monastery (choice a) is the second oldest wine estate, starting in 1114 AD.

10. **c. Sekt.** It is a German derived name for sparkling wines, coined first in Berlin in 1825. It was not until 1975 that it could be used as a name for other countries' sparkling wines. Austria was one of the few countries to do so. Any of Austria's 40 accepted grape varieties can be used in Austrian Sekt production. But the most commonly used are Pinot Noir, Chardonnay, Pinot Blanc, Riesling & Grüner Veltliner. Many of the Austrian quality Sekts are produced using the more expensive methode champenoise rather than the Charmat method. There are three quality levels, from the basic Classic level, to Reserve and the top level is Grand Reserve. On average around 25 million litres (33 million bottles) of Austrian Sekt are produced per annum (10% of all Austrian wine).

ANSWERS TO QUIZ 34 – WINES OF HUNGARY AND ROMANIA

1. *c. Romania.* Romania is the 6th largest producer of wine in Europe, and also the largest producer in Central and Eastern Europe. With an average of 5 million hl/year, or 650 million bottles, (circa 55 million cases), it ranks as 13th largest wine producing country in the world. But to put it in perspective, Romania only makes 1/10 of the wine volume produced annually by any of Italy, France or Spain, the top 3 wine producing countries in Europe. Answers a) and b) – both Austria and Hungary each make around 60% of the quantity of wine made by Romania, (circa 400 million bottles).

2. *a. Mad.* This is a wine town right in the centre of the best Tokaji single vineyard area in Hungary. Royal Tokaji was founded in 1990 by Hugh Johnson and others and is the first independent Tokaji wine company to be formed in the post-communist era. Royal Tokaji was also the first to re-introduce single vineyard names on its bottle labels. It concentrates on making single vineyard wines from 'first growth' vineyards and it has now won over 100 international awards, and exports to more than 30 countries.

3. *b. Bull's Blood.* This was Hungary's most famous international wine during the 20th century, made in Eger in north-eastern Hungary. It is now thought of as too common and rugged a name and was changed to Egri Bikaver. The Bull's Blood name arose from the siege of the walled town of Eger in 1552 by Suleiman the Magnificent's Turkish army. The town's fighters were so ferocious in resistance, with their beards stained red with wine, that the Turks gave up – believing that the Eger men were devil's drinking Bull's Blood, (not red wine). Egri Bikaver or Bull's Blood wine is a full bodied, rich and spicy red blend usually based on the Kekfrankos grape, with Merlot and Cabernet Franc added.

4. *b. Feteasca Regala.* This is a native Romanian white grape hybrid variety that first appeared in the 1920s in Transylvania. It is now the most planted grape in the whole of Romania. Plantings in Transylvania are now reducing as more international grape varieties are introduced including Sauvignon Blanc and Pinot Gris. Transylvania has the largest vineyard in Europe, owned by Jidvei, at almost 6,000 acres (2,400 hectares). Feteasca Regala is used for dry, still and sparkling wines and are fresh, crisp and with aromas of white fruit, roses and white flowers.

5. *a. Duna.* This is the largest of the seven larger wine regions of Hungary, stretching between the rivers Danube and Tisza. It is a mostly flat sandy area as it is on the wide Hungarian plain and was only officially formed in 2006 by merging formerly discrete wine districts in the Great Plain wine region.

Without a doubt, mentions of 'Great Plain wine' in the past decades meant cheap, industrial volume wines of the communist era made for the Soviet Union; hence the region's name change. Most of the wines made today are light whites with fresh floral aromas, sold at low prices and made from a wide variety of white grapes, including 22 indigenous varieties.

6.   *a. Germany.* Germany has imported increasing quantities of Romanian wines since the Soviet Union ended, and especially since Romania joined the EU in 2007. Germany now imports 21% by volume and 2nd is the UK (c) at 18% and it's also increasing because the low prices attract supermarkets. The 3rd largest importer is the Netherlands (b) at circa 14%. So only three countries import over 50% of all Romanian wine exports. The most imported grape varieties are all the international ones – Sauvignon Blanc, Chardonnay, Cabernet Sauvignon, Merlot, Pinot Noir and Syrah. Only 5% to 10% of total Romanian wine production is exported and from 2016, with rising consumer incomes, Romania is now a net importer of wines.

7.   *c. 65% to 75%.* The grape vine is part of a Romanian's life and most households have their own vines to produce wine for personal family consumption, with 65% to 75% of Romanian wine production represented by homemade self-production. Making wine at home is a form of personal emancipation, but it also means a lack of standards and resistance to change by most of the population. In Romania 50% of all wines consumed are still homemade, and only 10% come from imported wines. Most commercially grown Romanian wines are also sold for domestic consumption and 70% of that is white made mostly from indigenous grapes. Less than 10% of Romanian wine is exported nowadays.

8.   *a. Furmint.* Furmint is the grape variety that dominates the production of Tokaji sweet dessert wines. It is an ancient grape variety that seems to have originated in Tokaj, where it is by far the most planted grape, although there is also a little perfumed Hárslevelü and grapey Muscat. Unfortunately, modern tastes are against rich luscious perfectly balanced and expensive dessert wines. Sweet wines are much less popular compared to the 18th & 19th centuries when Tokaji was the most famous wine in Europe on the dinner tables of kings, queens and Tzars. The modern trend today is for dry Furmint which is becoming well known internationally. It can be fresh, fruity, with a pear and peach aroma and a distinctive delicate mineral freshness. Today most of the 120 producers in the Tokaj region tend to use up to 60% of their grapes for dry wine initially, and then leave the rest to hopefully turn into Aszús, shrunken berries to make Tokaji's sweet, golden, complex dessert wines. But with global warming, the arrival of 'noble rot' is becoming more uncertain.

9. **a. DOC Dealu Mare.** It is the most compact wine region in Romania. It's about 65 km long in the east-west direction and only about 3-12 km wide. Dealu Mare translates to Big Hill and is located in the south-east on the foothills of the Carpathian Mountains. It's regarded as Romania's premier red wine region with many smaller, newer wineries and more innovative winemakers. Many of the red wines are big, fruity, balanced, yet still often high in alcohol. Most producers grow a selection of red international grape varieties, led by Cabernet Sauvignon, with Merlot, Syrah, Pinot Noir, and sometimes the indigenous grape Fetească Neagră.

10. **b. 1700 to 1730.** This first in the world classification of the quality of vineyards and wines divided the Tokaji vineyards into First, Second and Third Growths. The classification of Tokaji wine quality depended on each vineyard's soil type, the sun exposure on the slope, and the potential to produce Aszús berries for sweet wine from 'noble rot'. Many of these vineyards remain highly prized to this day. The 1700 Classification was 56 years before the demarcation of the Douro Valley and 155 years before the 1855 Médoc Classification in Bordeaux.

ANSWERS TO QUIZ 35 – WINES OF BULGARIA, CROATIA AND SLOVENIA.

1. **b. Pamid.** In Bulgaria the most prolific planted red grape variety is Pamid, which also happens to be indigenous, at around 25% to 30% of all plantings of red grapes. Bulgaria has over 200 indigenous grapes which still produce wine, some are nowadays only used for domestic winemaking by private citizens. 65% of all wines produced are red, with the trend towards more international grape varieties such as Cabernet Sauvignon and Merlot which are now the joint second most planted red grapes at about 20% each. Pamid is considered to be one of the oldest local wine grape varieties in the country, and have been growing in Bulgaria since the Thracians' times. It is a light red thin skinned grape which produces a fresh fruity bright light red and should be drunk young and slightly chilled.

2. **a. 35%.** The percentage of plantings is growing, but it is still true that just over one third of all Bulgarian wine is made from International grape varieties. There are really only two red grape varieties dominating the non-indigenous

grapes with Cabernet Sauvignon and Merlot both at around 15% each and the remaining 5% made up from Pinot Noir, Chardonnay, Riesling and Viognier.

3. **b. Croatia.** The first underwater winery in Europe is Edivo Vina winery which is located about one hour by the coast road north of Dubrovnik in the Adriatic Sea next to the village of Drace on the Pelješac Peninsula. It was created in 2011, and the cellars are in a sunken ship on the bottom of the bay. Visiting the underwater cellars is for tourists and wine lovers who are also scuba divers, who are accompanied by one of the winemakers for the cellar tour. About 5,000 bottles of wine are aged above-ground for three months and then stored in clay amphorae on the bottom of the Adriatic Sea for one to two years. There is, of course, an above ground winery and shop for those visitors who don't fancy a scuba dive to the cellar in the sunken ship about 80 ft below the surface. Wine lovers can thus enjoy Navis Mysterium Amphora wine, a unique red wine which is aged in the Adriatic, by either diving down to grab it or buying it in the shop.

4. **a. Miljenko Grgic.** He is Croatian born and now a Croatian and American winemaker in Napa Valley, California. He was born into a winemaking family in the town of Desne in 1923 on Croatia's coastal region of Dalmatia. He first came to world fame in 1976 when at the 'Judgement of Paris' blind tasting the white wine he made in Napa Valley was judged to be the best white wine beating all the top white Burgundies from France. It was Chateau Montelena 1973. In 1977 he jointly set up his own Napa Valley wine estate with Austin Hills; he changed his name to Mike Grgich and launched Grgich Hills Cellar which has won many international wine awards in the past forty plus years. All the wines are high quality and premium priced, and he makes both red and white classic Napa varieties. The Miljenko Selection and Legacy range are the top two tier selections (Napa Selection is first tier) and are only made using the very oldest vines in single vineyard plots. In 1996 he founded Grgich Vina in Croatia and concentrates on producing Croatia's very best two varietals: Plavac Mali (red wine) and Pošip (white wine). They have twice been voted the best Croatian red and white wine.

5. **a. Blaufränkisch.** Slovenia (Lower Styria Region) is now thought to be the country of origin of Blaufränkisch, through DNA testing. This European grape variety accounts for over 20% of all the red grape vineyards in Austria and is grown extensively in Germany and in Hungary and other eastern European countries. It was called 'the Pinot Noir of the East' and thought to have been a clone of Gamay and to have originated in France or in Austria, until the extensive DNA testing was carried out. Blaufränkisch is a dark blue-skinned grape variety making red wines which remind one slightly of the Nebbiolos

of Piedmont or a Rhône Syrah with softer tannins. The name Blaufränkisch contains two geographical errors; ' blau' means blue in German, and 'fränkisch' refers to what was once thought to be the French origin of the grape.

6. *c. Zinfandel.* Plavac Mali was only discovered to be an ancient parent of Zinfandel in 1988, when researchers from Davis University Enology department did DNA testing on Zinfandel, the uniquely Californian red grape variety. Dr Carole Meredith with the help of Mike Grgich (a top Napa Valley winemaker and Croatian) and researchers from the University of Zagreb did extensive DNA fingerprinting of Zinfandel and worldwide red grape varieties and discovered a direct ancestor match to Plavac Mali, the most widely planted red grape in Croatia. Until that discovery it had been commonly claimed that Primitivo from Puglia in southern Italy had been the rightful ancestor and parent of Zinfandel. Plavac Mali makes good quality rich and powerful wines, which are dark red and smooth, similar to Zinfandel, with flavours and aromas of blackberries, dark cherries and often pepper and spices.

7. *c. Slovenia.* Slovenia is by far the most affluent country in Eastern Europe. Its other advantage is that it is a very small country in population terms with around 2 million people, compared to Croatia with 4 million, and Bulgaria with a population of just over 7 million. Therefore not in absolute terms, but per head of population Slovenia has more vineyards, wineries and tractors than any other Eastern European country. With 23,000 hectares of vineyards, Slovenia has a more extensive planting than Croatia at 21,000 hectares, but the much larger Bulgaria has 64,000 hectares. Wineries in Slovenia are on average very small, less than 1 hectare, with a total of over 28,000, compared to Bulgaria with only 300 enormous wineries, Croatia also has larger average size wineries with 400 registered for commercial wine production.

8. *c. Slovenia.* White grape varieties have always dominated volume wine production in Slovenia, now with over 75% being white. The 3 top white wine grapes by volume in Slovenia are Welschriesling, Chardonnay and Sauvignon Blanc. Croatia is second in terms of percentage of white wines produced at 67% and increasing, especially of dessert wines. Bulgaria has always been a red wine producing country; 10 years ago white wines only accounted for about 25% of all wines but in 2020 this has grown to around 37%.

9. *c. Klet Brda.* This is a cooperative winery in the Brda wine region of Slovenia with over 400 family wine producers as members, owning over 1,000 hectares (2,500 acres) of vineyards. The winery was founded in 1957 and is based underneath Dobrovo Castle, with enormous cellars housing over 100,000 bottles of older vintage wines. The wines are high quality and good value and

over 40% are exported, and 70% are white wines. Answer a) Bessa Valley is a top quality Bulgarian red wine estate producing Merlot, Syrah, Cabernet Sauvignon and red blends which are classically Bordeaux French in style with finesse and harmony. Answer b) Borovista is a cult boutique winery in northern Bulgaria which wins many national and international awards. It specialises in producing wines from indigenous grape varieties such as Bouquet, Evmolpia and Gamza, while also producing high quality Pinot Noir and Chardonnay.

10. *c. 400 years old.* The oldest wine producing vine in the world still producing grapes was planted before 1620 in the north-east of Slovenia in the old village of Lent in the Maribor Region. The vine is of a Žametovka red grape variety, which is one of the oldest noble indigenous wine grapes in Slovenia. The annual harvest of grapes is between 35kg to 55kg (up to 125 pounds) which are made into wine and then put into special 25cl bottles (a third of a normal wine bottle), designed by a famous Slovenian artist Oskar Kogoj. An average of 100 bottles are produced per year and are used as special gifts for foreign dignitaries. As well as being in the Guinness Book of Records, it is the only vine with its own museum attached and has its own annual festival. The old vine is now growing up the side of a village wall of Lent which houses the Vine House Wine Museum.

ANSWERS TO QUIZ 36 – WINES OF GREECE AND CYPRUS

1. *b. Peloponnese.* This is the largest wine region producing around 30% of all Greek wines.
There are 4 major wine zones or regions and 29 wine regions are now designated PDO or Protected Designation of Origin. Wine with this designation has to be made by one of the 300 Greek varietals, be indigenous, and historically grown and produced within the boundaries of the area.

2. *c. 300/350 million bottles.* Greece is a small country with fewer than 10 million population and is only 17th in world wine production by volume. Both its quality and volume of wine is increasing year on year with new quality wine estates springing up each year. Greece's average production of 2.5 million hectolitres produced by the 1,300 wineries, works out at an average of 20K cases per producer.

3. *c. Santorini.* This small volcanic island is the birthplace of the Assyrtiko white grape, which is fast becoming a favourite of wine writers and experts

worldwide. It is grown in little nests protected by low walls and planted on the windswept slopes of the dormant volcano. This top quality, dry wine can compare to a top Chablis or Sancerre. It can be austere, intense and floral with a scent of lemons and minerals. A Vinsanto sweet version is also made and has been used for Masses in the Greek and Russian Orthodox Church for centuries.

4. *a. Barolo.* Naoussa (Northern Greece) barrel aged red wines of top quality, made from the Xinomavro grape, resemble closely the finest Barolo wines of Piedmont, Italy, made with the Nebbiolo grape. Its bouquet is haunting and has a fine balance of fruit and power and is quite pale like fine Barolos. In 1971, it became Greece's very first wine area to be given its own official appellation title.

5. *c. 2,800 years.* Commandaria dessert wines from Cyprus have been produced continuously from Roman and Greek times. It was a most sought after wine in classical times being traded throughout the Mediterranean region. It is claimed to be the oldest named wine in the world in continuous production. It is made from the sun dried Mavro and Xynisteri grapes, left on mats to shrivel and concentrate the sweet juice.

6. *b. Cyprus.* Very unusually, with almost unique luck, Phylloxera never travelled to Cyprus. Their ungrafted vines are still protected by strict quarantine laws. This has slowed down the introduction of international grape varieties, so most Cypriot wines are still made from indigenous grapes. Cyprus has a very ancient history of wine production, back to 3500 BC. Mavro, meaning 'black' is the most planted grape variety (still over 50% of vineyards).

7. *a. Samos.* Their Muscats are fresh, clean and pure young sweet wines often made in concrete or steel. There are also some more complex older oak aged ones. Tinos is very small with only 6 wineries making mainly white wines. It is called the new Greek boutique wine frontier. Zante is best known for its lively red wines made from the Avgoustiatis grape.

8. *b. Pine resin.* Small pieces or chunks of Aleppo pine resin are added to the vats or barrels during the fermentation process. It gives the wine a resin flavour which can be subtle or overwhelming. It is often seen as the Marmite of wines. It has been made this way for at least 2,000 years.

9. *b. Emva.* Emva Cream Sherry was a huge part of the Cyprus wine Industry. It was born in 1844 and lived for over 150 years; still surviving today, owned by the ETKO winery. It is 15% ABV and relatively cheap and the taste is smooth and sweet. It is aged in wooden barrels. In the 1970s Emva sold over 12 million bottles per year to the UK. Its sales have now reduced hugely because of people's changing tastes since the 1980s, and the final nail was in 1996 when the EC ruled that only wine from the Jerez region in Spain could be called Sherry.

The end of Cyprus Sherry, but Emva Cream Fortified Wine still sells to niche markets.

10. **c. 55% to 65%.** In Greece currently around 61% of wines are white wines from white grapes. Savatiano is the most planted white wine grape variety which has traditionally been used in making Retsina wines. Savatiano is now also used in white blends using more acidic grapes to produce well balanced quality wines with aromas of citrus fruits and fresh flowers. Other top Greek widely planted indigenous white grapes are Debina, Robola, Roditis and Vilana. Assyrtiko is considered to produce the finest white wines in Greece from its home in Santorini and is now probably the most internationally well known grape variety from Greece.

ANSWERS TO QUIZ 37 – MATCH WINES OF EUROPEAN COUNTRIES

1. **c. Switzerland.** Michel Boven and his family have been making wines in the Valais region of Switzerland for over 60 years and is judged as one of the best wine estates in the whole of Switzerland. The Boven family winery is called 'Cave Ardévaz', and makes over 28 different wines from 20 grape varieties. The red and white wines are known for their finesse, delicacy and balance between fruit and minerality. Michel Boven has twice been voted winemaker of the year for Switzerland. The wine estate currently produces 12 different whites and reds and 2 types of rosé and sparkling wines. The estate's most popular wine is made from Petite Arvine the great indigenous white wine grape of the Valais region.

2. **a. Romania.** Davino Winery was established in 2003 and is judged to be one of the most iconic wineries in Romania. The winery is based in the Dealu Mare DOC region, the most compact wine region in Romania, and is situated on the southern Subcarpathian Hills, covering hills and valleys located around 40 miles north of Bucharest. Davino Winery is composed of 68 hectares of vineyards, mainly comprised of vines aged 40 years plus. The main grape varieties grown are Cabernet Sauvignon, Merlot, and Cabernet Franc, making red Bordeaux type blends.

3. **b. Greece.** Domaine Lyrarakis in Crete was founded in 1966 and is located in the mountainous commune of Alagni (440 metres above sea-level), south of the city of Heraklion. Domaine Lyrarakis uses modern winemaking techniques,

to produce single grape wines from obscure local varieties which they have rescued from extinction. These wines include the ancient white varieties of Plytó, Dafni, and Vidiano; also single varietal local reds including Kotsifali, Mandilaria and Liatiko. Domaine Lyrarakis is judged to have won more wine awards than any other Cretan winery, especially for their top flagship indigenous wines from single 'premium' vineyard plots. They also make wines from international varieties such as Syrah, Cabernet Sauvignon and Merlot.

4.   *e. Hungary.* The Szepsy Estate is located in the village of Mad in the Tokaji wine region of north-eastern Hungary. Istvan Szepsy, the Estate winemaker and owner, was also fundamental in helping to found the Royal Tokaji Wine Company in 1990, which is a joint venture of 63 local growers led by Istvan Szepsy, and is now part owned by Hugh Johnson. Also in 1990, after the communist era ended, Istvan Szepsy revived his own family wine estate, once again making and selling wines from family vineyards under the Szepsy label. Istvan Szepsy is regarded as Hungary's leading winemaker; one of his ancestors in 1630 was the first person to write down the process for making the legendary sweet dessert wines of Tokaji. The Szepsy Estate now only makes top quality wines. His 52 hectares of plantings produce fewer than 50,000 bottles, and his wines have an almost sacred reputation in Hungary and abroad. He makes all his wines from the white grape Furmint. His dry whites are elegant with expressive spices, lime and apple notes and his 6 puttonyos Tokaji Aszú dessert wine is sublime at over £200 per half bottle. Jancis Robinson has stated that Istvan Szepsy is a genius.

5.   *d. Austria.* Winegut Emmerich Knoll estate is in the wine growing region of Wachau in the village of Unterloiben in the Danube valley about 50 miles west of Vienna. It was established in 1825 and is still family-owned and operated. Nowadays Emmerich II and Monika Knoll are the winemakers of the hallowed 15 hectares where the famous wines are produced. About 45% of the vineyards are planted with Riesling and another 45% with Grüner Veltliner, and the remaining 10% is Chardonnay, Pinot Noir and indigenous grapes. The estate makes traditional concentrated yet tightly balanced wines with traditional colourful labels. Over 90% of his wines are white, most are dry and perfumed but luscious dessert wines are also produced. The Kellerberg Vineyard is one of the world's best individual terrains and makes exquisite and expensive flagship Riesling and Grüner Veltliner wines.

6.   *i. Assyrtiko.* Santorini is a small volcanic island close to Crete and is the birthplace of the Assyrtiko white grape, which is fast becoming a favourite grape variety of wine critics, experts and adventurous wine drinkers worldwide. It is grown in little nests, each of a curled up vine protected by

low round walls. They are planted on the windswept ash laden slopes of the dormant volcano. This top quality, dry wine is often compared to a top Chablis, Sancerre or even a New Zealand Chardonnay with a salty tang. It can be an austere wine, quite intense and floral with citrus fruits, also a scent of lemons and a taste of minerals and pears. A Vin Santo sweet version of Assyrtiko is also made and has been used for Masses in the Greek and Russian Orthodox Church for centuries.

7. **h. Furmint.** North-eastern Hungary, the Tokaji region, is the home of this white grape variety that produces intense perfumed dry wine as well as luscious sweet 'noble rot' versions. Furmint is the grape variety that dominates the production of Tokaji sweet dessert wines. It is an ancient grape variety that seems to have originated in Tokaj, where it is by far the most planted grape. Luscious dessert wines are much less popular today than they were in the 18th & 19th centuries, when Tokaji was the most famous wine in Europe presented on the dinner tables of kings, queens and tzars. Dry Furmint wines are now becoming well known internationally. They can be fresh, fruity, with a pear and peach aroma and a distinctive delicate mineral freshness. Today most of the current 190 wineries in the Tokaj region tend to use up to 60% of their grapes for dry wine initially and then hope that 'noble rot' occurs to turn the remaining 40% of grapes into the shrivelled bunches that produce the intense, concentrated sweet Tokaji Aszú dessert wines.

8. **j. Graševina.** This is Croatia's indigenous white grape and by far the most widely planted variety. It is a very adaptable grape making fresh dry wines all the way to sweet late harvest wines, and being used as the base variety for sparkling wines. It is also planted in Eastern Europe and called Welschriesling. Graševina's aromatic profile is often cited as flowery, fresh with elderberry and quince jam, and a taste of green apples and peach with mineral sensations. Graševina translates as 'green peas' as the early ripening tight bunches of grape berries resemble little peas.

9. **f. Grüner Veltliner.** It is indigenous to Austria and is the most planted variety making fine full bodied dry white wines which can age for a long time. The Grüner Veltliner variety accounts for well over 50% of all white grapes planted in Austria, and over 33% of all vineyards planted. It is a very versatile grape, making fresh young dry wines and sparkling sekt as well as rich, full yet dry and perfumed age-worthy whites to savour. Grüner Veltliner means literally 'the green grape from the village of Veltlin' in the Austrian Tirol.

10. **g. Chasselas.** Switzerland is the home to Chasselas which is the most important and widely planted white grape variety. Chasselas tends to ripen early on the vine, making it particularly good for Switzerland's cool and high alpine slopes. Recent DNA research suggests that it originated on the shores

of Lake Geneva; it is now most commonly grown in the Vaud and Valais wine regions. The best Chasselas wines can be complex and rich, showing a range of fruity, floral and mineral flavours, with very good balance of acidity and fruit, and can age for years in the cellar. Older Chasselas wines show more honeyed and nutty flavours, taking on a deep golden colour. The grape was usually called Fendant from the 1700s until the early 20th century, and now many producers in the Vaud region use Fendant on their labels instead of Chasselas.

ANSWERS TO QUIZ 38 – WINES OF ISRAEL, LEBANON, EGYPT, AND TURKEY

1. ***b. Lebanon.*** All 3 wine estates are in Lebanon. Belle-Vue, Ksara and Musar are called Chateau because of the French Influence in Lebanon. In 1920 soon after the end of World War 1, Lebanon became part of the French Colonial Empire. This lasted for over 20 years until January 1944 when Lebanese independence was granted. French is still the second language and taught in schools. French vines were imported and French winemaking methods were adopted, which helped the vibrant wine industry take off. Today Lebanon is still producing elegant quality predominantly red wines, from mainly Bordeaux grape blends.

2. ***a. 6th largest producer of wine in the world.*** This is surprising for a Muslim country where only about 2% of the population actually drink wine. Most wine is thus made for export or the tourist hotels. The quality of both the red and white wines is very high as are the average prices. Turkey is also the number one grower of raisins in the world, producing over 370,000 metric tonnes per annum. For wine production, 34 varieties of grapes are used in commercial wineries, with 22 of these being native grapes. Three countries take around 60% of all Turkey's wine exports, Northern Cyprus, Belgium and the UK.

3. ***b. Chateau Ksara.*** Many people have only heard of Chateau Musar in Lebanon, but it was Chateau Ksara which started Lebanon's modern wine industry, almost 80 years before Musar was founded in 1930. It was founded in 1857 by Jesuit priests who produced the country's first dry red wine. It is Lebanon's oldest, largest and most famous visited winery, attracting over

70,000 visitors per year. It is also located in the Bekaa Valley, near the Roman temple of Bacchus. The vineyard is planted at over 1,000 metres altitude (3,400 ft) and the vines enjoy a mild Mediterranean climate. It produces around 3 million bottles annually and exports to over 40 countries.

4. *c. 40 to 50 million bottles per year.* Israel's modern wine industry was founded by Baron Rothschild, owner of Château Lafite Rothschild in Bordeaux. In the 1880s he imported French grape varieties and helped set up Carmel Winery, which is now Israel's largest wine producer. Israeli wine is circa 70% red wine, and now over 75% are Kosher wine. Israel's wine industry is very concentrated with 5 large wineries producing 75% of all wines. The top 3 wineries are Carmel, Barkin and Golan Heights; there are a further 200 or so wineries but most are very small boutique producers. Red wines are the most popular, and all are French grape varieties lead by Cabernet Sauvignon and Syrah. Many of the top wines are Bordeaux blends.

5. *a. 3 to 5 wineries.* There are currently only 3 wineries in Egypt producing wines on a commercial basis. Ancient Egypt was a great wine drinking nation, with the Pharaohs and priests drinking the most prized wines. Their wines of 5,000 years ago were grown all over the Nile delta and they were made with relative sophistication, fermented and stored in clay amphorae, with the vintage year, region and winemaker's name etched on each amphora. It was even filtered before drinking. Nowadays wine is banned in Egypt and only allowed to be served in foreign tourist hotels and restaurants at exorbitant prices. Even Air Egypt does not serve any wines on board. The wines are some of the poorest quality in the world, often with an antiseptic nose and industrial harsh flavours. They are best avoided.

6. *b. 8 million to 14 million bottles.* Lebanon is a very small wine producer on the world stage – where Italy produces 5 to 6 billion bottles per year. Lebanese wine is high quality and sold at prices that put it amongst the top 5% of world wines. Local winemaking dates back to the ancient Phoenicians over 6,000 years ago. Lebanon lies further south than most northern hemisphere wine-producing nations, but has inviting mountains providing higher altitudes for vine planting, providing the cooler, drier conditions that high quality grapes need. The majority of the top wines are reds made in the Bordeaux blend manner. Chateau Ksara produces almost 35% of all wine volume, and the top 5 wineries produce over 60%, with 50 or so other small boutique wineries producing under 100,000 bottles per annum.

7. *a. Kalecik Karasi.* This is the Turkish love child grape to Pinot Noir with the same elegant, light fruit and acid driven taste. Kalecik Karasi often abbreviated as KK is a primary bluish black, thin skinned grape variety

of Turkey. Although it is considered as one of the country's top red wine producing varietals, it is largely unheard of outside Turkey. This grape and wine are called by the name of the area, the Kalecik district of Ankara Province. Narince (b) is a top quality white grape which makes wines like a slightly fuller less acid version of Sauvignon Blanc. Okuzgozu (c) translates as 'Bull's Eye' and is Turkey's most planted red grape.

8. *c. USA.* The USA is the main export market for Israeli wines by far, mainly for reds which get good write-ups from the wine critics, especially Robert Parker of Wine Advocate. Almost 60% of all wines exported are to the USA. But this is still a very small amount as 80% of Israeli wines are consumed domestically and only 20% exported – this amounts to only $25 million imported by the USA. Answer a) The European Union is the 2nd biggest export market for Israeli wines at around 20%. Answer b) Russia imports very little wine from Israel.

9. *b. 10% to 15%.* Less than 15% of all the grapes grown in Turkey are used to make wine, the rest are used for table grapes, raisins and jams, jellies and sweets. Although Turkey's viticultural history is one of the most ancient in the world, the modern Turkish wine industry is very young. Turkey only resumed producing wine in 1925, as a symbol of the nation's modernisation and Westernisation. The increasingly global red wine portfolio of Pinot Noir, Cabernet Sauvignon, Merlot and Syrah is now planted in Turkey, as is its white wine equivalent, consisting of Chardonnay, Sauvignon Blanc and Sémillon. Commercially, wineries also use 22 indigenous grape varieties including reds such as Kalecik Karasi, Okuzgozu and Bogazkere. The top 3 whites are Emir, Narince and Sultaniye.

10. *a. Chateau Isaac.* It is a Lebanese Bekaa Valley winery producing Cabernet Sauvignon. Very tricky to guess as it has a biblical Jewish name, but most wineries in the Middle East named 'Chateau' are from Lebanon. It was formed in 2000 and is the only winery in Lebanon that uses no sulphates or additives and is fully organic. Answer b) Golan Heights Winery Yarden Bar'on is a flagship Cabernet Sauvignon from Israel's largest winery. Answer c) Hevron Heights Winery Isaac's Ram Cabernet Sauvignon is made in a fairly new winery, founded in 2000 by a French winemaker, in the Judean Hills near Hebron. It is getting good reviews for its well balanced, elegant wines and exports most of its production. Worryingly their flagship wine is named Armagedon!

ANSWERS TO QUIZ 39 – WINES OF ASIA AND THE SOVIET BLOC COUNTRIES

1. **b. Château Lafite Rothschild.** This most famous Bordeaux first growth was the first prestige French Château to buy land and open a vineyard in China. Lafite bought 30 hectares of prime land in Shandong Province in 2007 and 10 years later their first vintage 2017 was produced. Their Chinese Grand Cru is named Long Dai and it came on sale in 2019 in China at a price of over £300 per bottle. This first vintage is a blend of Cabernet Sauvignon, Marselan and Cabernet Franc. It is aged for 18 months in French oak small barrels and is made to age for as long as a top Bordeaux Château. The second prestige French wine company to invest in buying vineyards in China was LVMH, with 'Chandon Me' a sparkling wine made only for the Chinese palate (much sweeter than Moët & Chandon champagne). LVMH have also planted Ao Yun red wine vineyards high up in the mountains, near Tibet and Shangri-La in Yunnan Province, at altitudes from 2,200 to 2,600 metres, enabling the Cabernet Sauvignon grape to express the full refinement of this unique terroir.

2. **b. Sparkling white blend.** This is an Indian sparkling methode champenoise wine, made by a Mumbai millionaire with technical help from Piper-Heidsieck Champagne. It was launched in 1984 and was very successful in the UK for over 25 years, being listed in supermarkets including Waitrose. It had 245 hectares high up in the Sahyadri mountains, but problems occurred and the company which had been exporting 400,000 bottles to Europe in 1990 finally imploded in 2011 and ceased exporting. The largest Indian wine producer since 1998 has been Sula Vineyards in the Nashik region of western India, annually selling over 1 million cases of mainly white wines per year.

3. **c. Tokyo.** The vineyards of Yamanushi are planted on the lower slopes of Mount Fuji. It is the largest quality wine growing area in Japan, with 80 of Japan's 300 top vineyards in Yamanushi. It is a very historic winemaking area, starting in 718 AD. Its main wine volume production is from white grapes, concentrating on Chardonnay and Sauvignon Blanc, and now there are some reds, mainly Merlot. The region now produces over 30% of Japan's wines.

4. **b. Merlot.** Now Merlot has exceeded Cabernet Sauvignon in plantings by hectares in Bulgaria. There are still around 200 different indigenous grape varieties cultivated in Bulgaria, but after the collapse of the Soviet Union the balance has moved in favour of international grape varieties. Local variety Pamid is still 3rd, but Mavrud is now only 4% of plantings. Some of the first European vineyards were in Bulgaria, 5,000 years ago when Thracian wines

were written about by Homer, and were favourites in Greece. Nowadays, the red wine grape varieties still dominate with over 60% of all cultivated vines. The trend is towards smaller high-quality wineries planting Merlot, Cabernet Sauvignon and Syrah.

5. *c. White.* Japan is not a major wine producing or wine drinking country. White grape plantings have always dominated, because of their fish based diet. Koshu grapes are now circa 20% of all grape plantings. It is high quality aromatic and very dry and elegant, similar to a Sauvignon Blanc. Only 5% of all wine consumed there is produced from Japanese vineyards. 15% is from imported grape juice and 80% is imported wines mainly from South America and Australia. The trend is now for more small high-quality wineries to produce Koshu wines for local consumption; very little Japanese wine is exported.

6. *c. Clay amphorae.* The unique qvevris are egg shaped clay vessels which make both red and white wines and are buried in the ground and sealed for fermentation and ageing. Georgia now claims to be the oldest wine producing country in the world, having started over 8,000 years ago. In the last few years Georgian wine is becoming more popular, as Orange wine is now becoming trendy worldwide. Decanter wine magazine had a cover and large part of the magazine on Orange wines in a 2020 edition. Georgian white wine was always orange or amber due to the way they were produced in qvevri clay pots with minimal interference. Georgia is finally investing in modernising its wine industry, and now both the quality of the wine and exports are increasing, especially of their Orange wine.

7. *c. 300 to 350.* The number of independent privately owned wineries is expanding quickly from a base of nil when Bulgaria was part of the Soviet Bloc. Up until 1989, in Communist times, all wines were made in enormous state wineries, which were factories producing cheap bulk wine all destined to be sent to Russia. In the early 1980s Bulgaria was the 4th largest wine exporting country, all to Russia. Then the Bulgarian wine industry nearly collapsed when President Gorbachev introduced his anti alcohol campaign from 1985 to 1988, and all wine exports to Russia from Bulgaria were banned. Many of the state run wine factories closed and never re-opened under state control. For the last 30 years Bulgarian wines have had to find new countries to export to and the UK and USA are their top targets. Supermarkets are keen to stock their Cabernet Sauvignon and Merlot, especially as they are low priced and soft smooth wines which have appeal to younger wine drinkers on a tight budget.

8. *c. Steven Spurrier.* Wine writer, critic and vineyard owner of the Dorset award-winning vineyard Bride Valley, who sadly died in early 2021, imported three high quality wines from India partnering with the Italian winery owner Piero Masi. The wine brand is called M/S (Masi/Spurrier). The M/S range

includes a Chardonnay/Sauvignon Blanc white blend, a Sangiovese rosé and a red made from Sangiovese, Cabernet Franc and Syrah. The vineyards are spread over 240 acres (96 hectares) across three sites 650m above sea level in Maharashta State, the home of Mumbai, and where most of India's best quality wines are made.

9. ***a. 10 to 20 bottles.*** Depending on the source, the expanding love of wine by the Russians has resulted in a per capita annual consumption of 12 to 15 bottles, which has more than doubled in 20 years. Russians still drink twice the volume of vodka compared to wine but the amount, and gap between the two drinks is decreasing. Russians still have a long way to go to match Italy and France's annual per capita wine consumption of circa 65 bottles.

10. ***a. Red wine.*** Red is the most popular type of wine in China by a long, long way. Roughly 80% of all the wine consumed in China is red, and experts largely put this down to its cultural significance in the country. 'Red is a symbol of luck and prosperity', Len Moser (top German wineries owner) said, who is investing in wineries in China. China overtook France and Italy as the world's largest consumer of red wine in 2014, and was the fifth largest wine-drinking nation overall. It's their huge 1.4 billion population of more affluent citizens that has done it. Cabernet Sauvignon is also the most widely-grown grape variety in the country, followed by Merlot and Carmenère, all used to make red wines and which have their spiritual homes in Bordeaux. c) white is nearly all the rest at 19%. b) Sparkling wines are hardly ever drunk in China, they don't have the celebratory tradition for champagne and sparklers. The average Chinese taste is not for cold, dry fizzy drinks. Champagne sales are only at 1.3 million bottles, which is less than one bottle per thousand Chinese people per year.

ANSWERS TO QUIZ 40 – WINES OF CALIFORNIA – PART 1

1. ***b. Mendocino.*** For years this most northerly Wine District in California provided grapes to the big more southerly estates, like Mondavi, Beringer and Duckhorn. Now there are many newer boutique wineries, making Chardonnay, Zinfandel and Cabernet Sauvignon. There are also some top sparkling wine producers. Currently there are over 60 wineries.

2. ***a. Canada.*** Canada is the largest export market for California wines for value and volume. In value terms Canada takes around 35% of all California wine

exports at $450 million. By volume Canada is still the largest market at 22%. For both value and volume Germany is 2nd and Hong Kong 3rd.

3. *a. Sideways.* The hit film about the adventures of two friends (Miles and Jack) on a wine trip, visiting wineries in the Santa Ynez Valley as Jack's bachelor party before his wedding. It was released in 2004. It was nominated for 5 Oscars and won 1. Sideways is based on the Book by Rex Pickett and 'Sideways' is a term for being intoxicated. It is a great feel good factor film to see especially if you are a wine lover.

4. *c. Screaming Eagle.* It is a small winery in Oakville in Napa Valley. There is a waiting list to buy their famous Cabernet Sauvignon wines. It only makes 500 cases per year. Jean Phillips bought the 57 acres (23 hectares) site in 1986 and totally replanted it.

5. *Zinfandel.* It was unique to California, but is now only 10% of total production. It used to be the widest planted red grape up until the 1970s. Its origins are traced to Primitivo in Puglia Italy, or latterly some scientists say Croatia is its indigenous home.

6. *a. Central Valley.* This is the home of Gallo and many other enormous wineries producing vast quantities of jug and easy drinking wines. Chardonnay, Sauvignon Blanc and Chenin Blanc are the best offerings. Napa Valley, the king of quality wine, only produces 4% of California wines.

7. *b. 3,800.* These commercial wineries are four times as many as the next biggest wine producing state, which is Washington State with around 930 wineries. California houses over 60% of all wineries in the USA. They also tend to be large estates as California produces about 80% of all US wines; and if it was a country it would be the 4th largest wine producer in the world.

8. *a. Chardonnay.* This is the most widely planted grape variety in California at 30%. It also accounts for around 60% of all white grapes grown for wine in California. Pinot Grigio is the 2nd most planted white grape at 23% and Sauvignon Blanc is 3rd most planted at 12%. An increasing proportion of the Chardonnay in California is used in the production of sparkling wines.

9. *a. Cabernet Sauvignon.* This is the top red grape at 50%, (and the 2nd most widely planted grape at 27%). For red varieties Merlot is next at 22%, then Pinot Noir at 18%. Cabernet Sauvignons are produced as single varietal wines or as part of top quality Bordeaux blends. The highest quality and most expensive examples are produced in the Napa Valley wine area.

10. *b. Buena Vista.* This Winery is in Sonoma and started production in 1857. It produces 100K cases of wine from 8 major grape varieties and small amounts from historical indigenous grapes. It is predominantly red grapes, Cabernet Sauvignon and Pinot Noir.

ANSWERS TO QUIZ 41 – WINES OF CALIFORNIA – PART 2

1. *a. Krug champagne* is only made in Reims, in the Champagne region of France. Roederer Estate started their California vineyard in Mendocino in 1981. Mumm Napa was even earlier in 1979. Other top champagne houses producing top quality sparkling wines in California are Taittinger with Domaine Carneros, and Moët & Chandon's sparkling wine Californian outpost is called Domaine Chandon in the Napa Valley.

2. *b. Chardonnay.* The most planted grape variety in California at around 28%, followed by four red grapes – Cabernet Sauvignon at circa 24%, Zinfandel at 14%, Pinot Noir at around 12% and Merlot at about 10%. Thus only 5 major grape varieties account for almost 90% of all wine produced in California, although there are more than 60 different varieties of grapes planted for use in making wine.

3. *c. 30%.* California is a major volume producer of wines in the world. It has circa 600,000 acres (240,000 hectares) of vineyards compared to France which has 2 million acres (800,000 hectares). California produces around 17 million gallons (77 million litres) of wine per year and 80% of all USA wine produced. If it was a country it would be the 4th or 5th largest wine producer in the world.

4. *c. 75%.* Thus, California is 75% of the size of France. It is an enormous US state, 30% larger than Italy and 20% bigger than Germany. California is the most populous US state at over 40 million residents and is the 3rd largest in area after Alaska and Texas. California vineyard acreage is limited because more than 25% of California is desert.

5. *a. San Antonio Winery.* It is the oldest winery in downtown Los Angeles, a historical landmark which was founded in 1917. They are one of the most awarded wineries in California. The other two wineries are also near Los Angeles but not as close to Hollywood.

6. *a. Cabernet Sauvignon.* In the Napa Valley it is around 70% of all red grape varieties planted. It accounts for 40% of all volume and 55% of value for all Napa grape varieties. For other red varieties Merlot is circa 20% and Pinot Noir is at 10%.

7. *c. Wine Country.* A comedy film released in 2019 of six female friends celebrating a 50th birthday by going on a boozy fun wine weekend in Napa Valley. it is beautifully filmed in northern California where the sun shines on rolling hills of vineyards and the wine flows freely. Wine Country is directed by Amy Poehler who also acts in it as a lead character. It's worth watching if you like wine based films, and is also on Netflix.

8. ***c. Schramsberg Vineyards.*** Founded in 1862, near Napa Valley, by a German immigrant, Jacob Schram. It has always aimed to produce top quality sparkling wines using the same method as champagne. Domaine Carneros is another top quality sparkling wine producer, also in Napa, and owned by Taittinger. Fetzer is a quality table wine producer from Mendocino County, but not known for sparkling wines.

9. ***b. 80%*** of all USA wine comes from California. 20 years ago it was over 90% of all wines produced but other states are exploding in the growth of new wineries,but from a small base. Washington State is the second largest wine producer followed by New York State and Oregon. These are the big 4 producers accounting for over 90% of USA wine. Nowadays almost all US states have wineries, but commercial production is very small.

10. ***c. Steven Spurrier.*** He organised the blind tastings of top quality First Growth red Bordeaux wines, and Grand Cru white Burgundies set against Cabernet Sauvignons and Chardonnays from Napa Valley. Stag's Leap Wine Cellars was the outright winner for reds. Chateau Montelena California Chardonnay also won against 4 top white burgundies. It was a long lasting embarrassment for the French top winemakers, and launched Californian wines onto the world stage. Sadly Steven died in early 2021.

ANSWERS TO QUIZ 42 – WINES OF OREGON AND WASHINGTON STATE

1. ***c. Washington State.*** It is the second largest producer of wine and produces over three times as much wine as Oregon, and twice New York State's volume. It has over 900 wineries with around 50,000 acres (20,000 hectares) of vineyards, which is about the same acreage as Napa Valley.

2. ***c. Pinot Noir.*** This variety represents almost 70% volume (80% by value) of all wines produced in Oregon. Pinot Noir has always dominated, but in the last 10 years other varieties are growing in usage. The next three grapes in volume terms are all white – Pinot Gris, Chardonnay and Riesling making up to 20% of Oregon wines.

3. ***a. 90%.*** Almost 90% of all wines in the USA are produced in California, Washington and Oregon, although it is reducing slowly as more states start producing wine commercially in increasing volumes, especially New York State.

4. **a. Oregon.** Domaine Drouhin is situated in the Dundee Hills area of the Willamette Valley, with a large 235 acres (94 hectares) estate encompassing around 85 acres (34 hectares) of hillside vineyards. It produces circa 400,000 bottles a year of mainly Pinot Noir. The first vines were planted in 1988 from Burgundy clone cuttings from their own Drouhin vineyards near Beaune, France. There are now around 74 acres (30 hectares) of Pinot Noir and 11 acres (4.5 hectares) of Chardonnay grapes.

5. **c. Treveri Cellars.** This winery only makes handcrafted sparkling wines. It is a family owned winery in the Yakima Valley. It only began in 2010, but has already been served at White House dinners and State Banquets. Treveri is owned and run by the Grieb family (originally from the Mosel in Germany) producing sparklers of traditional champagne blends as well as from Riesling and other varietals.

6. **a. Rogue Valley.** This wine valley is in southern Oregon extending to the California border. Most of the 90 vineyards are higher up on the valley slopes between 1200 ft and 2000 ft high for coolness and maximum sunshine. It comprises three separate river valleys coming together and extending for 70 miles long by 60 miles wide. Rogue Viognier is a grape variety on the increase and the quality is outstanding. Answer b) Walla Walla (means place of many waters) is a wine region mostly in Washington State but extends into Oregon. Answer c) Yakima Valley was the first wine region AVA in Washington State founded in 1981; the first Washington Syrah was also produced in Yakima.

7. **b. Pinot Gris.** This grape variety is actually a descendant of Pinot Noir, but is a white grape, and is known as Pinot Grigio in Italy, and Grauburgunder in Germany. It grows best in the Willamette Valley and up until the year 2000 Chardonnay was the dominant grape. Now, just over 20 years later, Oregon makes over four times as much Pinot Gris as it does Chardonnay. The third most prolific grape grown in Oregon is Riesling.

8. **c. Willamette Valley.** It Is a large wine area which is 150 miles long and up to 60 miles wide and home to over 750 vineyards and 600 wineries. It is the largest AVA in Oregon, famous for producing top quality Pinot Noirs (around 70% of wines) followed by Pinot Gris at circa 20%. Modern winemaking in Willamette Valley only goes back just over 50 years when Californian winemaking pioneers came to the valley, because of the height and cool climate (and lower land prices) to plant and make high quality Pinot Noirs. It worked.

9. **a. Cooper Mountain Vineyards.** A family venture started by Dr Robert Gross that became the first fully biodynamic winery in Washington in 1999, and produces Pinot Noir, Pinot Gris, Chardonnay and Pinot Blanc. Situated in

the Portland metropolitan area, and sited on the slopes of Cooper Mountain, an extinct volcano.

10. ***a. Chardonnay.*** It used to be much more dominant but now there is a trend in Washington towards red wines, especially Cabernet Sauvignon and Merlot. Both of these red varieties look like they may, on present trends, overtake the volume of Chardonnay in a few years. These three grape varieties account for 60% of all wine production in Washington State.

ANSWERS TO QUIZ 43 – WINES OF OTHER USA WINE AREAS

1. ***b. 20 – 29 states.*** In the USA 27 states have more than 10 wineries operating commercially as of 2020. Every state in the USA apart from Alaska has at least one winery operating commercially. The three western states of California, Washington and Oregon produce almost 90% of all USA wines. Total USA wine production accounts for about 12% of worldwide wines and is the fourth or fifth largest producer country.

2. ***c. Concord.*** This is a native American cultivar (called a fox grape); it is used for wines, table grapes, juices, and jellies. It is named after the town in Massachusetts where it was first developed in 1849 by Ephraim Bull who planted many wild vine seedlings, before choosing Concord. It has always been the dominant grape variety in New York State and is very popular for making kosher and sacramental wine. It is most often used to produce fruity and sweet red wines, but it can also be made into dry versions, which is a growing trend.

3. ***a. New York.*** This is the third biggest wine state producer in volume and value. The Brotherhood Winery was started by monks in 1839 mainly producing altar sacramental wines for Holy Communion. Because of this it was allowed to continue producing wine during the Prohibition period and never had to close its doors and cease production. It is also stated to be America's oldest winery still producing wines today. They now make a wide range of red and white table wines from classic grape varieties. Their flagship wine is 1839 Cabernet Sauvignon celebrating 180+ years of passionate winemaking.

4. ***c. 200 to 300 wineries.*** As at 2020 there are 270 wineries operating in Pennsylvania. Over the past 25 years the growth of new vineyards in the state has exploded. There were only 50 wineries in 1995. It was one of the first US

states to start planting vineyards, when William Penn in 1683 planted cuttings taken from Bordeaux vineyards.

5. **a. Flat Creek.** Texas has over 200 wineries now, after experiencing a huge growth of new openings in the past 10 years. High quality whites especially Chardonnay are produced, also with new red varieties, including many Italian and Spanish grape varieties, such as Garnacha, Sangiovese, and Tempranillo. Answer b) Ridge Vineyards are in the San Francisco Bay area. Answer c) Standing Stone Vineyard is in Washington State.

6. **a. Finger Lakes.** This is by far the largest New York wine region with around 150 wineries producing over 70% of all New York State wines. It is a cool climate zone with a short growing season and icy winters and mainly produces high quality Riesling wines similar to the dry German style, and sweeter versions, even a luscious sweet Ice Wine. The second largest NY wine region is Long Island with 75 wineries, 3rd is Hudson River, and 4th is Lake Erie.

7. **b. Michigan.** Has over 150 wineries and it has experienced growth of over 50% by volume in the last 3 years. It mainly produces Pinot Noir, Riesling and Chardonnay. Missouri now has over 130 wineries, and Maryland (although one of the smallest states) now has over 80 commercial wineries.

8. **a. The highest vineyard in the USA.** Continental Divide has vineyards at 10,361 ft on the Rocky Mountain slopes. It claims to be the highest commercial vineyard in the world. But Chile and Argentina have claims to this as well. A tiny vineyard in Lhasa Tibet is in the Guinness Book of Records as the world's highest vineyard with vines planted at 11,700 feet above sea level.

9. **a. Barefoot Wines.** This brand, since 2005 owned and produced by E & J Gallo in Modesto California, sells almost $700 million worth of wine within the USA per year. It was started by David Bynum in his garage attached to his Californian ranch home in 1965, when he crushed the grapes barefoot, hence the name. His first wine in 1965 was 'Barefoot Bynum Burgundy' which became very popular. The second biggest wine brand is Sutter Home at circa $400 million, and the third is Woodbridge Wines at circa $350 million.

10. **c. Virginia.** Trump Winery was planted in 1999 and is very close to Charlottesville. It was bought by Donald Trump in 2011, and is run by Eric Trump the second oldest of the President's sons. It is of course Virginia's largest ever 'Great Again' winery. It also claims it has the largest vineyard planting of European vines on the east coast of the USA. It produces around 36,000 cases per year, made from varieties including Chardonnay, Sémillon, Sauvignon Blanc, Cabernet Sauvignon and Merlot.

ANSWERS TO QUIZ 44 – MATCH FAMOUS CALIFORNIA AND USA WINES

1. ***d. Napa Valley, California.*** Stag's Leap Cabernet Sauvignon was the wine that beat all the French top red wines at the 'Judgement of Paris' in 1976. It had only been founded in 1970 and is now considered a Napa Valley first growth estate, and has just celebrated its 50 years anniversary.

2. ***c. Central Valley, California.*** Gallo Thunderbird Fortified Blend was launched in 1957 and at 17.5% ABV was drunk by winos and down and outs. It was a mixture of wine, a spirit dosage and added fruit flavouring. It sold in the millions in poor neighbourhoods and made E & J Gallo huge profits. It is now the largest winery in the world, with a turnover of over $4 billion per annum. Central Valley is the largest wine grape growing region of California; largely hot, dry and flat, it supplies a humongous quantity of grapes to other wineries in the state as well as producing strong cheap table wines and fortified wines.

3. ***a. Willamette Valley, Oregon.*** Domaine Drouhin Pinot Noir was one of Oregon's pioneer 'Burgundian' style wines. Not surprising, as J Drouhin was started in Beaune, Burgundy in 1880. It has been one of Burgundy's top quality producers for over 140 years. Drouhin's Oregon outpost in the Dundee Hills (just south-west of Portland) was started in 1987 and creates Chardonnays and Pinot Noirs of great elegance and finesse. Willamette Valley is the home to over 500 wineries and is known for its world class Pinot Noirs.

4. ***e. Columbia Valley, Washington State.*** Chateau Ste Michelle Riesling. Washington State, and Columbia Valley, is the largest Riesling producing region in America. Chateau Ste Michelle is Washington State's founding winery, with many award-winning wines including Riesling; In fact it is one of the largest producers of Rieslings in the world. It has also been named American Winery of the Year in 2004. Additionally it produces Chardonnay and two reds, Merlot and Cabernet Sauvignon.

5. ***b. Santa Barbara, California.*** Firestone Vineyard was founded in 1972 and was a pioneer icon of Santa Barbara County. Founders were Leonard and Brooks Firestone, the son and grandson of the famous car tyre inventor and manufacturer, Harvey Firestone. It was the first sizeable Ynez Valley winery and after 35 years of winemaking the family sold it to a winemaking friend in the valley, Bill Foley. Santa Barbara wine area is home to over 200 wineries predominantly making Chardonnays and Pinot Noirs (with some Syrah) and all of these can be very good value California wines.

6. **j. Cabernet Sauvignon.** Opus One was a shared dream of two winemaking friends, Baron Philippe de Rothschild of Château Mouton Rothschild in Medoc, Bordeaux, and Napa Valley vintner Robert Mondavi. Their plan and dream was to create the most perfect Cabernet Sauvignon dominated Bordeaux type blend and handcrafted wine grown in the Napa Valley. For its first 3 years, until 1982, it was called Napamedoc. Opus One Bordeaux Blend releases around 25,000 cases a year at an average bottle price of $330. Cabernet Sauvignon is the most planted grape in Napa Valley at over 60% of all varieties.

7. **f. Pinot Noir.** Clos du Bois was founded by Frank Woods in 1974 in Sonoma County. It is known for producing some of the best value approachable Pinot Noirs in the USA. They are around $15 a bottle and have a fruity yet classic refined taste to them. The winery's production is now over 1 million cases a year of mainly Pinot Noir and Chardonnay.

8. **i. Chardonnay.** Cakebread Cellars makes very celebrated and award-winning Chardonnays amongst their varietals. Jack Cakebread bought the vineyard land in 1972 and Cakebread Cellars was born in Rutherford in the Napa Valley. Now around 50 years later the Cakebread children and grandchildren are still involved in the family winery. It now mainly produces Chardonnay and some Sauvignon Blancs with annual sales of around 200,000 cases. Chardonnay is the most planted grape variety in California providing about 30% of all wine grapes.

9. **g. Sparkling Blend (Ch + PN).** Domaine Chandon is the Californian outpost of Moët & Chandon Champagne House (the largest in the world producing around 30 million bottles per year) sited in Epernay, France. Domaine Chandon was founded in 1973 in the town of Yountville in the Napa Valley, and became the first French-owned sparkling wine producer in the Napa Valley. There are now many French Champagne Houses producing 'Sparklers' in California, including Mumm, Roederer and Taittinger. It was not until 2005 that the EU managed to ban California sparkling wines calling themselves champagne. But there are loopholes with, at the bottom end of the market, cheap sparkling wines still calling themselves 'Californian Champagne' – some even sold in cans.

10. **h. Zinfandel.** Ravenswood Zinfandel from Lodi County is one of the best and largest, good quality 'old vines' producers at value prices. Joel Peterson started making Ravenswood Zinfandel from 1976 using bought-in grapes, and produced the red wine in his cabin in the woods which was surrounded by the calls of many noisy ravens – hence the wine's name. Zinfandel is a very dark thick skinned red grape, and was thought to have come to California from Puglia, Italy (Primitivo grape) but recent tests prove it is a Croatian grape used for many centuries called Tribidrag.

ANSWERS TO QUIZ 45 – ANAGRAMS – WINES OF USA

Prime Wine-Producing States

1. **California.** The most important, and largest, wine region in the USA, with around eighty per cent of all the wine produced in the USA coming from California. All the best-known grape varieties are grown here, including Pinot Noir, Cabernet Sauvignon, Syrah and Merlot reds, and Sauvignon Blanc, Chardonnay, Riesling and Sémillon whites. Running along the western Californian coast, the relative position of the vineyards to the Pacific Ocean is crucial to the style and quality of wine that is produced.

2. **Washington.** Even though Washington State is a neighbour to Oregon, their wine regions experience very different climates indeed, owing to the location of the vineyards in relation to the Cascade Mountain Range which slices through both states from north to south. Washington produces fine Cabernet Sauvignon, Syrah, and Merlot reds, and Riesling, Sauvignon Blanc, and Pinot Gris whites. The state is second only to California in size of wine production.

3. **New York.** New York State wines are produced from six major winegrowing regions, Lake Erie, Long Island, Finger Lakes, Niagara Escarpment, Hudson Valley, and Champlain Valley. Vines have grown in the State since Dutch settlers planted them in the seventeenth century. Important grape varieties here are Concord and Cabernet Franc reds, and Chardonnay and Riesling whites.

4. **Oregon.** Producing a huge range of grape varieties, but the one that Oregon is world-famous for is their cool climate, high quality, Pinot Noir. For their white wines, Chardonnay, Pinot Gris, and Riesling are important. The vast percentage of Oregon's Pinot Noir is produced in the iconic Willamette Valley, which is home to many hundreds of wineries.

5. **Colorado.** Miners working in the south of Colorado in the nineteenth century, first brought vine cuttings to the state. Today, there are over 150 wine producers in Colorado, with important grapes being Cabernet Sauvignon, Syrah, and Riesling, as well as some decent Petit Verdot and Gewürztraminer.

Californian Wine Regions

6. **Sonoma.** The Sonoma wine region is about an hour's drive north of San Francisco. With over five hundred wineries, it is one of the most important winegrowing areas, not just in California, but in the whole of the USA. Vines have been planted here since the 1850s, and important grapes today include Cabernet Sauvignon, Pinot Noir, Merlot, and Zinfandel reds, plus Chardonnay and Sauvignon Blanc whites.

7. **Mendocino.** California's northernmost wine region. The principal sub-region is the Anderson Valley, and other important sub-regions include the Potter Valley, Redwood Valley, and Yorkville Highlands. Mendocino's cooler areas can produce fine Pinot Noirs and Chardonnays, and Mendocino has been an increasingly important player in establishing organic vineyards.

8. **Monterey.** About an hour's drive south of California's famous Silicon Valley, Monterey has many beautiful vineyard landscapes. An immense amount of wine is produced in the Monterey district, much of it being sold in bulk and used in blends with wines from other regions. However, some good quality Pinot Noir, Chardonnay, and Riesling wine is also made here.

9. **Napa Valley.** The most famous region in California, and one of the most revered wine regions in the world, producing some of the best wines on the planet. The high percentage value of California's wine produced in Napa Valley bears little relation to the lower percentage volume that Napa produces compared with California as a whole. Such is the quality and reputation of the Napa Valley. In particular, premium wines are made from Cabernet Sauvignon and Merlot grapes, along with Chardonnay and Sauvignon Blanc.

10. **Santa Cruz.** Located about fifty miles south of San Francisco, at the northern end of Monterey Bay. The rough terrain of the Santa Cruz Mountains can make life very difficult for winegrowers. However, some of California's best wines are made here, particularly from Cabernet Sauvignon grapes. Santa Cruz is a relatively large region, and covers mountainous, valley, and marine terrains.

ANSWERS TO QUIZ 46 – WINES OF CANADA

1. **a. Less than New Zealand.** Canada produces around 60 million litres of wine per year. As a comparison NZ produces circa 320 million litres, so Canada is less than 20% of NZ, and Australia produces over 800 million litres per annum. Canada's wine industry is growing fast but from a really small base. It is only the 30th largest producer in the world, but is the sixth largest importer of wine.

2. **b. Ontario.** Ontario wine country represent 60% to 65% of all Canadian wines. Ontario province has three official wine-growing regions, the Niagara Peninsula, the north shore of Lake Erie, and Prince Edward County. The Niagara Peninsula is by far the largest wine region in Canada with over 100

wineries producing over 2 million cases of wine per year. British Columbia province produces 30% to 33% of all wine. All the other provinces produce only 5% to 10% maximum of Canadian wine.

3. *c. Sweet dessert wine.* Canada now produces around 90% of the world's Ice Wine. Germany is in second place at 7%, and Austria next. With global warming Canada has become much more dominant in the production of Ice Wine. In 2019 it was too warm to produce any Ice Wine in Germany for the first time ever. Ice Wine has to be picked at temperatures below -8°C from frozen grape berries, and has to have an ABV of 7% to 13%.

4. *c. White wine.* White grapes still make up the majority of Canadian grown wines at about 60%. The five most popular white grape varieties planted in Canada are Vidal, Riesling, Chardonnay, Pinot Gris, and Sauvignon Blanc, and these 5 grapes account for around 90% of all white wine produced in Canada. Vidal, because of its importance in Ice Wine production is about 40% of all white grapes planted. Red volume is increasing fast but is still at only 38%. The most planted red grapes are Cabernet Franc, Merlot, Cabernet Sauvignon and Pinot Noir. Sparkling wine is only 2% of volume per annum.

5. *c. Tawse Winery.* It is a family owned organic winery on the Niagara Escarpment in southern Ontario. It was only founded in 2005, yet has won over 100 wine awards and has been awarded Canadian winery of the year 4 times, in 2010, 2011, 2012, and 2016. Moray Tawse's love of Burgundian Pinot Noir and Chardonnay is reflected in his traditional winemaking techniques combined with state-of-the-art technology. Tawse Winery now produces 30,000 cases of wine and has one of the largest portfolios of organic wines in the Niagara region. Answer a) Mission Hill is a good quality volume white winemaker, Answer b) Pillitteri Estates is famous for its Ice Wines.

6. *a. Cabernet Franc.* In Ontario it is now the dominant red grape variety, and represents around 30% of the 20 or so other varieties of red wine grapes that are grown in Ontario Province. The second most planted red variety is Baco Noir which is similar to the Gamay grape variety famous for making Beaujolais in France. Merlot is the third most planted red grape in Ontario. The most planted red grapes differ in British Columbia, the smaller but second largest wine producing province in Canada, with Merlot first and Pinot Noir catching up as more new vineyards are planted.

7. *b. Pelee Island.* It is the most southerly part of Canada, and the largest island in lake Erie. Vin Villa was Canada's first ever commercial winery, which was founded in 1866. It is now part of Pelee Island Winery, both the most southerly and oldest vineyard in Canada. At over 700 acres (280 hectares) of vineyards, Pelee Island Winery is also the largest private estate winery

in Canada. It grows both red and white grape varieties with Chardonnay, Riesling, Pinot Noir, Cabernet Franc, Gewürztraminer, Pinot Gris, and Merlot being their most planted varieties.

8. **a. Baby Duck.** It was a sweet red or pink sparkling wine that sold over 8 million bottles per year in the 1970s and 80s. Created by Andres Wines and still produced today (in small volumes), it was launched in the UK in 1979 with a big advertising campaign, but it flopped. The London Times said 'It tastes like blackcurrent wine gums dissolved in Andrews Liver Salts'. Answer c) Whispering Angel is an iconic and expensive rosé wine from Provence in France. Answer b) Pink Diana does not exist, it is just a made up name.

9. **a. 28 Wineries.** British Columbia has grubbed up many apple and peach orchards in the past 40 years to create new high quality vineyards. The biggest explosion in vineyard growth was from the year 2000, when there were only around 65 commercial wineries. By 2020 the number of wineries had increased to over 370. The Okanagan Valley, which is 1,000 miles north of the Napa Valley in California, is the largest wine growing area of British Columbia. Twenty years ago there were only 31 wineries in the region, and now there are over 160.

10. **c. Vidal.** This grape variety was created in France in 1930. It is a cross between Ugni Blanc and Rayon d'Or. Canada has the most Vidal grapes planted in the world and New York State in the USA has the 2nd highest plantings. This hardy variety is designed to produce high sugar level grapes with lots of natural acidity for balance, and thrives in very cold climates. This is the ideal variety for producing Ice Wine, especially in Ontario province in Canada with its short growing season and freezing cold winters. Vidal Ice Wine has to be picked when at least -8°C, and the individual grapes are frozen solid. Both the other Answers a) and b) Cabernet Franc and Riesling are also used to make Ice Wine but in much smaller quantities.

ANSWERS TO QUIZ 47 – WINES OF CHILE – PART 1

1. **True.** As well as table grapes and other fruit growing abundantly in the Atacama Desert, wine is also made there, including Pinot Noir, Syrah, Chardonnay, and Sauvignon Blanc. Chile's most northerly vineyards are situated in one of the driest regions on earth.

2. **Casablanca.** Situated about 50 miles west of Chile's capital, Santiago, and close to Valparaiso, the country's premier port city. The terroir and temperatures of the coastal region of the Casablanca Valley produce good quality wines, including Pinot Noir, Chardonnay, and Sauvignon Blanc.

3. **b. Concha y Toro.** One of the leading wine producers in South America, Concha y Toro employs well over 3,000 people. Their headquarters are in Santiago, and they own vineyards all over Chile. The winery was founded in 1883 by Don Melchor de Santiago Concha y Toro, and his wife Emiliana Subercaseaux, and they started by bringing in grape varieties from Bordeaux, including Cabernet Sauvignon, Merlot, Sémillon, and Sauvignon Blanc.

4. **a. Pinot Noir.** Literally meaning 'southern cone' with reference to its geographical origins, Cono Sur is also a play on words with 'connoisseur'. A very wide range of wines are produced, including sparkling wine, but they're particularly famous for their excellent Pinot Noir. Their Bicicleta Pinot Noir is well-known, as is the Reserva Especial Pinot Noir from the San Antonio Valley, just south of the Casablanca Valley on the Chilean coast.

5. **Wine Regions.** Maule is one of Chile's oldest wine regions situated in the central part of the country. Leyda lies west of Santiago, between the San Antonio and Casablanca Valleys. Elqui is in the far north of Chile, about 300 miles from Santiago.

6. **Wine Region.** Maipo is one of Chile's most prominent wine regions. Located just south of the capital, Santiago, and east of Casablanca and San Antonio Valleys. Maipo is essentially red wine country, and is particularly famous for its Cabernet Sauvignon.

7. **Both.** Originally, the wine map of this long and narrow country was split west to east into geopolitical valleys. But because of the huge significance, geographically, of the Pacific Ocean to the west and the Andes to the east, it is now divided north to south as well.

8. **French-owned.** Casa Lapostolle is owned by the Marnier-Lapostolle family, producers of Grand Marnier liqueur. Located in the Colchagua Valley, they

are still managed today by a member of the Marnier-Lapostolle family. Using organic and biodynamic practices, their wines are consistently highly rated.

9. **a. País.** This red grape was the most widely planted variety in Chile until it was overtaken by Cabernet Sauvignon at the end of the 1990s. Since then it has been made as a general table wine, but in recent years producers have been making much higher quality País, with a light, fresh, and fruity character.

10. **c. Curicó.** Miguel Torres invested heavily in Curicó by introducing many modern technologies that put the region on the international wine map. This action also had a significant impact in strengthening Chile's presence in the global wine market.

ANSWERS TO QUIZ 48 – WINES OF CHILE – PART 2

1. **a. Aconcagua.** Located about 60 miles north-west of Santiago, as opposed to Curicó and Colchagua which are both well south of the capital. Aconcagua is an important Chilean wine region. It runs from inland to the Chilean coast, just north of Valparaiso. The Aconcagua river runs through part of the region, from the Andes Mountains to the Pacific Ocean. A very wide variety of grapes are grown here, including some fine Pinot Noirs.

2. **c. Merlot.** Chilean wine growers believed for over a hundred years that their vines were Merlot until they, in fact, turned out to be Carmenère. They were often pressed and fermented along with actual Merlot grapes until the truth was discovered! However, Chile does produce quite a lot of actual Carmenère grapes, as well as Merlot. The origins of both grapes are in the Médoc region of Bordeaux, and were introduced to Chile in the nineteenth century.

3. **Phylloxera.** So far, Chilean vineyards have been free of this pest but, of course, producers are always conscious and aware of the possibility of its arrival. Phylloxera is a microscopic louse or aphid that lives on, and eats, the roots and leaves of grape vines, thereby destroying them. From the late nineteenth century, indeed from the late 1860s in France, vast swathes of vineyards in Europe, and elsewhere in the world, were totally devastated by Phylloxera. Since then, vines have usually been grafted onto certain species of American rootstocks, which are resistant to the aphid.

4. **Cono Sur.** The name refers to the company's geographical position in South America's Southern Cone. The vineyards and winery were founded in 1993. As well as using a range of other grape varieties, Cono Sur is a huge producer of Pinot Noir, and their Bicicleta Pinot Noir has been a great success.

5. **Maule.** One of Chile's oldest and largest wine regions, situated in the Central Valley. A wide variety of grapes are grown here, including País, Malbec, Carmenère, Cabernet Sauvignon, Carignan, and Pinot Noir. Maule experiences the same dry summers as Santiago, though twice the rainfall.

6. **b. Almaviva.** Established in 1996 in the Maipo Valley, by Baron Philippe de Rothschild of Château Mouton-Rothschild, and Concha y Toro. The aim was to produce a top quality 'First Growth' Chilean wine. Almaviva is the name of both the winery and the wine, and the grapes are a Bordeaux-style blend.

7. **b. Miguel Torres.** Established in the Curicó Valley in 1979, the family company of Miguel Torres produces wine from a wide range of grape varieties in a number of different regions. Torres was one of the first foreign wine companies to set up a base in Chile, pioneering modern winemaking techniques.

8. **Santiago.** A large cluster of major wine regions is situated around Chile's capital city of Santiago, including Aconcagua, Casablanca, Leyda, San Antonio, Maipo, and Cachapoal. Not far away are Curicó and Colchagua. For a country with vineyards extending nearly 900 miles, Santiago is the focal point for many of them.

9. **c. Bío Bío.** This region lies almost 300 miles south of Santiago, between the Andes Mountains and the Coastal Range. Bío Bío is known for its crisp, aromatic, range of wines, from grapes such as Riesling, Gewürztraminer, Chardonnay, and Sauvignon Blanc. The region's cool climate and higher rainfall make for more challenging conditions than those in the northern Chilean vineyards. Some first class Pinot Noirs are produced here.

10. **Patagonia.** South America's southernmost wine producing region, Patagonia straddles the base of both Chile and Argentina. Even though this region appears to be the least obvious place for growing quality vines, its cool, dry, climate has proved to be well suited to producing some excellent Chilean Pinot Noir.

ANSWERS TO QUIZ 49 – PART 1. MATCH THESE FAMOUS CHILEAN WINE PRODUCERS WITH THEIR PRIME REGION

1. **d. Aconcagua Valley.** Errazuriz was founded in 1870 by Don Maximiano Errazuriz, and a direct descendent, Eduardo Chadwick, still owns the company today. Aconcagua is the region that the company is most associated with, but they also have vineyards in other Chilean wine regions.

2. **c. Maipo Valley.** Founded in 1879 by Francisca Underraga Vicuña, who brought grape vine cuttings from Europe back to his Chile homeland, including Cabernet Sauvignon and Pinot Noir from France, and Riesling and Gewürztraminer from Germany.

3. **e. San Antonio Valley.** A relatively new, but highly successful winery, started by María Luz Marín in the year 2000. Together with her husband and two sons, she still runs the business today. Casa Marín produces wine from a range of different grape varieties, and have won many international awards.

4. **a. Casablanca Valley.** Founded in the 1990s by the Kingston family, who had a dairy and cattle ranch, and decided to expand into wine production. They produce a range of high quality wines, in particular from Pinot Noir, Syrah, Chardonnay, and Sauvignon Blanc. They are recognised as one of the best wineries in Chile.

5. **b. Colchagua Valley.** Founded in 1976, Luis Felipe Edwards is one of the largest family-owned wine companies in Chile. As well as their prime Colchagua Valley estate, vineyards are also owned in the Maule and Leyda regions. Luis Felipe Edwards exports to over 85 countries around the world.

ANSWERS TO QUIZ 49 – PART 2. FIVE OF THE FOLLOWING REGIONS ARE IN THE NORTHERN PART OF THE MAIN CHILEAN WINE GROWING AREA, BUT WHICH FIVE ARE IN THE SOUTHERN PART?

Southern Part

6. **f. Maule**
7. **g. Bío Bío**
8. **i. Malleco**
9. **l. Itata**
10. **m. Curicó.**

These five regions are all well south of the capital, Santiago, which is situated in the north of the main winegrowing area. Bío Bío and Itata are the furthest south of the five. The other five regions are in the northern part of the main winegrowing area, and are all within a relatively short distance of Santiago, with Aconcagua being the furthest north of the five.

ANSWERS TO QUIZ 50 – ANAGRAMS – WINES OF CHILE

CHILE

Well-Known Chilean Wines

1. **Montes.** Founded in the late 1980s, Montes is one of the most highly respected and successful wineries in Chile, producing a range of high quality wines. Still led by one of the founders, Aurelio Montes, the company exports their wine to over 100 countries in every continent around the world.

2. **Santa Rita.** Founded in the late nineteenth century, Santa Rita pioneered the modernisation of Chilean vineyards, and are heavily involved in sustainability today. An extensive range of wines is produced from an array of grape varieties, including very high quality wine such as the iconic Casa Real.

3. **Morandé.** Viña Morandé was established in 1996, with Pablo Morandé being one of the founding partners. Their wines are distributed worldwide to over 45 countries. They were pioneers in creating and planting vineyards in Casablanca, and in believing in the great potential of the Maule Valley. They are one of relatively few producers who are making quality wine from the once beleaguered local País grape.

4. **De Martino.** Pietro de Martino Pascualone founded the De Martino estate in 1934, after he moved from his native Italy to Chile looking for perfect land on which to grow grapes and make wine. He found it in the Maipo Valley, just south of the capital, Santiago. Producing a very wide range of grape varieties, the estate is still run today by the De Martino family.

5. **Caliterra.** Originally established in 1996 as a partnership between the families of Robert Mondavi and Viña Errazuriz, run by Eduardo Chadwick. The aim was to produce high quality wines that reflected the best of Chilean terroir. The name comes from the Spanish words 'Calidad', meaning quality, and 'tierra', meaning land.

Chilean Wine Regions

6. **Limari.** One of the northernmost wine regions in Chile, about 250 miles north of Santiago, and close to the Pacific Ocean. The Andes Mountains and the Atacama Desert are also both nearby. The Limari Valley has a winemaking history that dates back to the sixteenth century, but it has only been in relatively recent times that it has emerged as a region with great quality winegrowing potential.

7. **Maipo.** One of Chile's most prominent wine regions. Located just south of the capital, Santiago, and east of Casablanca and San Antonio Valleys. Maipo is essentially red wine country, and is particularly famous for its Cabernet Sauvignon.

8. **Casablanca.** Situated about 50 miles west of Chile's capital, Santiago, and close to Valparaiso, the country's premier port city. The terroir and temperatures of the coastal region of the Casablanca Valley produce good quality wines, including Pinot Noir, Chardonnay, and Sauvignon Blanc.

9. **San Antonio.** A small wine region located around the city of San Antonio, and to the west of the capital, Santiago. It's relatively new, with the first vines planted in the late 1990s. The region produces particularly fine Pinot Noir, Chardonnay, and Sauvignon Blanc.

10. **Maule.** One of Chile's oldest and largest wine regions, situated in the Central Valley. A wide variety of grapes are grown here, including País, Malbec, Carmenère, Cabernet Sauvignon, Carignan, and Pinot Noir. Maule experiences the same dry summers as Santiago, though twice the rainfall.

ANSWERS TO QUIZ 51 – WINES OF ARGENTINA – PART 1

1. **b. La Rioja.** Situated at the foothills of the Andes Mountains, in western Argentina, and north of the huge Mendoza wine district, La Rioja is one of Argentina's most important wine regions. Syrah, Malbec, and Bonarda are important red grape varieties here, and the white Torrontés grape is particularly suited to the mountainous terroir of the region.

2. **Yes.** Many vineyards and wineries have been established in Patagonia. Despite being one of the least obvious regions for making wine, Patagonia

produces elegant Pinot Noir, Merlot, and Malbec. Indeed, a wide variety of wines, both red and white, are produced here.

3. **Mendoza.** Approximately 600 miles west of Argentina's capital, Buenos Aires, and on the edge of the Andes Mountains, Mendoza is easily the largest wine region in the country. Some of Argentina's most highly-rated Malbec wines originate from Mendoza's high altitude sub-regions of Luján de Cuyo and the Uco Valley. However, the region grows a very wide variety of wine grapes, both red and white. Central Mendoza tends to produce the finest wine, and a lot of important producers are based there.

4. **a. Norton.** Bodega Norton was founded in 1895 when the British train engineer, Edward Norton arrived in Mendoza during the building of the first railway that linked it with Chile. Today, Norton wines have won a huge number of international wine awards. Their most successful grape varieties are Cabernet Sauvignon, Cabernet Franc, and Malbec.

5. **Salta.** This is a breath-taking mountainous wine region in the north of Argentina, bordered by Chile, Bolivia, and Paraguay. The Salta wine region is home to some of the world's highest altitude vineyards. Red grapes include Cabernet Sauvignon, Syrah, and Malbec, and whites include Chardonnay, and Salta's jewel-in-the-crown grape, Torrontés.

6. **Zuccardi/Claudio Zucchino.** Sebastian Zuccardi is currently the third generation owner of the family business, started by his grandfather in Mendoza in 1963. Zuccardi is one of the leading wine producers in Argentina. In 2019 the Zuccardi wine estate in Mendoza's Uco Valley, was crowned World's Best Vineyard. Red wines include Malbec, Cabernet Sauvignon, Cabernet Franc, Bonarda, and Tempranillo. Whites include Torrontés and Chardonnay. Less well-known is Claudio Zucchino who grows some of Argentina's highest, and most northerly vines, close to the Bolivian border.

7. **Malbec.** Despite its roots being French, and mainly in Bordeaux, as well as Cahors, it was Argentina that really put this grape on the map as a single varietal and, indeed, in a reverse role it was Malbec that put Argentine wine on the map! The country has been producing high quality full-bodied, plump and juicy Malbecs since the 1990s, and Argentina is now seen as the Malbec capital of the world.

8. **The Andes.** As well as running between Chile and Argentina, the Andes is the world's longest continental mountain range, at about 4,500 miles long, and also runs through Venezuela, Columbia, Ecuador, Peru, and Bolivia. The terroir in the vineyards on either side of the Andes has a direct bearing on the type of Argentine and Chilean wines produced there.

9. **Uco Valley.** A sub-region in the huge winegrowing area of Mendoza, the exceptional Uco Valley is one of Argentina's most important wine districts. The prime red grapes include Malbec, Cabernet Sauvignon, and Merlot. And the main whites are Torrontés, Chardonnay, Sémillon, and Sauvignon Blanc.

10. **White.** In recent years, Torrontés has been a hugely successful white wine in Argentina and, indeed, it's increasingly being grown elsewhere in the world. The character of Argentine Torrontés varies, depending on where in the country it is grown, but essentially it has a light peach, apricot, and rose petal aroma on the nose, with a fresh, smooth texture and moderate acidity on the palate.

ANSWERS TO QUIZ 52 – WINES OF ARGENTINA – PART 2

1. **c. Uruguay.** Historically grown in the Madiran wine region in south-west France, the Tannat grape has become increasingly important in Uruguay. Its easy adaptation to Uruguay's climate and soil has made it the leading grape variety in the country. Traditionally, the wine is full bodied with spicy aromas, but does vary according to local terroir and winemaking techniques.

2. **b. San Juan.** Immediately abutting the northern end of the Mendoza region, and the south-western side of the La Rioja region, the San Juan wine region sits on the foothills of the Andes Mountains. In recent years, San Juan has moved from an area best known for its table grapes, to an area known for producing top quality wines, particularly the reds of Malbec and Syrah.

3. **a. Moët & Chandon.** Until the early 1990s Argentine wine was largely sold locally, and was usually known to the rest of the world as 'jug wine'. In other words cheap, low quality, quaffing wine with little sign of finesse. In this climate, the house of Moët & Chandon had no qualms in calling the wine it produced there 'Champagne', thinking that it would go unnoticed. However, that had to change when quality Malbec started being produced and the world started to sit up and take notice of Argentine wine.

4. **c. Catamarca.** Situated in the north-west of Argentina, the Catamarca wine region nestles in the midst of the Andes Mountain Range, and borders the Salta region. It is not nearly as well-known as other Argentine wine regions, and lags slightly behind them in the quality wine stakes, producing a lot of wine for domestic consumption. However, production is progressing, and

some good quality Torrontés, Bonarda, Malbec, and Syrah wines are now being produced.

5. ***Bonarda.*** Before the explosion onto the scene of Malbec, Bonarda was considered to be Argentina's main red wine. It tends to be lighter-bodied than Malbec, but is full of fruit with moderate acidity. It has great colour and soft tannins, adapts well to local climate and soil, and is grown all over Argentina.

6. ***Syrah.*** It is also Syrah in Chile, but Shiraz in Brazil. It's Shiraz in Australia, but Syrah in New Zealand. No one knows why different countries choose to call this grape either Syrah or Shiraz. It's just a matter of preference!

7. ***c. Luján de Cuyo.*** Containing some of the oldest vines in Argentina, the Luján de Cuyo wine region, situated within Mendoza, is known as 'The headquarters of Malbec' because more than half of its 15,000+ hectares of vines are Malbec, almost a fifth of all Argentina's Malbec vineyards. Indeed, Luján de Cuyo has more Malbec vines planted than the whole of France.

8. ***Pedro Giménez.*** Ampelographers (those concerned with the identification and classification of grape vines) are uncertain as to whether or not this grape is related to the famous sherry grape of Pedro Ximénez, even though the names are so close. It is little-known to most people, but is still grown in Argentina, predominantly in the Mendoza wine region.

9. ***b. Buenos Aires Province.*** During the first decade of the current century, Buenos Aires Province started to produce premium wine. It is not a wine region that immediately comes to mind, unlike Mendoza, Salta, San Juan, La Rioja etc. But it is producing high quality wine, particularly in the southern part of the Province, around Médanos. The terroir there is ideal for quality vineyards, and a wide range of grape varieties are grown.

10. ***Norton.*** Bodega Norton was founded in 1895 when the British train engineer, Edward Norton arrived in Mendoza during the building of the first railway that linked it with Chile. Today, Norton wines have won a huge number of international wine awards. Their most successful grape varieties are Cabernet Sauvignon, Cabernet Franc, and Malbec.

ANSWERS TO QUIZ 53 – WINES OF SOUTH AMERICA, EXCLUDING CHILE AND ARGENTINA

1. **Tannat.** In the nineteenth century, the oenologist, Harriague, planted the first vines in Uruguay of what is now commonly known as Tannat, but is often locally named after the eponymous Harriague. Since then, the Tannat vines have adapted perfectly to the soil and climate of Uruguay, producing a rich, full-bodied red wine. It is the country's most famous grape variety.

2. **a. Grape Brandy.** In the sixteenth century in Peru, the Spanish conquistadors, who had colonised the region, grew grapes to make wine, and then distilled the wine to make Pisco, after the city of the same name near Lima, the capital. It's also produced in Chile, and both countries claim its origins. The drink is famous for the Pisco Sour cocktail, where it is mixed with lime juice and Angostura Bitters.

3. **c. Brazil.** The vast majority of Brazilian wine is produced in the two areas of Campos de Cima da Serra, and Serra Gaúcha, in the southern Brazilian state of Rio Grande. Merlot and Chardonnay are important grape varieties here, and some decent sparkling wine is made from Moscatel grapes.

4. **a. A Pisco-type drink.** Singani is Bolivia's answer to Peru's Pisco, and is a grape brandy made from the distillation of the white Muscat of Alexandria grape variety, which has been grown in Bolivia for 500 years. Until recently, Singani has only been available inside Bolivia itself. The drink originated in the valleys near the silver mining city of Potosi, around 300 miles south-east of Bolivia's capital, La Paz.

5. **a. 10,500 ft.** Local grapes, particularly Muscat of Alexandria, have been grown in Bolivia since the sixteenth century, but recently international grape varieties, such as Malbec and Merlot, have been planted on some of Bolivia's highest vineyards, rising up to 10,500 feet. The Tannat grape also performs very well at high altitudes here.

6. **c. Southern Coast of Uruguay.** With the capital city of Montevideo located roughly in the middle, most of the country's wine production is spread along the Atlantic-influenced southern coast of Uruguay, starting at the mouth of the Rio de la Plata. The Tannat grape is famous here, but Chardonnay, Sauvignon Blanc, Viognier, and Albariño also do very well.

7. **a. Wine Regions.** Ica and Tacna are two of Peru's main wine regions, along with Lima and Moquegua. All these regions lie along Peru's Pacific Ocean coastline. Ica is close to Lima, whereas Tacna and Moquegua are both much further south. Many vineyards are dedicated to the production of the

grape brandy, Pisco. However, a wide variety of wines are also produced, both from local grape varieties and international grapes, such as Cabernet Sauvignon, Malbec, Syrah, and Chardonnay.

8. **b. Grape Variety.** Isabel is a hardy American grape variety that was widely grown in Brazil when there was little viticultural knowledge of ideal sightings for vines. Isabel grew just about anywhere, producing often questionable wine. It is still extensively grown in the country today, but with the introduction of international grape varieties in the early 1990s, producing higher quality wine, Isabel is generally either drunk locally or turned into grape juice.

9. **c. 16th Century.** Muscat of Alexandria was one of the first grapes grown in Bolivia, back in the sixteenth century. It was mainly used for the production of Singani grape brandy. Today, several other local grape varieties are grown, and Tannat is doing well. Increasingly, international grapes are being produced, including Cabernet Sauvignon, Syrah, Merlot, and Malbec reds, as well as Riesling, Chenin Blanc, and Torrontés whites.

10. **c. Wine Producers.** Tacama, and Santiago Queirolo are two of the most prominent wine companies in Peru, and are both family-owned. Tacama is one of the oldest wineries in South America, and has been producing wine for almost 500 years. The company also exports its wines to countries around the world. Santiago Queirolo are best known for their range of wines under the Intipalka brand. Intipalka means 'valley of the sun' in Quechua, the language of the ancient Incas.

ANSWERS TO QUIZ 54 – ANAGRAMS – WINES OF SOUTH AMERICA

South American Grape Varieties

1. **Marselan.** Not a well-known red grape variety, Marselan is a cross between Cabernet Sauvignon and Grenache. First grown in the early 1960s, near the town of Marseillan, not far from Montpellier in southern France, it is still planted in parts of the Languedoc. It is also grown in South America, chiefly in Brazil and Uruguay. Often used in blends, but also as a single varietal.

2. **Niagara.** Native to North America, the white Niagara grape variety is used for both eating and making wine. Little known elsewhere in the world, it does have a place for producing wine in both Uruguay and Brazil.

3. **Criolla.** A red grape variety commonly grown in Argentina. It has mainly been used to make ordinary, everyday, table wine. However, in recent years some Argentine producers have been attempting to make quality wine from this grape, in a similar way to Chilean producers raising the quality of the local País grape.

4. **País.** This red grape was the most widely planted variety in Chile until it was overtaken by Cabernet Sauvignon at the end of the 1990s. Since then it has been made as a general table wine, but in recent years producers have been making much higher quality País, with a light, fresh, and fruity character.

5. **Bonarda.** In South America, the red grape Bonarda is grown chiefly in Argentina. Before the explosion onto the scene of Malbec, Bonarda was considered to be Argentina's main red wine. It tends to be lighter-bodied than Malbec, but is full of fruit with moderate acidity.

Argentine and Chilean Wine Regions

6. **Mendoza.** Approximately 600 miles west of Argentina's capital, Buenos Aires, and on the edge of the Andes Mountains, Mendoza is easily the largest wine region in the country. Some of Argentina's most highly-rated Malbec wines originate from Mendoza's high altitude sub-regions of Luján de Cuyo and the Uco Valley. However, the region grows a very wide variety of wine grapes, both red and white. Central Mendoza tends to produce the finest wine, and a lot of important producers are based there.

7. **Aconcagua.** Located about 60 miles north-west of Santiago, Aconcagua is an important Chilean wine region. It runs from inland to the Chilean coast, just north of Valparaiso. The Aconcagua river runs through part of the region, from the Andes Mountains to the Pacific Ocean. A very wide variety of grapes are grown here, including some fine Pinot Noirs.

8. **Leyda.** Another important Chilean wine region, Leyda is situated about sixty miles west of the capital, Santiago. It's sandwiched between the wine regions of San Antonio to the south, and Casablanca to the north. Red grapes include Cabernet Sauvignon, Pinot Noir, Syrah, and Merlot, and whites include Chardonnay and Sauvignon Blanc.

9. **Rio Negro.** Situated in Patagonia, in the south of Argentina. The climate is cooler than most of the rest of Argentina, and elegant cool-climate styles of Pinot Noir, Malbec, and Sauvignon Blanc are produced here, as well as some good examples of Cabernet Sauvignon, Merlot, Sémillon, and Torrontés.

10. **Rapel.** Located well south of Chile's capital, Santiago, the Rapel wine region is close to both the Cachapoal and Colchagua districts. It's principally a red wine producing region, and Cabernet Sauvignon, Syrah, and Carmenère are important examples. There are also some plantings of Chardonnay and Sauvignon Blanc.

ANSWERS TO QUIZ 55 – WINES OF AUSTRALIA – PART 1

1. **a. China.** Wine is no exception, China is the largest importer of most of the goods that Australia exports. China imports around 40% of all Australia's exported wines. USA is the next largest Importer at 16%, third is the UK with 13%, and fourth is Canada at 8% by value and volume. This means that only 4 countries account for 77% of all Australia's wine exports. The big change in the last 20 years is China, it is now the top Importer but around the year 2000 it imported very few wines from Australia.

2. **a. Barossa Valley.** Langmeil's The Freedom 1843 Shiraz Vineyard is said to be the world's oldest Shiraz vineyard. In 1838 Christian Auricht emigrated from Prussia and became a blacksmith and winemaker in the Barossa Valley. In 1843 he purchased the Freedom vineyard and planted Shiraz grapes. It is still today producing top quality Shiraz wines from vines which are over 150 years old. The vines are now low yielding, but the concentration and complexity of the must (fermented grape juice) is exquisite. This single vineyard is 3.5 acres (1.5 hectares) of loam and red clay sited on the banks of the North Para River in the Barossa Valley. Part of the vineyard is of pre-Phylloxera ungrafted Shiraz vines which are very rare in the world of wine.

3. **a. Red wine.** Nowadays the majority red wine production of Australia varies between 55% and 60%. Red wines are led by the Shiraz grape which is the most planted red grape variety in Australia at circa 40%. There are four main varieties of red grapes producing the vast majority of Australian red wines. The other three varieties after Shiraz are Cabernet Sauvignon, Merlot and Pinot Noir, in that order. Over twenty years ago the reverse was true, when in the year 2000 63% of all wines produced were white, but over two decades Australian reds have become much more popular.

4. **a. South Australia.** Of all the Australian States, South Australia produces by far the most wine in volume and value terms at circa 50% to 55% per annum. South Australia has 18 wine regions producing 610 million litres of wine a year, equivalent to 820 million bottles. It has many historic and very high end premier wine areas mainly producing red wine including Barossa Valley, McLaren Vale, Coonawarra, and Clare Valley. These four wine areas produce about 30% of the wine in South Australia by volume (50% by value). Then there is Riverland Wine Area which alone produces around 60% of SA total wines due to large international wine brands producing good value wines for the world's supermarkets. It is the giant wine area nobody has heard

of, silently selling over 500 million bottles a year of major wine brands such as Banrock Station and Oxford Landing.

5. **c. Shiraz.** Shiraz is the red grape, or any grape, success story of Australian wine. It now produces approximately 40% of all red wines from Australia and has become an iconic legend. Shiraz first made its way to Australia over two hundred years ago from the Rhône Valley, where it was called Syrah. John MacArthur is widely credited with importing the first cuttings in 1817 and then throughout the 19th century Shiraz was used for blending, often with Grenache, Cabernet Sauvignon or Mourvèdre, and mostly for fortified wines rather than table wines. It was not until Max Schubert, a real pioneer winemaker, who in 1951 set out to produce a 100% Shiraz wine from very old vines that Shiraz became world famous. He produced Penfolds Grange Bin 95 the iconic flagship red wine of Australia, named by wine critics as the Southern Hemisphere's only First Growth.

6. **b. Penfolds Grange.** Robert Parker found it more concentrated and exotic than Petrus from Pomerol, which had been his favourite wine previously. Answer no. 5 mentions Penfolds Grange Bin 95 as the 100% (or 95% in some years), Shiraz wine begun in 1951 and made from 70 year old plus vines. Penfolds is one of Australia's oldest wineries having celebrated its 175 year anniversary lately. Up until 1951 the very old Shiraz vines on the estate, some over 100 years old and also pre-Phylloxera, which is incredibly rare, were used in Bordeaux type blends to add smoothness and intensity. Penfolds Grange Bin 95 if stored well is one of the world's best wines for ageing for a long time. The most recent global average price we have for Penfolds Grange Bin 95 1954 is £12,148 a bottle, and it is said to be at peak maturity.

7. **c. Tasmania.** Tasmania is an island 150 miles south of the state of Victoria and is Australia's coolest, most distinctive wine region with a varied cool and sometimes damp temperate climate. The cool temperatures and high rainfall make it the ideal growing area for Tasmania's five major grape varieties which make subtle wines with finesse and minerality. Tasmania thus makes classic European wine styles of Pinot Noir, Sauvignon Blanc, Chardonnay, Pinot Gris, and Riesling. These five grape varieties account for about 96% of all wines produced, with Pinot Noir being 45% and Chardonnay 24%, mainly because they are also used for the production of Tasmanian Sparkling wines, including Bay Of Fires, Jansz, Ninth Island and Pirie. In the past twenty years the number of wine producers has doubled to around 250 but only about 10% of wineries have more than 10 hectares (25 acres) of vineyards. Tasmania is a very high quality wine area but is the smallest Australian wine region with less

than 1% of production, fewer than 17 million bottles per year, but they are worth seeking out.

8. ***b. James Busby.*** James Busby was a Scottish gentleman who sailed to Australia in 1824 determined to create a new wine industry there. He had studied winemaking and viticulture in France, and for his journey he had collected a large selection of grape vine cuttings from France and Germany. He developed the first vineyard in the Hunter Valley region of New South Wales, then continued to import more cuttings of new grape vine varieties and he also wrote the country's first wine books. They were practical tomes on the cultivation and best production techniques for quality wines. He sailed back to France to collect more vine stock in 1832 and this included vine cuttings from the Rhône Valley which would later become the iconic grape variety of Australia. The first wines produced from these cuttings were labelled 'Hermitage', or 'Claret' or 'Burgundy'. It was not until the 1850s that Australia adopted the name Shiraz for these vine cuttings imported in 1832.

9. ***c. Vasse Felix in Margaret River.*** Vasse Felix was the first vineyard and winery to be established in the Margaret River wine region of Western Australia. It was founded in the small town of Wilyabrup in 1967 by Dr Tom Cullity. The winemaker and owner's aim from the start was to produce ultra-premium Cabernet Sauvignon and Chardonnay. These varieties were planted in 1967 and much later Shiraz and Sémillon Sauvignon Blanc blends were also made at Vasse Felix. The Margaret River wine region produces just 3% of Australia's total wine production, but accounts for over 20% of the Australian premium wine market. Now over 50 years on from Vasse Felix as the founding vineyard, there are around 200 vineyards producing circa 50 to 55 million plus bottles of premium wine per year. About 45% is red wine dominated by Cabernet Sauvignon at 20% and Shiraz at 15% on average. The two major white grapes by volume are Sauvignon Blanc at 20% and Chardonnay at 15%. Way less than 1% of plantings are of Pinot Noir.

10. ***b. 40% to 50%.*** The population of Australia tries its best, but even with heroic efforts only manages to consume 40% of the Australian wine produced per year. Australians have switched some allegiance from beer to wine and nowadays they drink over five times as much wine per head as they did in the 1960s. Australia is now the 5th largest exporter of wine in the world at an average range of 1.6 billion to 2 billion bottles per year. The quality levels achieved and the prices the exported wines are sold for continue to rise each year.

ANSWERS TO QUIZ 56 – WINES OF AUSTRALIA – PART 2

1. **Shiraz.** It is the grape name used in Australia and some other New World wine countries for the Syrah grape variety mainly grown in the southern Rhône region of France. Shiraz is an identical clone, which was first used by this name in Australia, and now in some other countries, such as South Africa. Some New World wine producers have started to name their wines Syrah if they are more 'French' in style (dark savoury fruit, peppery and herbal) or name them Shiraz to indicate a richer, raspberry-fruited, soft and less herby style of wine. The Syrah/Shiraz grape variety originally came from 9th century vineyards in the town of Shiraz in Persia/Iran.

2. **c. New Zealand.** Over 55% of all wine by volume imported into Australia is from New Zealand. France is 2nd with about 20% and Italy is 3rd with 15%. Then, measuring Australia's wine imports by value, New Zealand's dominance is reduced, as the French imports are mainly expensive château and domaine wines from Bordeaux and Burgundy. New Zealand's share becomes 40% by value and France climbs to 38%, with Italy third at 12%. So these three countries alone represent about 90% of all wine imports into Australia by volume and value.

3. **a. Chardonnay.** The Chardonnay grape dominates white grape varieties in Australia. Around 40% to 45% of all white grapes planted in vineyards are Chardonnay. This is over twice the amount of any other white grape variety. Traditional Australian Chardonnays used to be 'fruit salad' wines, often a bit overblown and sweet with ripe melon flavours and sometimes too woody. But nowadays you can also find cool climate Australian examples of unwooded 'Chablis' style Chardonnays. The second most planted white variety, increasing now at about 15%, is Sauvignon Blanc. The next two most popular white grapes are Sémillon and Pinot Gris both at around 10% of all whites planted.

4. **a. Melbourne.** The Yarra Valley in Victoria State is only 30km (20 miles) north of Melbourne and the Mornington Peninsula is only 50km (30 miles) south. Both of these wine areas produce very fine quality Pinot Noir, and there are very popular vineyard wine tours to both regions run from Melbourne. Three of the best wines in the Yarra Valley are Coldstream Hills, Yarra Yerring and Oakridge, all with a 'Burgundian' feel to them. In Mornington Peninsula, three popular top quality Pinots are Moorooduc Estate, Stonier, and Ten Minutes by Tractor. All six wines are widely available in the UK.

5. **c. Sauvignon Blanc.** The most planted grape variety in Margaret River is Sauvignon Blanc, although this Western Australia wine area is best known for

its top quality Cabernet Sauvignon and Chardonnay. Margaret River vineyards were only started in the 1960s, now it is one of the most experimental in Australia for introducing new grape varieties, such as Chenin Blanc, Verdelho and even Nero d'Avola and Vermentino. The plantings are still expanding with over 12,000 acres (4,800 Hectares) of vineyards and more than 150 wine estates.

6. *b. House of Arras.* This wine estate situated in Tasmania has won many sparkling wine trophies in Australia and internationally. It makes both vintage and non vintage sparklers. Answer c) Jansz is also a top sparkling wine producer from Tasmania. Answer a) Domaine Chandon was started well over 30 years ago in the Yarra Valley in Victoria and it is the Australian outpost for Moët & Chandon.

7. *b. Penfolds Estate.* This wine Estate was founded in 1844 and has produced Grange Hermitage since its inception. Grange Hermitage bin 95 is made from 90% to 95% old vine Shiraz grapes, with a small dash of Cabernet Sauvignon added. The first Penfolds Grange Bin 95 was made in 1951 and one bottle sold at auction in 2004 at around £40,000. Answer a) Hardy's Estate is also one of Australia's oldest and was planted in 1853. Answer c) Wynn's Estate founded in 1891 is the largest vineyard in Coonawarra wine region.

8. *b. 65 Wine Regions.* There are 65 designated wine regions situated in all of Australia's 6 States. The Riverland in South Australia is the largest wine producing region, with Chardonnay and Shiraz being their most planted grape varieties. South Australia is by far the country's largest wine producing state responsible for almost 50% of Australia's annual wine by volume. Over 100 different grape varieties are planted in Australia for commercial production.

9. *b. Wyndham Estate.* The brand started internationally in 1970, but wine has been planted and continually produced on George Wyndham's land since 1828 making it Australia's oldest vineyard/wine estate. Answer c) Yalumba is the oldest family owned winery in Australia started in 1848. Answer a) Tyrrell's was founded in 1858 and is still a family run wine estate.

10. *a. Henschke cellars of Eden Valley.* The Hill of Grace vineyard was planted in 1860, with grape vine cuttings brought over from vineyards in the Rhône Valley. These same vines nowadays are still producing small quantities of expensive very concentrated wine. Answer c) Yalumba, in the Barossa Valley was started by Samuel Smith of Dorset in 1848; they use hundred-year-old vines in their top blends today. Answer b) Mount Horrocks is by far the newest vineyard not planted until 1980.

ANSWERS TO QUIZ 57 – MATCH AUSTRALIAN WINES

1. **e. Tasmania.** Tamar Ridge and Bay of Fires are two top producers of cool climate classical 'Burgundian type' Pinot Noirs located in the island state of Tasmania. It is the most southerly state of Australia and is sited 240 kilometres (150 miles) off the southern coast of Victoria, on the opposite side of the Bass Strait. Tasmania's most common grape varieties are closer in style to those grown in New Zealand than Australia, reflecting their shared cool maritime climate. They are Pinot Noir, Chardonnay, Sauvignon Blanc and Merlot, which account for about 70% of all wine produced in Tasmania. High quality sparkling wines using Pinot Noir and Chardonnay are also a Tasmanian speciality. Tamar Ridge just about only makes award-winning 'Burgundian' Pinot Noir and have done so for over 25 years, and they also produce Australia's most awarded non-vintage sparkling wine, 'Pirie' which is the 'brother brand' of Tamar Ridge Pinot Noirs. Bay of Fires is located in Pipers River area which is also part of the Tamar Valley wine region. Hardy's purchased the winery and developed the Bay of Fires brand in 2001 and it has been producing gold medal wines ever since.

2. **c. Margaret River.** Both Vasse Felix and Leeuwin Estate are wineries in Margaret River in the south-west corner of the state of Western Australia. The region is famous for producing a more 'European' wine style with finesse and delicacy. There are now over 180 wine estates producing refined Chardonnays, Bordeaux Blends and Sauvignon Blancs as well as other varieties. Vasse Felix was established in 1967 by regional wine pioneer Dr Tom Cullity, and is famous for being Margaret River's founding wine estate. Leeuwin Estate is family owned, and is also one of the five founding wineries in Margaret River, having begun wine production in 1971. It now produces the 'flagship range' called the Art Series with a different artist painting the label of each vintage (copied Château Mouton Rothschild). It quickly gained the reputation of Australia's finest Chardonnay producer. Oz Clarke has described the Chardonnay as Australia's 'Montrachet', and many other wine experts agree with that judgement.

3. **b. Barossa Valley.** Yalumba and Château Tanunda are both historic wine estates situated in the heart of the Barossa Valley in South Australia state. The Barossa Valley is Australia's largest high quality wine district (like the Napa Valley of California) and is most famous for its rich, bold, spicy and chocolatey Shiraz, and concentrated and big rounded 'Bordeaux Blends'. Some of the vines still used in quality wine production in the Barossa are amongst the oldest in the world. Yalumba's motto is 'Fiercely independent since 1849' and is still a

family run wine business. There have now been six generations of the Smith family since Samuel founded Yalumba over 170 years ago. They are well known for their red blends including their signature Cabernet Sauvignon and Shiraz blends. Château Tanunda was founded over 40 years later in 1890, now with over 130 years of winemaking experience. This historic estate specialises in world class red wines made from very old vines. Their signature wine uses grapes from their 150 year old vines and is called '1858 Field Blend'. It has become a very exclusive and rare collectors' item.

4. *a. Hunter Valley.* Both Mount Pleasant and Tyrrell's wineries are in the Hunter Valley of the state of New South Wales; the valley starts at about 80 miles north of Sydney. They both make famous Sémillon wines as well as other varieties. Mount Pleasant was founded in 1921 on vineyards that have vines going back to 1880; of their 5 separate vineyards Old Hill is by far the oldest. Mount Pleasant's most famous Sémillons are the cellar aged Elizabeth and Lovedale. They have won many awards for their Sémillons and also won the title of winery of the year in 2017. Tyrrell's wines are located very close by, also in Pokolbin. They have been family winemakers since 1858 and have won over 5,000 prizes/awards for their wines especially for their flagship Sémillon 'Vat 1 Sémillon'. This was first made in old oak in 1963, but since 1990 has been the archetype of the Hunter Valley style – fermented, settled, and blended in stainless steel before spending a couple of years ageing in bottle. Murray Tyrrell and his son Bruce have been given the title of Champion of Hunter Valley whites.

5. *d. Adelaide/Coonawarra.* Shiraz from Chapel Hill and Bird in Hand are judged to be two of the top producers of the variety in Australia, and both are based in the Adelaide Hills and Coonawarra Valley. Chapel Hill's Michael Fragos took over winemaking in 2004 and endless titles and trophies worldwide have since followed. He was also named best winemaker on the planet at the world's biggest wine show, with the judges verdict that 'his wine quality is unfailingly excellent'. Bird in Hand Winery was founded in 1997 on land that had previously been a large dairy farm and was very near to the 19th century gold mine 'Bird in Hand'. Their flagship wine is called M.A.C. Shiraz, and Kym Milne, their winemaker, is the second ever Master of Wine in Australia and was named Australian winemaker of the year not once but twice. The secret of Adelaide Hills region's restrained, elegant wines is the altitude of its vineyards, which range from 400 to 650 metres (1,300 to 2,100ft) and thus produce 'cool climate' Shiraz with finesse and restraint, yet still powerful and rich.

6. *h. Sparkling Blend.* Domaine Chandon and Jansz are two of Australia's best examples of sparkling wines made by the champagne method, and using

the same blend of grape varieties as used in the champagne region. Australia annually makes around 7 million cases and is the 7th largest sparkling wine producer in the world, way behind the top 2 – Italy with around 60 million cases and France with just over 50 million cases. Domaine Chandon is the OZ outpost of Moët & Chandon, and started their winery in 1986 up in the high Yarra Valley in Victoria State at a place called Green Point, which had been a large dairy farm. Jansz winery was founded in the same year (1986) and had partnered with Roederer Champagne. It is situated high in the northern hills of Tasmania in the cool climate Piper River region. Both wineries have won many international sparkling wine awards and are worth seeking out in the UK.

7. *i. Shiraz Blend.* Both Penfolds Grange and Wolf Blass are famous for their Shiraz wine blends, the former for the Southern Hemisphere's sole 'Grand Cru' or '1st growth' wine and the latter for widely available and affordable great quality volume Shiraz blends. Shiraz is Australia's most planted grape variety and is increasingly being created as a blend with Cabernet Sauvignon added. Penfolds Grange is usually a blend of around 95% Shiraz and 5% Cabernet Sauvignon, and on its 50th birthday in 2001, Grange was listed as an Australian heritage wine icon, while the 1997 and 2008 Grange vintages achieved a perfect score of 100 'Parker Points'. Wolf Blass is also in the centre of the Barossa Valley in South Australia and was founded in 1966 by Wolfgang Blass a German immigrant winemaker. It is now owned by Treasury Wine Estates and produces around 60 million bottles of wine a year. Its flagship wine is the Black Label blend and it also has an entry level Shiraz blend called Red Label.

8. *j. Riesling.* Pewsey Vale in the Eden Valley and Mount Horrocks in Clare Valley are both situated in cool climate high altitude winemaking areas of South Australia, perfect for making intense yet elegant Rieslings. Historic Pewsey Vale was founded by an Englishman named Joseph Gilbert in 1847. It was the first vineyard to plant the Riesling grape variety in Australia, (now still the only winery to solely grow Riesling), and also the first vineyard planted in the Eden Valley. Now after over 170 years of trying and experimenting they make some outstanding age-worthy Rieslings including single vineyard '1961 Block' and 'The Contours'. Mount Horrocks may be small with only 10 hectares and it limits its production to approximately 3,500 cases (42,000 bottles) but it is perfectly formed, with owner/winemaker Stephanie Toole winning many international trophies especially for her 'Cordon Cut' Rieslings.

9. *f. Pinot Noir.* Coldstream Hills and Yarra Yerring are both located only about 3 km apart in the Yarra Valley, the signature area for Pinot Noir in Victoria State. Along with the nearby Mornington Peninsula (smaller wine

area) Yarra Valley has the largest concentration of Pinot Noir vineyards in Australia, accounting for 40% of all the vines planted there. Similar to Burgundy, it is mainly a two grape region, Pinot Noir and Chardonnay. Coldstream Hills was founded by James Halliday in 1985, who was Australia's favourite wine writer, and the flagship wines are Reserve and Single Vineyard Pinot Noirs. Yarra Yerring next door was started up In 1969 by Dr Bailey Carrodus after a lengthy search for the perfect vineyard site to produce elegant classic 'Burgundian, Rhône & Bordelais' style wines. These iconic wines tend to totally sell out on their annual release weekend as soon as they are offered for sale.

10. **g. Chardonnay.** Both Bannockburn and Cullen make distinctive and iconic Chardonnay wines along with other varieties. Bannockburn is a family-owned winery with 27 hectares of vineyards, which are some of the earliest established in the Geelong wine region of Victoria. Stuart Reginald Hooper planted the vineyards in the late 1970s and their flagship wine from 40 year old single vineyard vines is S.R.H. Chardonnay. Cullen wines is also family-owned and was started in the 1970s by Kevin John Cullen, but is thousands of miles away in the Margaret River wine region of Western Australia. The flagship wine in the Cullen portfolio is the Kevin John Chardonnay, crafted from 35-year-old vines and aged for nine months in oak. So both flagship Chardonnays are named after the founder of their winery, a bit of an Australian trait. The grape Chardonnay used to be the most planted grape variety in Australia, but has nowadays been overtaken by the Shiraz grape.

ANSWERS TO QUIZ 58 – ANAGRAMS – WINES OF AUSTRALIA

Australian Famous 'Valley' Wine Regions

1. **Barossa.** Situated in South Australia, about thirty five miles north-east of the state capital, Adelaide. South Australia is the most important wine state in Australia, producing around half the nation's wines, and the Barossa Valley is one of the country's most important wine regions. Many different grape varieties are grown here, but the grape that the Valley is most famous for is Shiraz (Syrah). The often ungrafted vines here (this state has not yet encountered Phylloxera) produce a rich, earthy, spicy and delicious Shiraz.

2. **Yarra.** Located in the state of Victoria, about an hour's drive north-east of Melbourne, the Yarra Valley is another region producing high quality wine. It has many micro-climates, so different parts of the region are ideal for certain grape varieties. Some excellent Cabernet Sauvignon, Riesling, and Shiraz wines are produced, and the Valley also makes superb Pinot Noir and Chardonnay, which are often used here to produce some excellent sparkling wines.

3. **Tamar.** Located in eastern Tasmania, not far from the city of Launceston, the Tamar Valley is a cool climate wine-growing area, with maritime influences from both the Bass Strait and the Tasman Sea. Some excellent Pinot Noir, and sparkling wine, is produced here. Indeed, Tasmania, generally, is justly famous for producing outstanding Pinot Noir and high quality sparkling wine. The island is on the same latitude as New Zealand's South Island, which is also well-known for producing superb Pinot Noir.

4. **Alpine.** Positioned in the eastern end of the state of Victoria, the Alpine Valleys region is close to Victoria's 'Alps' and is an area that is cooled by the mountain breeze. One of Australia's most famous producers, Brown Brothers, are based not far away in the town of Milawa. A wide range of grape varieties are produced in the Alpine Valleys, including Chardonnay and Shiraz. Owing to the region's rich history of Italian culture dating back to the Second World War, grapes such as Nebbiolo and Barbera are also grown here.

5. **Derwent.** Located just north-west of Tasmania's capital city, Hobart, the Derwent Valley is a relatively dry region, owing to the sheltering presence of nearby Mount Wellington. The prime grape varieties here are Pinot Noir, Chardonnay, and Riesling, including producing some excellent sparkling wine. The Derwent Valley is also one of Tasmania's most beautiful valleys.

6. **Eden.** Situated in South Australia, the Eden Valley butts up against the Barossa Valley, north-east of Adelaide. Unsurprisingly then, the most important grape in Barossa, Shiraz, is also a principal grape variety here in the Eden Valley. However, equally impressive are the splendid Rieslings that this valley produces, and which compare well with the excellent Rieslings of Clare Valley, which is also located in South Australia.

7. **Blackwood.** Lying east of the famous Margaret River wine region in Western Australia, and tucked into the south-west corner of this huge state, the Blackwood Valley is less well-known than Margaret River. But it's a very scenic area of rolling hills, valleys, forests, orchards, charming country towns, and rivers, including the River Blackwood. It also has dozens of vineyards growing a very wide range of grapes, including Cabernet Sauvignon and Merlot reds, along with the more unusual Tempranillo, and Chardonnay, Sauvignon Blanc, Viognier, and Sémillon whites.

8. **Hunter.** One of Australia's most famous wine Valleys, the Hunter Valley lies about 100 miles north of Sydney in New South Wales. Shiraz and Sémillon are the most important grape varieties here and, indeed, the Hunter Valley is world-famous for producing some of the best Sémillon made anywhere on the planet.

9. **Clare.** Situated about 75 miles directly north of Adelaide in South Australia, Clare Valley is justly renowned for producing superb Riesling wine. Excellent Shiraz and Cabernet Sauvignon are also made here. It's one of Australia's oldest wine regions, and produces wines from light and elegant to rich and robust.

10. **Coal River.** Located not far from Derwent Valley, the Coal River Valley is north-east of Hobart in Tasmania. It's a fast-growing wine region, but a relatively recent one, with the appearance of the first commercial vineyards in the 1970s. A number of different grape varieties are produced, but the most important are Pinot Noir, Chardonnay, and Sauvignon Blanc.

ANSWERS TO QUIZ 59 – WINES OF NEW ZEALAND – PART 1

1. **North Island.** Hawke's Bay is New Zealand's second biggest wine region, after Marlborough on the South Island. This wide bay on the east coast of the North Island has a beneficial combination of low rainfall and high temperatures. Full-bodied red wines are produced here from grapes that include Cabernet Sauvignon, Merlot and Syrah. Rich and complex Chardonnays are also made.

2. **a. Martinborough.** One of the leading producers of red wine in New Zealand, Ata Rangi is located in the Martinborough wine region situated at the foot of the North Island. Terroir is combined with a winemaking philosophy that produces consistently high quality wine, winning countless awards and accolades along the way.

3. **b. Brancott Estate.** Well-known in Marlborough on the South Island, the name change from Montana Wines to Brancott Estate took place in 2010, by the parent company Pernod Ricard, in order to reduce confusion in the United States market with wines from the state of Montana. A very wide range of red, white and sparkling wines are produced in the Marlborough region.

4. **Pinot Noir.** New Zealand's Central Otago Pinot Noir has the same sort of prestige around the world as their Marlborough Sauvignon Blanc. Central Otago is New Zealand's southernmost wine region, and is home to mountains,

lakes, and dramatic skies. The region is very firmly on the world stage for producing very fine Pinot Noir.

5. **Sauvignon Blanc.** This was Cloudy Bay's flagship wine, launched in 1985, and Sauvignon Blanc is still the grape variety that they are most associated with today. It is one of the world's most prestigious Sauvignon Blancs, and has consistently scored 90+ Parker points every year.

6. **c. Sparkling Wine.** The champagne house, Deutz, produces one of New Zealand's best sparkling wines in the Marlborough wine region on the South Island. It's made by the traditional method of secondary fermentation in bottle, and has won multiple awards.

7. **a. Hawke's Bay.** Gimblett Gravels is an acclaimed wine growing area within the Hawke's Bay wine region on the North Island. Hawke's Bay's largest river, the Ngaruroro flows through the Gimblett Gravels district, and it was the river that formed the extraordinary gravelly soil after which this area was named. In particular, superb examples of Merlot, Cabernet Sauvignon, Cabernet Franc, and Syrah are produced here.

8. **c. Gisborne.** Situated on the east coast of the North Island, just above Hawke's Bay. It was where Captain James Cook first landed in New Zealand in 1769. White wines dominate the region, particularly Chardonnay and Pinot Gris. A comprehensive 'Wine Trail' through the region leads to a number of boutique wineries.

9. **Waipara.** Situated about 40 miles north of Christchurch on the South Island. One of New Zealand's premier wine regions, Waipara is a picturesque valley, and is particularly well-known for producing top quality Pinot Noir and Riesling.

10. **Marlborough.** The Nelson wine region lies on the north-west edge of the South Island, adjacent to Marlborough. The region produces excellent Pinot Noir, and Sauvignon Blanc, Chardonnay, Pinot Gris, and Riesling. Marlborough is the largest wine producing region in New Zealand, producing a wide variety of grapes.

ANSWERS TO QUIZ 60 – WINES OF NEW ZEALAND – PART 2

1. *False.* The Bay of Plenty is situated on the North Island, just around the coast from the wine region of Gisborne. As well as having spectacular beaches, and growing juicy kiwifruit, the Waikato Bay of Plenty wine region has been steadily expanding its vineyard plantings and producing wine from mainly Chardonnay, Cabernet Sauvignon, and Sauvignon Blanc grapes.

2. *a. Central Otago.* Situated in North Otago, within the wider Central Otago wine region, Waitaki Valley is one of New Zealand's newest and, indeed, smallest, wine regions. The main grape varieties grown here are Pinot Noir, Chardonnay, Pinot Gris and Riesling.

3. *Syrah.* There's no particular reason why this grape is called Shiraz in Australia and many other countries in the world, and Syrah in New Zealand, France, and various other countries. It's the same grape, and each country has made its own choice as to whether they call it Syrah or Shiraz.

4. *Yes.* One of the most southerly wine regions on the planet, Central Otago is home to dramatic scenery, and is world-famous for producing high quality, elegant, Pinot Noirs. Relatively little Syrah is grown here, but it does exist. Nanny Goat Vineyard Syrah is a good example!

5. *b. Marlborough.* As well as the lion's share of sparkling wine production, the Marlborough wine region also has the lion's share of producing New Zealand wine generally. The sparkling wines in Marlborough are not only produced by the traditional method of secondary fermentation in bottle, using Pinot Noir and Chardonnay grapes, but are also made from some other grape varieties, such as Sauvignon Blanc. Some excellent premium sparklers are made here, a classic example being Cloudy Bay's Pelorus.

6. *b. Over 200 years ago.* The first planting of grape vines in New Zealand was on 25 September 1819. Reverend Samuel Marsden was the driving force behind the establishment of Anglican mission stations in New Zealand. Together with his missionaries, his work built a relationship of trust with the Maori chiefs. His diary shows that he planted the first vine in New Zealand at Kerikeri, a town next to the Bay of Islands, very near the northern end of the North Island.

7. *c. Auckland.* Waiheke Island is about 12 miles east of Auckland City on the mainland of North Island. It is the second largest island in the Hauraki Gulf. This hilly island is home to some of Auckland's most famous vineyards. The main grapes grown include Cabernet Sauvignon, Merlot, Syrah, and Chardonnay.

8. **True.** Situated just north of Hawke's Bay, on the North Island, Gisborne grapes include Pinot Gris, which tend to be grown in the cooler areas in the southern part of the region. Since the 1990s, New Zealand's Pinot Gris has enjoyed a dramatic rise in popularity, including being successfully grown in Gisborne, where it produces ripe, rich, and full-bodied wine.

9. **a. Hawke's Bay.** Located on the Te Awanga coast in Hawke's Bay, on the North Island, within a stone's throw of the Pacific Ocean. Elephant Hill produces high quality wine through careful attention to detail, ensuring the winemaking is driven by tradition, without losing sight of the advantages of innovation.

10. **b. 1970s.** Nelson's first grape vines were planted in the mid-nineteenth century. But it was not until the 1970s that pioneering producers established the modern wine industry there, and are now making high quality wine from Pinot Noir, Chardonnay, and Sauvignon Blanc grapes, as well as a number of other varieties.

ANSWERS TO QUIZ 61 – MATCH WINES OF NEW ZEALAND

1. **d. Central Otago Pinot Noirs.** Both Felton Road and Two Paddocks are most famous for their Pinot Noirs made in Central Otago, one of the most southerly vineyard areas in the world, vying for that status with Patagonia in Argentina. Felton Road is a totally biodynamic vineyard, situated by the old gold fields in the Bannockburn area; its best Pinot Noirs are Block 3 & 5. Sam Neill the film actor, (Jurassic Park, The Piano etc) is the wine loving owner and winemaker of Two Paddocks which he founded in 1993 in the Gibbston area of Central Otago. He only makes single vineyard Pinot Noirs and a very small amount of Riesling.

2. **e. Hawke's Bay Merlots.** Church Road and Mission Estate both produce famous top quality Merlots, as well as other varieties. Mission Estate was founded in 1851 by pioneering French missionaries and is said to be the oldest vineyard in New Zealand, and became the start-up of the New Zealand wine industry. Church Road Winery is almost next door to Mission Estate, on the same Church Road. It started up a bit later in 1897 and is one of the most awarded wineries in Hawke's Bay for its Merlots and Bordeaux Blends. Hawke's Bay in North Island is the main wine area for top Merlots with around 80% of all New Zealand plantings. With more than 200 vineyards and 90+ wineries it is the second largest wine region in New Zealand.

3. **b. Marlborough Sauvignon Blancs.** Vavasour & Greywacke both produce star quality Sauvignon Blancs with a concentrated grassy and zesty nature. Vavasour is the first winery to be located in the small and cooler Awatere Valley within the Marlborough region; it was founded in 1986 and before that the whole valley had been used exclusively for sheep farming. Greywacke is one of the most recent star award-winning Sauvignon Blanc labels from Marlborough and was only started in 2009 by Kevin Judd who had previously been the founding winemaker at Cloudy Bay winery for 25 years until he started Greywacke. Marlborough region is the top producer of New Zealand Sauvignon Blancs by far, responsible for almost 75% of all Sauvignon Blancs produced per year. Marlborough also exports almost 85% of all wines from New Zealand, again mostly Sauvignon Blancs.

4. **a. Auckland Red Blends.** Coopers Creek & Man of War both produce powerful and intense classic Bordeaux blends of Cabernet Sauvignon, Merlot and Petit Verdot. Man of War is the largest vineyard on Waiheke Island in Auckland Bay. Auckland in the north of North Island is one of New Zealand's oldest wine regions, established in the early 1900s by overseas settlers, mainly Croatian, Lebanese and English winemakers.

5. **c. Canterbury Rieslings.** Giesen and Mud House make top quality Rieslings, dry yet fruity like Alsace. Canterbury is south of Marlborough near Christchurch, and is the 5th largest New Zealand wine region. Riesling plantings are almost exclusively in Canterbury and Marlborough regions of South Island, with a small amount in Nelson. They still account for only around 1% of all NZ wines produced. The cool plains of Canterbury surrounding Christchurch produce crisp, flinty Riesling characterised by green apples and citrus, and from their small base they are growing in popularity. .

6. **h. Sauvignon Blanc.** Oyster Bay and Cloudy Bay are in Marlborough and produce large quantities of classy, herbaceous and aromatic Sauvignon Blanc. Cloudy Bay was the first superstar winery in NZ, started back in 1985 by David Hohnen, who sold it to Veuve Clicquot in 2003, now part of LVMH. Oyster Bay was established by family-owned company Delegats, and its inaugural vintage was named best Sauvignon Blanc at the 1991 International Wine and Spirit Competition. It is now one of the largest New Zealand wine brands, producing well over one million cases a year with around 40% being imported by the USA. Sauvignon Blanc still accounts for around 70% to 75% of all NZ wines and over 85% of all their wine exports. New Zealand is 2nd to France's position as the number one global producer of the variety at around 23,000 hectares and is fast catching up on France's 27,000 hectares.

7. *i. Merlot.* Elephant Hill and Squawking Magpie are multi award-winning wineries in North Island, Hawkes Bay area (the 2nd largest wine area in NZ). They produce wines from 3 or 4 grape varieties, with the most impressive being their Merlots, which are bold, yet soft and classic Bordeaux style wines. Elephant Hill Estate was founded in 2003 by German businessman Roger Weiss and he has since won the trophy for best New Zealand Red Wine. Squawking Magpie from their first vintage in 1999 has consistently collected awards and earned high praise from wine critics at home and internationally. Vines were first planted in Hawke's Bay back in 1851 by French missionaries who established Mission Estate. Hawke's Bay produces well over 90% of all Merlot in New Zealand; a proportion does go into red blends with Cabernet Sauvignon, and Merlot only accounts for about 3% of all NZ wines.

8. *g. Chardonnay.* Milton (the first organic winery in NZ), and Poverty Bay wine estates are both in Gisborne, North Island (the 3rd largest wine region). These Chardonnays are vegan and organic with soft complexity of stone fruits, with some vanilla and honeyed notes. They vary from freshly scented, with ripe tropical fruit flavours for early consumption through to concentrated, complex Chardonnays with elegance and finesse, which will mature well for up to 10 years. Chardonnay still accounts for only 6% of all New Zealand wines. Gisborne and Hawke's Bay in North Island and Marlborough in South Island are the 3 major regions producing over 95% of all NZ Chardonnays.

9. *J. Pinot Noir.* Brancott Estate (formerly Montana until 2010) was the first vineyard to export New Zealand Pinot Noir to the UK (1977). It is now owned by Pernod Ricard and is one of the largest NZ producers. Both are based in Marlborough, South Island. St Clair founded over 30 years ago and still family run makes many intense award-winning Pinot Noirs. The entry level is Vicars Choice and the top wines are numbered Pioneer Blocks. Marlborough region produces around 50% of all New Zealand Pinot Noir and almost twice as much in volume as Central Otago. Both Brancott and St Clair produce Pinots with bright raspberry, cherry and plums on the palate, with freshness from subtle acidity that is complemented by soft tannins. Pinot Noir accounts for around 8% of all New Zealand wines.

10. *f. Riesling.* Pegasus Bay and Greystone make stylish fresh, floral and citrus Rieslings in the Canterbury region of South Island. Greystone is a newly formed winery. The Thomas family's first wine was produced in 2008 and over the past few years Greystone has grown with international awards and accolades to be recognised now as one of New Zealand's best wineries. It has won many awards for its organic Rieslings and other wines. The first vines were planted at Pegasus Bay by the Donaldson family in 1986 and the estate

is family-owned and operated. There are now around 40 hectares (100 acres) of vineyards which are mainly award-winning Rieslings or Pinot Noirs. Riesling only accounts for about 1% of all New Zealand wine, but is growing fast in popularity.

ANSWERS TO QUIZ 62 – ANAGRAMS – WINES OF NEW ZEALAND

New Zealand Wine Regions

1. **Canterbury.** On the South Island, just north of Central Otago, Canterbury's wine region stretches around the South Island's capital city, Christchurch. The region tends to be too cool to ripen the famous Bordeaux grapes, but it does produce high quality, almost Burgundy-like Pinot Noir and Chardonnay.

2. **Nelson.** The Nelson wine region lies on the north-west edge of the South Island, adjacent to Marlborough. The region produces excellent Pinot Noir, and also Sauvignon Blanc, Chardonnay, Pinot Gris, and Riesling.

3. **Bay of Plenty.** The Bay of Plenty is situated on the North Island, just around the coast from the wine region of Gisborne. As well as having spectacular beaches, and growing juicy kiwifruit, the Waikato Bay of Plenty wine region has been steadily expanding its vineyard plantings and producing wine from mainly Chardonnay, Cabernet Sauvignon, and Sauvignon Blanc grapes.

4. **Martinborough.** Situated at the southern end of the North Island, and about an hour's drive from New Zealand's capital, Wellington. The small town of Martinborough, and its surrounding district, are home to some of New Zealand's most highly respected boutique wineries. In particular, the region produces excellent Pinot Noir.

5. **Waipara Valley.** Situated about 40 miles north of Christchurch on the South Island. One of New Zealand's premier wine regions, Waipara is a picturesque valley, and is particularly well-known for producing top quality Pinot Noir and Riesling.

New Zealand Wine Producers

6. **Cloudy Bay.** Based in Marlborough, Cloudy Bay takes its name from a bay at the northern tip of the South Island named by Captain Cook in 1770. Their

Sauvignon Blanc, launched in 1985, was their flagship wine and is still the grape variety that they are most associated with today. Cloudy Bay Sauvignon Blanc was the wine chosen by the New Zealand Prime Minister, John Key, in 2014 to serve to the Duke and Duchess of Cambridge during their royal tour of the country.

7. **Wither Hills.** Named after the hills that border them, Wither Hills vineyards are sited throughout the Wairau Valley sub-region of Marlborough on the South Island. One of Marlborough's best-known wineries, it was established in the 1990s and consistently produces high quality Pinot Noir, Sauvignon Blanc and Chardonnay.

8. **Te Mata.** Situated in the Hawke's Bay wine region on the North Island, Te Mata estate has the oldest winery building in New Zealand, and is surrounded by some of New Zealand's oldest vineyards. Their Pinot Noir, Chardonnay, and Sauvignon Blanc are particularly famous, as are their wines made from some of the Bordeaux blends. Other grapes produced include Syrah and Viognier.

9. **Elephant Hill.** Located on the Te Awanga coast in Hawke's Bay, on the North Island, within a stone's throw of the Pacific Ocean. Elephant Hill produces high quality wine through careful attention to detail, ensuring the winemaking is driven by tradition, without losing sight of the advantages of innovation.

10. **Saint Clair.** Particularly famous for their multi award-winning Sauvignon Blanc, Saint Clair are based in the Marlborough wine region on the South Island, and are one of New Zealand's most well-known producers.

ANSWERS TO QUIZ 63 – WINES OF SOUTH AFRICA – PART 1

1. **a. Chenin Blanc.** In South Africa, Chenin Blanc is the most widely planted grape variety, accounting for nearly one-fifth of all vineyard  plantings in the 21st century so far. In 2018 there were almost 50,000 acres (20,000 hectares) of Chenin Blanc planted, which is nearly twice the amount planted in France. Chenin Blanc originated in the Loire Valley, in France, and the South African version is more fruity and soft without the sometimes austere and delicate mineral notes. The variety was introduced to the country in the collection of vine cuttings sent to South Africa in the early 1700s by the Dutch East India Company. For the next couple of hundred years of South African wine history, the variety was known as Steen. It was not until 1965

that it was definitely authorised as Chenin Blanc, but many wineries still called it Steen until the early 2000s.

2. *c. The Netherlands.* The first non-indigenous white settlers arriving in South Africa were from the Netherlands, living in settlements around the port of Cape Town. This started as a trading post set up on the East India route by the Dutch East India Company. The foothold of small farming communities was established by Jan van Riebeeck, a Dutch explorer who became head of the Cape Colony, following his arrival with three ships on 6th April 1652. This is taken by the Dutch Afrikaners to be the start of the 'history' of South Africa. The Afrikaners were then the majority owners of farms and wineries in South Africa for over 300 years. The post-apartheid era since 1994 has resulted in foreign investors now owning over 16% of wine estates (over 100), while there has also been a dramatic growth of wineries in black ownership, from nil to over 3%; still a very long way to go.

3. *c. 101 plus.* In South Africa, around 100 to 110 different wine grape varieties are grown on an area of approximately 120,000 hectares. This sounds quite impressive, but of course many of these varieties are grown in very small quantities, but are still part of the country's commercial wine production. The South African safari industry has 'the Big Five', and the South African wine industry has two more, 'the Big Seven', which refers to these grape varieties – Chenin Blanc, Pinotage, Shiraz, Cabernet Sauvignon, Merlot, Chardonnay and Sauvignon Blanc. Pinot Noir is the 8th grape variety in quantity planted, but some say the 1st or 2nd best in quality terms.

4. *b. Fairview.* They position themselves as a vineyard and goat farm offering wine & cheese tasting sessions, plus a Mediterranean-style restaurant. This is an example of Charles Back's typical modesty. The Fairview farm started growing grapes in 1693, and the first Fairview wines were produced in 1699. A Lithuanian refugee arrived in 1901 and bought the farm. In 1996 (his grandson) Charles Back II was announced by South African Wine Magazine as the second most influential person in the South African wine industry – after Nelson Mandela. Also later in 2017 Charles Back II was awarded the 1659 Wine Industry Medal of Honour, becoming the most awarded winemaker in South Africa. He still makes goats cheese and his most famous Rhône style wine is still 'Goats do Roam'.

5. *c. Walker Bay.* This wine producing district surrounds the seaside town of Hermanus, south-east of Cape Town and is famous for whale watching. It makes the most elegant and classic European style Chardonnay and Pinot Noir wines especially from Hamilton Russell, Bouchard Finlayson and Newton Johnson. The Walker Bay District is also now producing outstanding

and consistent Pinotage, especially Southern Right. Recently plantings of Sauvignon Blanc, Merlot and Shiraz are also being experimented with. The cool climate is the sought after attribute in this area where vineyards benefit from persistent cooling winds from the very nearby ocean.

6. *a. Ernie Els.* The Big Easy is his biggest selling wine range exported worldwide. The great South African golfer also loved wine almost as much, and in the Millennium Year 2000 his wine estate crushed its first grapes and after ageing, his first vintage was released in 2004. The north-facing vineyards on the slopes of the Helderberg Mountain, near Stellenbosch made for ideal growing conditions especially for red varietals. His flagship Bordeaux blend is Signature, and his first love was Cabernet Sauvignon and Bordeaux blends. In 20 years he has expanded greatly, buying a neighbour's winery and now producing famous quality ranges of wines, some whites as well as his beloved reds. His range of wine brands are all based on golf terms, the Major Series, The Big Easy range and The Clubhouse Selection.

7. *a. Graham Beck.* In 1983 Graham Beck, an industrialist and entrepreneur bought the Madeba farm close to Robertson, which is inland east of Cape Town, in order to produce quality still wines and especially sparkling wines in the champagne manner. After some years the plantings became mainly Chardonnay and Pinot Noir grapes and Graham Beck became the hot spot for the Methode Cap Classique in South Africa. In 1994 Nelson Mandela served the Graham Beck Brut for his inauguration as President. Exactly 14 years later Barack Obama celebrated his Presidential win in 2008 with Graham Beck Brut, which he then continued to serve at many State Dinners held at the White House.

8. *c. Spier.* The winery is located close to the South African town of Stellenbosch. The history of this beautiful and sprawling winery dates back to as early as 1692, which makes it one of the most ancient wineries in South Africa. As well as a wide range of quality red and white wines, a hotel, restaurants and an entertainment centre, there is an eagle sanctuary. Their long-term Cheetah Outreach Centre has now moved 20 miles south of the wine farm. Spier's winery is owned by Dick Enthoven a South African billionaire businessman, who is also the owner of the global casual dining restaurant chain Nando's. In 2018 Spier won the Trophy award for the world's best Chenin Blanc from the IWSC Global Wine Competition.

9. *c. 29 Wine of Origin Districts.* The Wine of Origin Scheme set up in 1973 divides South African vineyards into geographical based regions, then districts and finally wards. There are five regions in the geographical unit of the Western Cape – Breede River Valley, Cape South Coast, Coastal Region,

Klein Karoo and Olifants River. Another five geographical units exist: Eastern Cape, Free State, KwaZulu-Natal, Limpopo and Northern Cape. The total South African winelands are divided up into 29 Wine of Origin Districts and within these there are 92 smaller wine wards.

10. *c. **Vin de Constance*** dessert wine was the favourite sweet wine of Napoleon, and served by kings at European palaces and the Tzars of Russia in the 18th and 19th centuries in preference to Yquem, Tokay, Madeira and Port. After losing the Battle of Waterloo, Napoleon was finally exiled by the British to the very remote Atlantic island of St Helena, and he arrived there on 15th October 1815, after ten weeks at sea. He died there 6 years later at the age of 51, of stomach cancer. Little exercise, over-eating and drinking wines to excess probably didn't help either. Over 300 litres of Vin de Constance were shipped over every year for his exclusive use, and he usually drank over a bottle of it a day. He called for and drank a last glass on his deathbed. Vin de Constance vineyards were destroyed by the Phylloxera wine blight in 1866. Then 120 years later the same Muscat grapes were planted and re-introduced, with the first 'new era' vintage being 1986. So once again Vin de Constance appears on lists of the world's top dessert wines.

ANSWERS TO QUIZ 64 – WINES OF SOUTH AFRICA – PART 2

1. *c. **KWV**.* KWV stands for 'Co-operative Winemakers Union of South Africa' in the Afrikaans language, and it was founded on 8 January 1918, the same year in which Nelson Mandela was born. KWV was created with Government funds and controls to provide minimum quality standards and unity for the wine farmers of South Africa and to ensure continuous improvement in the quality of South African wines and brandies. It weathered the international trade embargoes and restrictions placed upon it because of apartheid. In 1997 Nelson Mandela presented KWV with the President's Award for export achievement; in the same year it converted from a co-operative to a private company. For over 100 years it has been producing and exporting wines and brandies, nowadays to over 100 countries. Roodeberg is KWV's iconic wine brand, known worldwide for its red blend which was launched in 1949 and thus the 2019 release celebrated its 70th year as a wine legend.

2.   ***a. Delaire Graff Estate.*** The estate is owned by Laurence Graff the billionaire founder of Graff Diamonds which he started in London in 1960, and is now internationally renowned as one of the world's most exclusive diamond jewellery designers. He was born in Stepney, East London, and his father was a Jewish tailor. His estimated worth is currently over £4 billion. Laurence Graff bought the wine estate located near Stellenbosch in 2008 on his 70th birthday, and immediately began to build the luxury 5 star hotel, spa, restaurant, and state-of-the-art winery. The estate has around 20 hectares (50 acres) which are 50% planted with Bordeaux red varieties and then two whites, Chardonnay and Sauvignon Blanc. The most iconic wine is Laurence Graff Reserve which is almost 100% Cabernet Sauvignon; depending on vintage it sells for over £350 a bottle. It is probably the most expensive red wine from South Africa.

3.   ***c. Pinot Noir.*** Bouchard Finlayson, Newton Johnson and Paul Cluver produce some of South Africa's best quality Pinot Noirs, but the pioneer of top quality Pinot Noir is Hamilton Russell who in the 1970s planted his vineyards in the Walker Bay area. Before then nearly all Pinot Noir had been used in the production of sparkling wines. Professor Abraham Izak Perold in the 1920s introduced the Swiss BK5 Pinot Noir clone to South Africa and in 1927 Muratie Estate in Stellenbosch produced the first South African Pinot Noir. In the same year Professor Perold crossed this Pinot Noir with the Rhône Cinsaut grape, called Hermitage at that time, and invented the unique South African grape variety and wine, Pinotage. Pinot Noir plantings have grown by 60% in 10 years but still accounts for only 1.4% of total vines (Pinotage is 7.5%). Pinot Noir is the 7th most planted red grape and 12th overall grape variety.

4.   ***c. Vin de Constance Muscat.*** President Mandela drank less and less wine the older he got. Of course he could not drink when he was imprisoned on Robin Island for 27 years. On his inauguration he served Graham Beck sparkling wine to celebrate the momentous occasion, but later on in life the virtually teetotal Mandela preferred sweet wines – and Vin de Constance in particular – just to sip and contemplate. A 100 year gala international charity dinner was held in Washington DC in the United States, marking the centenary of Nelson Mandela's birth on 18 July 2018. It was attended by past US Presidents, royalty and many celebrities and all the 4 matching wines were donated by Klein Constantia, culminating in Vin de Constance Muscat with the celebratory dessert.

5.   ***c. Vergelegen Wines.*** Queen Elizabeth II has stayed at this historic house in extensive gardens and vineyards in Somerset West near Cape Town. In fact when it comes to British Royalty being entertained in the winelands of South

Africa, Vergelegen is second to none. Over the years it has hosted overnight stays for the Prince of Wales and the Duchess of Cornwall in 2011, Prince Philip the Duke of Edinburgh and Prince Edward the Duke of Kent in 2000, Prince Edward in 1997, Queen Elizabeth II and Prince Phillip in 1995– and not forgetting US President Bill Clinton and Mrs Hilary Clinton as guests of President Nelson Mandela in 1998. Queen Elizabeth still serves Vergelegen wines at functions held at Buckingham Palace. Their flagship wine is 'V' a 100% Cabernet Sauvignon.

6. *c. **Walker Bay.*** The first 'Burgundian' Chardonnays and Pinot Noirs were planted by Tim Hamilton Russell in the mid 1970s. He purchased the undeveloped 170 hectare vineyard site in 1975, after an exhaustive search for the most southerly place on which to make South Africa's top cool climate wines with enough sun and height. It is one of the closest vineyards to the sea, just behind the old fishing village of Hermanus (famous for whale watching) in Walker Bay, or more formally, the Hemel-en-Aarde appellation area. Before his pioneering stance nearly all Pinot Noir and Chardonnay were used in the production of sparkling wines. Pinot Noir and Chardonnay are still minority grapes for still table wine in South Africa, but in over 45 years the plantings of Pinot Nor have increased fivefold up to 1.4%, while Chardonnay has increased to 8%. Nowadays other top star producers of 'Burgundian' wines in Walker Bay are Bouchard-Finlayson and Newton Johnson. These Pinot Noirs are not now bargain buys any longer, except compared to the prices of Burgundies. If you like red and white Burgundy try one of these 'classic Burgundy style' wines and you won't be disappointed.

7. *c. **1,300 million bottles.*** South Africa on average produces 1.3 billion bottles of wine a year, or 10 million hectolitres. 2017 to 2019 were difficult years for wine production with extensive droughts occurring. It is the 9th largest wine producing nation in the world in terms of volume and the 8th largest exporter. About 40% of all wines are consumed domestically and 60% exported. There has been a great increase in prices and quality over the past 25 years (the post-apartheid era). The estimated 550 South African wine estates base some of their appeal on their 300 year heritage and history. Many South African wine farms claim starting dates before the year 1700, with the first wines having been produced in 1659. Here are 10 of the very highest quality wine estates still excelling after 300 years and stating their foundation year on their wine labels, Rustenburg 1682, Blaauwklippen 1682, Klein Constantia 1685, Groot Constantia 1685, Boschendal Winery 1688, Allée Bleue 1690, Spier 1692, Meerlust 1693, Rust en Vrede 1694 and Vergelegen 1700.

8. **c. Whale.** The Southern Right whale is quite rare but often still seen (giving swimming and diving lessons to their calves) just off the Hermanus town cliffs less than 2 miles from the vineyards. Southern Right wine estate is a small Pinotage and Sauvignon Blanc winemaking specialist, located on a strikingly beautiful 448 hectare property in Walker Bay. It was founded by Tim and (son) Anthony Hamilton Wright in 1994. With each bottle sold, Southern Right wine estate makes a contribution to worldwide whale conservation and the whale conservation in the immediate area.

9. **b. 1925.** The uniquely South African Pinotage grape had its beginnings in South Africa in 1925. Professor A. I. Perold (the first Professor of Viticulture at Stellenbosch University), wanted to develop a vine which was robust and resilient, and also made great red wine. He experimented with trying to clone a Pinot Noir vine with a Cinsaut vine (Hermitage), this resulted in the production of four seeds which he planted in his back garden. When he moved house the young vine stocks were forgotten, but saved by his junior colleague just before they were being grubbed up. The vines were grown and tasted yearly, and culled with only the strongest vines being propagated. After years of experimenting the first Pinotage wine was produced in small casks during 1941, and the first commercial planting was made in 1943. Thus the first vintage was in 1945, 20 years after the mating of the two different grape varieties. It was not until 1961 that Pinotage was mentioned on a wine label in South Africa.

10. **c. United Kingdom.** The United Kingdom is still in love with South African wines in terms of the value versus high quality dimension. From volume supermarket wine brands through to flagship wines stocked by the UK's top independent wine merchants, sales per annum are still increasing. The UK imports circa 25% of all South African wine exports in terms of value and volume. Germany is the next largest importer at circa 18% and the Netherlands is third at 10%. The Dutch import amount is the highest by far per capita/consumer figure, as the Netherlands only has 25% of the population of the UK, so their wine loyalty goes back well over 300 years to the Dutch East India Company starting the wine industry and trade in South Africa in the 17th century.

ANSWERS TO QUIZ 65 – MATCH WINES OF SOUTH AFRICA

1. **e. Cabernet Sauvignon.** Cederberg Five Generations is one of the top iconic wines of South Africa. It is made from old vines from a single vineyard and is then aged for 18 months in barriques. Expert wine critics say it has a classic French feel, and a taste of blackcurrants with tobacco and spice tones. Cabernet Sauvignon is the widest planted red grape variety in South Africa. Other great Cabernet Sauvignons are V from Vergelegen, Paul Sauer from Kanonkop and Kruger Family Reserve.

2. **c. Chenin Blanc.** Ken Forrester's FMC is a top Chenin Blanc from Ken the 'King of Chenin'. FMC is purported to stand for 'F– Magic Chenin'. It is an iconic wine made from using the best grapes from old vines which are all over 30 years old. FMC is fermented using natural yeasts, just on its lees, for 12 months in French oak barrels. Chenin Blanc is the most planted white grape variety in South Africa at about 20% of all wine grapes. Chenin Blanc is thought to be amongst the first cuttings planted in South Africa, brought over from France in 1655. It was called 'Steen' until the 1960s and only later appeared on wine labels as Chenin Blanc. It is a very versatile grape making immediate easy to drink fresh, fruity wines to oaked wines to age, and also Noble Late Harvest dessert wines.

3. **a. Pinot Noir.** This is still only a small minority grown grape in South Africa at around 1.4% of all plantings, but it is always of very high quality. Hamilton Russell is the pioneer 'Pinot' winemaker from Walker Bay, one of the most southerly vineyard areas in South Africa. Hamilton Russell only makes Pinot Noir and Chardonnay and has been doing so since 1975. Paul Cluver and Bouchard Finlayson are two other top quality Estates making both varieties in the same area.

4. **b. Pinotage.** Kanonkop Black Label at over £125 a bottle is an iconic Pinotage. It is made from the unique South African grape variety created in 1925 by Professor I.A. Perold, and is a cross between Pinot Noir and Cinsaut grape varieties. Other great Pinotages are Beyerskloof, Delheim and Rijks. Pinotage is now the third most planted red grape variety in South Africa.

5. **d. Chardonnay.** Warwick Wine Estate's, The White Lady was planted as a single vineyard wine in 2006. It has a silky yet an austere feel with rounded fruit and citrus limes and mineral finish. The first vintage released was not until 2011. Warwick Estate also have a range of wines called First Lady; this is because their winemaker is one of the first women to make wines in South

Africa. Chardonnay only really became popular in South Africa during the 1990s and is now the fourth most planted white grape.

6. *i. Stellenbosch.* Delaire Graff Wine Estate is one of the finest wine producers in South Africa. It was only launched in 2003 when Laurence Graff, a London diamond merchant and jeweller bought the Avantuur estate near Stellenbosch and then turned it into a world-class winery and exclusive retreat with luxury accommodation, a spa and fine dining. They now produce a wide range of wines from sparkling blends to still whites and red wines. Their entry wines are great quality and value and include a vibrant Sauvignon Blanc and a fruity Chenin Blanc. They also produce single vineyard Merlot, Shiraz, Pinotage and Cabernet Sauvignon reds. Their flagship wine is Laurence Graff Reserve which is a Cabernet Sauvignon blend and vintages sell for over £350 a bottle. Stellenbosch, which nestles in a valley of the Western Cape, just 30 miles east of Cape Town, is probably South Africa's most famous wine area. It is known predominantly for its top quality red wines including Cabernet Sauvignon, Merlot, Pinotage and Shiraz.

7. *h. Franschhoek.* Chamonix Wine Farm on the outskirts of Franschhoek is on a high south facing hillside. It has been making classic 'Burgundian style' Chardonnay and Pinot Noir wines for over three decades. It is owned by German-born entrepreneur and adventurer Chris Hellinger. The original farm has been making wines for around 350 years as it was part of one of the first wine estates in Franschhoek, the Huguenot Estate, La Cotte, which dates back to 1688. Franschhoek (French Corner), is a very pretty small wine town with some of the best restaurants in South Africa and only 50 miles east of Cape Town.

8. *f. Elgin.* Paul Cluver is the pioneer winemaker from the Elgin wine region which is 40 miles south-east of Cape Town. This cool valley has been the home of the Cluver family since 1896, when they planted the first vineyards in Elgin. The Cluver estate is now part of a UNESCO World Heritage Site. Its vineyards are planted up to a height of 450 metres on steep hillsides, and it is only 7 miles from the south coast. It is the only South African wine region surrounded by four mountains, which create a unique cool microclimate that produces some spectacular wines. Elgin produces cool climate Pinot Noirs, Chardonnays and Sauvignon Blanc wines which are elegant, restrained and aromatic with subtle stone fruit flavours.

9. *j. Walker Bay.* Southern Right is a wine estate owned by Hamilton Russell and founded in 1994 in the Walker Bay wine area. It is situated on the hills just behind the old fishing village of Hermanus, which has become the whale watching capital of South Africa. Their wine label features the rare Southern

Right whales which are often seen with their calves swimming and diving in Walker Bay, and with each bottle sold, Southern Right makes a contribution to their conservation in the area. They specialise in making two varieties, Pinotage and Sauvignon Blanc. Walker Bay is the nearest wine area to the Atlantic Ocean and one of the most southerly. It is famous for the 'Burgundian' stylish Pinot Noir, Chardonnay, and fresh, flinty Sauvignon Blancs.

10. *g. Paarl.* KWV was established by the South African government in 1918, (the same year Mandela was born) and became for decades the sole exporter of wines from South Africa. In 1997 it became one of the largest private wine companies in South Africa. It also has the largest capacity wine cellars in the world. Roodeberg their legendary red blend celebrated its 70th anniversary in 2019. Paarl is just 40 miles inland from Cape Town and just north of Stellenbosch. Today, there are over 14,000 hectares of vines; the first vineyards were planted surrounding the town of Paarl in the 17th century by Dutch settlers. Paarl also makes some of the best wine brandies in South Africa.

ANSWERS TO QUIZ 66 – ANAGRAMS – WINES OF SOUTH AFRICA

South African Wine Regions

1. *Walker Bay.* Situated on the Cape South Coast, and south-east of Cape Town, Walker Bay contains the well-known Hemel-en-Aarde Valley, home to the famous Hamilton Russell winery, with their distinguished duet of Pinot Noir and Chardonnay wines, assisted by the cool maritime climate off the Atlantic Ocean. Sauvignon Blanc also does well here.

2. *Elgin.* Located between the Walker Bay and Stellenbosch wine regions, and only about forty miles south-east of Cape Town, Elgin was, before the turn of the current century, primarily an apple-growing region. Only since the early 2000s have commercial vineyards started to be planted, sometimes converted from orchards. As with Walker Bay, some top quality Pinot Noir, Chardonnay, and Sauvignon Blanc are produced here.

3. *Constantia.* A tiny wine district on the outskirts of Cape Town. In the late eighteenth and early nineteenth century Constantia was famous for its sweet dessert wine. Indeed Jane Austen mentioned it in Sense and Sensibility, and so did Charles Dickens in his unfinished novel The Mystery

of Edwin Drood. Nowadays, Constantia is more well-known for its excellent Sauvignon Blanc. Other grapes grown in the region include Cabernet Sauvignon, Merlot and Chardonnay.

4. **Stellenbosch.** Situated close to Cape Town, the Stellenbosch wine region is the most prestigious in South Africa, and famous for containing so many of the Cape's top wine producers, including Meerlust, Vergelegen, and Kanonkop. Stellenbosch produces some of the greatest red wines in South Africa, from Cabernet Sauvignon, Syrah, and Merlot grapes, and some very fine white wines from Sauvignon Blanc, Chardonnay, and Chenin Blanc grapes.

5. **Swartland.** Lying north of Cape Town, in the Western Cape, Swartland was not particularly well-known as a wine region up to the end of the twentieth century. But from the early 2000s, talented young winemakers have transformed the region and are making seriously good wine, particularly from Cabernet Sauvignon, Syrah, and Pinotage reds, and Chenin Blanc and Sauvignon Blanc whites. The wines are complex and full of character, and produced from a myriad of microclimates, soils and vineyard sitings.

South African Grape Varieties

6. **Chenin Blanc.** Sometimes called 'Steen' in South Africa, Chenin Blanc was, until the late twentieth century, the first white grape that came to mind when one thought of South African white wine. To many people that remains the case, and indeed it is still the most widely planted grape variety in South Africa, though many other grapes are now competing for that space. Today, Chenin Blanc is also widely grown around the world.

7. **Cinsaut.** Spelt either Cinsaut or Cinsault, depending on where you are in the world, this grape variety, well-known in the Languedoc, is not as favoured these days with wine producers in South Africa as it used to be, owing to the rising popularity of Cabernet Sauvignon, Syrah and Pinotage. However, it has been grown here since the mid-nineteenth century, and is still produced for making both red and rosé wine.

8. **Pinotage.** This red grape is a crossing of Pinot Noir and Cinsaut. Cinsaut used to be known as Hermitage in South Africa, which explains the 'age' part of Pinotage. Even though it is now also grown, usually in small quantities, elsewhere in the world, it is South Africa that immediately comes to mind when one sees or hears the name Pinotage. The character of the wine can vary, depending on viticulture and vinification, but it is usually a fruity, full-bodied wine.

9. **Chardonnay.** Now widely grown in South Africa, particularly in the Cape's cooler vineyards, Chardonnay is also, of course, ubiquitous around the world.

Chardonnay is a well-loved noble grape variety, and in South Africa it is produced by both oaked and unoaked methods, producing rich flavours with notes of citrus and tropical fruits.

10. ***Colombard.*** This is a less well-known white grape variety, but is still widely grown in South Africa. It has been planted here since the early twentieth century, and was originally a crossing of Chenin Blanc and a grape called Heunisch Weiss (also known as Gouias Blanc). In South Africa, as well as being used as a base wine for distilling into brandy, it also produces single varietal, blended, and sparkling wines.

ANSWERS TO QUIZ 67 – WINE AND THE HOLLYWOOD MOVIES

1. ***a. Bollinger.*** In the Bond films, James Bond's favourite champagne was Bollinger, which was featured in 14 films. Back in 1978 Bond film franchise producer Cubby Broccoli struck a deal with the Bollinger family for it to become James Bond's exclusive choice of champagne in all the films from then on. In the Bond books by Ian Fleming (probably because Fleming was an avid drinker and knowledgeable fan of champagne and wine), James Bond is very fickle on his choice of champagne, dependent on his mood and the book; choosing between Bollinger, Dom Pérignon, Krug, Pommery, Taittinger and Veuve Clicquot, which were six of the best champagnes around when Ian Fleming wrote the Bond books.

2. ***b. Merlot.*** It is called Marilyn Merlot and the first vintage was launched in 1984 by a group of winemaker friends who were also fans of Marilyn Monroe films. It is made in Napa Valley and the 30th anniversary edition, vintage 2014, again sold out fast, even though it sells for over $50. Each year the wine label features a different historic colour photograph of Marilyn Monroe in one of her movies. The first label of 1984 was entitled 'Maneater' with a sexy face close-up photo. The wines regularly win awards for quality and are so popular that other Marilyn wine ranges have been successfully launched including Norma Jean, Marilyn Cabernet, Marilyn Meritage, Sauvignon Blonde and Blonde de Noir, many of these wines sell out on release.

3. ***b. Princess Leia.*** Corellian wines were a favourite of Galactic smugglers Han Solo and Chewbacca, especially when hiding out on the planet of Monsua Nebula from Imperial TIE Fighters. Han Solo offered Princess Leia a glass of

Corellian wine, but as she thought he was a 'scoundrel' trying to seduce her, she threw the wine in his face. What a waste, as it is obviously very high quality wine mentioned and shown in seven of the Star Wars films.

4. **b. Chianti.** In the film Silence of the Lambs, Hannibal Lecter says to Dr Clarice Starling that 'I ate his liver with some fava beans and a nice Chianti'. It is in fact a coded message and warning to Dr Starling stating clearly (to the medically trained) that he is not taking his psychiatric medication of MAOI drugs, as they are the three foods that could be fatal if you are taking that particular strong anti-depressant. In the book Hannibal Lecter says 'Amarone' not 'Chianti' which would have been the ideal wine match for liver, but the film director felt that most of the audience would not know what an Amarone was, so it was changed to Chianti.

5. **c. Ratatouille.** In the Pixar/ Disney animated film an ambitious young country rat named Remy aims to be a top chef in Paris. Along the way in the film some very famous great wines are mentioned and consumed, including Côte-Rotie, 1961 Château Latour and 1947 Château Cheval Blanc. After the film was released Disney marketed a Ratatouille wine of French Chardonnay which was sold in 18 US states.

6. **c. Brad Pitt.** He paid £30,000 for a Château d'Yquem dessert wine in Mirabelle, a top London restaurant. He is well known for buying top rated wines in restaurants around the world. Brad Pitt is a great lover of fine wines and drinks a lot of the best vintages and has a large fine wine collection. He and Angelina Jolie own a large wine estate in Provence making Château Miraval, which is one of the best rosé wines in Provence.

7. **c. The Judgement of Paris.** The film is fact-based, telling the story of the 1976 blind tasting in Paris at which a selection of top Napa Valley Californian wines, both reds and whites, defeated the best French First Growth wines of Bordeaux and Burgundy. Best of all, the judges were all French. The results shook the wine world to its foundations and showed that France no longer ruled the world of premium wines.

8. **b. Bardolino.** Michael Corleone and Kay drink a lot of red Italian wines especially Bardolino, and at his son's communion party in The Godfather II Bardolino is served to everyone. The Godfather films have a code for alcohol, scotch for male only business, red wine for family occasions and wives, and white wine only at summer parties.

9. **c. Withnail and I.** This British film was made in 1987, and the film is about two out of work actors who love wine, having a very boozy holiday weekend in a cottage in the Lake District. Withnail summed up the good life as 'we want the finest wine available to humanity' and it was Uncle Monty who

brought it along; it was Château Margaux 1953. Château Margaux vineyards have been making wine since the 12th century but it was not until 1815 that the beautiful Château 'the Versailles of the Medoc' was built. In the 1855 Official Classification only Margaux got a score of 20 out of 20. It became the first of the 1st Growths.

10. **b. Goldfinger.** In this 1964 film James Bond (Sean Connery), as we know, has exquisite taste in champagne and he can be a bit of a champagne snob, you must serve it at the right temperature. Modern taste would state that he is serving Dom Pérignon much too cold at 38F (3c) The recommended temperature now is minimum 45F to 50F maximum (7c to 10c).

ANSWERS TO QUIZ 68 – WINE AND POLITICS

1. **c. Over 50,000 bottles.** It has been estimated that Winston Churchill drank at least that amount of vintage champagne during his whole lifetime. Even when Prime Minster during World War II Churchill drank two bottles of vintage champagne a day, mainly with meals. Well over 80% of this total (42,000 bottles) was Pol Roger vintage champagne. It was the only champagne he drank for the last 50 years of his long life. After he died Pol Roger launched their flagship vintage champagne named Cuvée Winston Churchill, which is 80% Pinot Noir and 20% Chardonnay as he liked it, and it is aged 10 years before being released.

2. **c. President Nixon.** He was notorious for drinking only the finest wine himself, especially Château Lafite Rothschild, his favourite red wine. At large parties he would serve inferior wine to the large number of invited guests with all the wine bottles including his personal 'Lafite Rothschild' wrapped in white linen to hide the labels.

3. **b. Parliament House of Commons.** The cellars under the House of Commons store over 30,000 bottles, kept in seven vast cellar rooms. A further UK Government store of wine is in St. James, with a further estimated 40,000 bottles. Buckingham Palace stores another cellar of special bottles of wine for government and state occasions. So London is awash with government wine. Answer a) the French wine store is only 15,000 bottles of wine in cellars under the Elysée Palace. The French tend to drink their wine much earlier/younger than the British who love old vintages, and therefore they don't store and age as many wines. Answer c) The USA Government does not have a large store of

wine, except some quantities of champagne kept in a small Senate cellar. The White House has no official wine cellar, just a small storage area about the size of a walk-in cupboard.

4. **b. Mateus Rosé.** Saddam Hussein loved this sweet, semi sparkling rosé wine from Portugal. He wasn't alone in loving Mateus Rosé, it was drunk by the Queen and by Jimi Hendrix, Elton John, Cliff Richard and many other celebrities. It was launched in 1942 and has sold over 1 billion bottles since its launch. The unique and iconic flattish bottle (inspired by the flasks used by soldiers in the First World War) has contributed to the wine's enormous success worldwide. In the late 1970s over 4 million cases were sold worldwide and this one wine accounted for about 40% of all Portuguese table wine exports. After the Iraq War was over it was discovered that each of Saddam Hussein's palaces had large stockpiles of Mateus Rosé, by far his favourite wine.

5. **c. UK.** This is a huge change that has happened over the last 20 years. The House of Commons cellars and all the Government wine store used to be full of French wine, especially old vintages of red Bordeaux classed growths and vintage champagne. Now over 60% of all the wines stored are English. The sparkling wine mostly served at State Banquets at Buckingham Palace is also English sparkling wine not champagne.

6. **a. Neville Chamberlain.** He was an avid wine drinker, especially reds. He said he needed to drink fine wine after his meetings negotiating with Hitler. Answer b) Hitler was a teetotaller and a vegetarian. His father had been an alcoholic so he never drank. Answer c) President Donald Trump now never drinks alcohol. This is said to be due to his older brother Freddie's death from alcoholism.

7. **b. Fixin.** It is at the northern end of the Côte de Nuits in Burgundy. It is not a very famous commune, and is known for producing good value red village and premier cru Burgundies. Napoleon did once visit the Clos vineyard for refreshments, so the vineyard owners immediately renamed it Clos Napoleon. Chambertin was always Napoleon's favourite red wine, which he always travelled with on his expeditions.

8. **c. Donald Trump.** Trump Winery was bought by President Trump in 2011 (it was formerly the Kluge Estate). It had been planted in 1999 with a selection of French grape varieties. At 227 acres (91 hectares) of vineyards it is claimed to be the largest wine estate in Virginia, and the largest vineyard planted with European grapes on the whole of the East Coast wine area of the USA. It is now operated and managed by Trump's eldest son Eric. It produces around 36K to 40K cases of wine a year. Some of the wines have won medals and international wine awards including their Blanc de Blancs sparkling wine.

9. ***c. Pol Roger.*** This filly was one of Churchill's favourite racehorses and one of his most successful. He asked permission to name it after his favourite champagne and the Roger family agreed. He continued throughout his lifetime to be one of Pol Roger's most illustrious admirers and loyal customers. Vintage Pol Roger was the only champagne he drank by choice for his last 50 years of life. After his death a new flagship champagne was launched – Cuvée Winston Churchill Vintage Pol Roger.

10. ***c. Pol Pot.*** He was a revolutionary and the ruler of Cambodia from 1975 to 1979. During his short rule Cambodian society was decimated by his party the Khmer Rouge who were trying to take the country back to a pre-industrial age and agrarian socialist society and utopia. During the fewer than 5 years of his rule, a quarter of the population was killed (circa 2 million people). It was termed the Killing Fields or the Cambodian Genocide. Pol Pot seemed sophisticated and charming and had spent over 5 years in Paris being educated and gaining a great love of French wine, especially fine reds. When back in Cambodia he imported fine wines from France for himself and his elite Khmer Rouge comrades to drink on a daily basis while the general Cambodian population was starving.

ANSWERS TO QUIZ 69 – WINE AND RELIGION

1. ***c. 12th century.*** It was not until the Middle Ages, in 1215, that Pope Innocent III brought in transubstantiation of wine in the Eucharist Mass of the Catholic Church, when it was then believed that the holy wine changed into the actual blood of Jesus Christ. Before that time wine had been used in the service as only a remembrance of the blood of Jesus Christ, shed for us sinners. It was first challenged by various 14th century religious reformers, John Wycliffe in particular.

2. ***Dionysus.*** He was worshipped by Mycenaean Greeks as early as 1100 BC, especially at harvest time. He was the son of Zeus. As well as the Greek God of Wine he was also the God of fertility, orchards and fruit, vegetation, insanity, ritual madness, religious ecstasy, festivity and theatre in ancient Greek religion and myth. He was quite a busy fellow.

3. ***Bacchus.*** He was the Roman God of Wine, Fertility and Agriculture, really copied from Dionysus the Greek God of Wine. Bacchus was revered since the 5th century BC. He was the son of Jupiter (Zeus in Greek mythology) and

he wandered the earth, showing people how to grow vines and process the grapes for wine. Many celebrations were called Bacchanalian because of the copious wine drinking, and the resulting Roman orgies and debauchery sometimes went on for days.

4. **c. Renetutet.** She was depicted as a woman with the head of a cobra. As Goddess of Wine she enabled abundant harvests and wine was drunk copiously to honour her. In her other role of fertility goddess, Renetutet was known as the 'Lady of Fertile Fields' and 'Lady of Granaries'. She often had shrines dedicated to her near a wine press or vat, so she could receive the offerings of the winemakers.

5. **c. Tuscany.** Italian Vin Santo was born in the 14th century in the province of Siena. It was holy wine used in church services and to heal the sick. It is a sweet dessert wine now produced all over Italy, especially Tuscany. Vin Santo can be produced in various sweetness levels, ranging from dry to luscious and can vary in colour from gold to deep amber. It is also called Vino Santo in Italy.

6. **a. Armenian.** The first wine production used in religious services was in Armenia in 4200 BC. The first evidence of wine made from grapes is from Georgia in 6000 BC, but not used in religious services then. The Armenian Cave winery was right next to a cemetery, and it is thought that their religious drinking rituals were likely to involve ceremonies in honour of the dead.

7. **b. New York.** The Brotherhood Winery is still producing wine today and was started by monks in 1839. It was the only winery in NY State producing wine throughout Prohibition, as it made altar wine for the Catholic Church. It now makes a range of classic varieties, as well as altar wine.

8. **c. Noah.** He planted his vineyard after the Great Flood. It is the first mention of alcohol in the Bible and Noah becomes the first drunk! Thus the discovery of fermentation is also attributed to Noah.

9. **b. France & Spain.** These two countries now dominate altar/communion wine sales to the Catholic and Anglican churches in the UK. Altar wine used to be produced from UK British wine and Cyprus wine. They are now usually fortified wines of 15% to 18% so they keep longer.

10. **a. Egyptian.** Since 4000 BC, the Feast of Drunkenness originated as a once a month religious festival, but priests soon felt that this was too frequent as it disrupted daily life. It then became an annual event. Ideally, those involved in the religious celebrations are served with large amounts of alcohol and are allowed to drink until they get completely drunk and fall asleep. Some experts claim that the participants of this sacred festival engaged in drunken sex orgies as a way of celebrating Hathor, a goddess of love and fertility of the land.

ANSWERS TO QUIZ 70 – WINE SCANDALS AND FRAUDS

1. **a. Austria.** In 1985 some Austrian vineyards were convicted of adding antifreeze to their wines to make them seem sweeter, and more full-bodied, in the style of a late harvest wine. The scandal was uncovered by German laboratories doing tests on imported wines from Austria. Headlines of the wine scandal went around the world. The short-term effect was total collapse of Austria's exports of wine. The longer term effect was that Austria replanted many vineyards and concentrated on high value dry white wines from the Grüner Veltliner grape variety, instead of previously producing cheaper sweet wines. Austria also introduced the strictest wine laws in the world to stop another scandal from ever happening again. Unfortunately, many people are still prejudiced against Austrian wine, yet the price and quality are now high, and 30% of their production, at 200 million euros, is exported mainly to Germany and Switzerland.

2. **c. Death by hanging.** This was the extreme penalty for adulterating or diluting wines in medieval Germany. This could also be the maximum sentence for knowingly selling adulterated or diluted wine. If this fraud had not been done on a large scale, the two other penalties of branding, or being put in the local stocks and beaten, were usually administered. The stocks were used as a penalty for a first offence.

3. **b. Thomas Jefferson.** In 1985 a single bottle claiming to be a Château Lafite vintage 1787, and once owned by Thomas Jefferson, was auctioned at Christie's in London for £105,000. It was in an 18th century hand-blown green glass bottle, with the year and the initials TJ engraved on it. It became the most expensive old wine single bottle ever to be sold at auction. It was from a collection of 18th century bottles of wine said to be found behind a wall in a Paris cellar. They are deemed to be fakes but nobody has been successfully prosecuted. A very readable book entitled 'The Billionaire's Vinegar' by Benjamin Wallace was published in 2007, about the strange story behind the world's most expensive bottle of wine.

4. **b. Sassicaia.** In the year 2000 Italian police found a warehouse full of over 20,000 bottles labelled as the Super Tuscan Sassicaia 1995. They were all fakes and were being sold across Italy, sometimes out of the back of one of the fraudster's Peugeot van, for over 100 euros a bottle. The wine in the fake bottles of Sassicaia was cheap Sicilian Nero d'Avola red, a totally different grape variety to Sassicaia, and worth less than 10 euros per bottle. It is estimated that over 1 million bottles of fake wine is exported from

Italy annually, but with better wine testing many of these fakes are being discovered early. Sassicaia (Bolgheri, Tuscany) is the only single vineyard DOC in Italy, and they now insert electronic chips in their labels to stop fraud.

5. *b. Merlot & Syrah.* Gallo Wines of Modesto, California sourced its Red Bicyclette Pinot Noir wine brand from a large wine cooperative in the Languedoc in the South of France. It very quickly became a best seller in the USA and 18 million bottles were sold between 2006 and 2008. Unfortunately, it was proved that only a tiny amount of Pinot Noir was in the bottles, if any; nearly all the contents were a Merlot and Syrah blend which was much cheaper to source than Pinot Noir. The Fraud was discovered in 2008 when the French Wine Fraud Agency realised that the cooperative was selling Gallo more Pinot Noir than was produced in the entire Languedoc, and at a price below that normally charged for bulk Pinot Noir sourced from that region. In 2010, ten people from the cooperative, wine merchant, broker, and wine growers were all prosecuted and only given suspended sentences and fines. Who says crime does not pay, as it has been estimated that the fraud made 7 to 8 million euros extra profit for the perpetrators. Gallo was never implicated and there were no complaints by the drinkers in the USA, they loved the taste!

6. *a. Rudy Kurniawan.* He made a great fortune trading in rare old wines, the trouble was he was bottling them himself. The world's biggest wine forger faked over £100 million of rare old wines which were mainly sold at auctions worldwide. In one auction alone in 2006 Kurniawan sold $24.7 million of wine. He was young, charming, mysterious, and seemingly wealthy. He had a connoisseur's knowledge of old fine wines and a super-taster's palate. In blind tastings he could usually identify all the fine wines, so he impressed a lot of wine experts. At his cellar in his home in Arcadia, just north of LA, he had all the tools he needed, a printing press, old bottles and correctly aged paper for labels. He travelled extensively, buying up very old bottles of mediocre wine. He then did his magic of blending the old wine within his stock of young wines from California. He made them taste plausible and his tampered bottles looked perfect for the vintage and Château or Domaine. He managed to fool eminent wine experts for over seven years. He was not arrested and jailed until 2013. Sour Grapes is a TV documentary on Netflix, and a book entitled 'In Vino Duplicates' by Peter Hillman; both tell the story of this, the world's largest wine fraud.

7. *a. Beaujolais.* 53 Beaujolais vineyard owners and winemakers were arrested in 2008 for admitting that they had illegally added extra sugar to their Beaujolais wines to increase alcohol levels by 2% to 3% in poor unripe vintages, especially 2004. They were trying to increase the ABV level to 13.5%

from 11%, which they said was unsaleable. All the winemakers were convicted and given high fines averaging £20,000. The supermarkets selling them 600 tonnes of sugar were also convicted and fined. Chaptalisation (the adding of sugar) is sometimes allowed by the French wine authorities in particularly poor vintages, but only to add up to 2% alcohol. Beaujolais Crus now seem to have improved in sales and quality.

8.   *b. Penfolds.* Police in China in 2018 arrested 11 people and seized more than 50,000 fake bottles of wine labelled as Australian Penfolds bin 707, and China's top wine, Changyu. Other branded fake wines were also found in the police raids. The total value is estimated to top £11 million. Penfolds bin 707 retails for circa £400 plus; these fake bottles were being sold online for £100 throughout China. China is now the third largest importer of bottled wine, and fakes and forgeries are increasing enormously. Fakers are much more expert, and the days when they misspelled back labels have gone. Forgers misspelled Austrlia (sic) on a back label of Oxford Landing wines in 2008, which was not noticed for 2 years.

9.   *a. Languedoc.* British consumers have recently been victims of one of France's biggest ever wine frauds, when 66 million ordinary bottles of wine, worth £4 each, were passed off as Châteauneuf-du-Pape selling for £30 plus, or other Côtes du Rhône top appellations. An investigation by the French trading standards agency has found that up to 15 per cent of the annual output of the Côtes du Rhône appellation from 2013 to 2016 was counterfeit. The CEO of France's largest bulk wine négociant, and wholesaler Raphaël Michel, were charged with passing off Vin de Table and Vin de Pays as top quality Rhône wines, using Rhône bottles and fake labels. They were just cheaply made Languedoc wines from ripe grapes that tasted like a Rhône wine.

10. *a. Domaine de la Romanée-Conti (DRC).* Maureen Downey is the world's leading expert on wine forgeries. She testified for the United States government in Kurniawan's wine fraud trial in 2013, when he was convicted for the largest ever wine fraud, by forging between £100 million and £200 million of fine old wines (see answer 6 above). The experts' consensus is Domaine de la Romanée-Conti is the most counterfeited wine, especially as so many of its vintages are stratospherically priced, and thus worth forging. Luckily for the rich and famous wine lovers, the list of fine wines that counterfeiters like to make is very short. The top 20 are all European wines from decades past, the top 14 are from France (Lafite, Latour, Le Pin, Petrus etc), and the other 6 are from Italy. Unfortunately, today with good digital technology and winemaking/faking expertise rising, some wine experts are

saying that between 10% and 20% of all fine wines sold in the world are fraudulent. They may taste fine, but they are not what the labels on the bottles state them to be.

ANSWERS TO QUIZ 71 – CRAZY AND WEIRD W

1. ***c. Sauvignon Blanc.*** It is from New Zealand, a and acidic 'kittenish' wine from Coopers Creek wine Marlborough region. Odd name but a good quality drink youngest available. Chenin Blanc a) is a fruitier and fuller bodied wine, where the best examples are from South Africa and the Loire Valley in France. Catarratto (b) is a prolific white wine grape grown extensively in Sicily.

2. ***b. Fairview.*** The owner and winemaker is Charles Back; he was originally and primarily a goat cheesemaker, with a small vineyard attached. One day his herd of goats escaped and ran through his vineyards, where they ate only the plumpest and ripest grapes. This inspired him to name his new wine 'Goats do Roam'. It is made from a blend of Rhône grapes and became an instant bestseller in the UK and USA. The French tried but failed to ban the new wine, as it sounded and tasted like Côtes du Rhône.

3. ***a. Amarone.*** These special red wines are made from Valpolicella in the Veneto wine region, between Verona and Venice. They are made mainly from Corvina grapes, blended with up to three other grape varieties, including Rondinella, and the usual ABV is 15%+. Before fermentation they are left on mats in the sun, or hung on trellises to semi dry out, concentrating the grape juice. Ripasso Valpolicella is made from adding left over Amarone partially dried grape pulp to the grape juice must, then put in large barrels to add body and sweetness. It is often a bargain, especially compared to Amarone.

4. ***b. New York.*** Birthday Cake Vineyards of Upper New York State, make 5 or 6 varieties of cake inspired wines. The best seller is cheesecake white, with a tangy vanilla taste. Their rosé is a wine called Strawberry Shortcake, and the best selling red is Black Forest Gateau. They're not cheap, and sell mainly to the young set in New York and California.

5. ***b. Germany.*** Lukas Krauss is a rebel winemaker; his Pornfelder wine is made from Dornfelder grapes, and a changing blend of Portuguese grapes. Pornfelder's label has an erotic design of two scantily clad porn stars embracing a bottle.

6. ***c. 20% ABV.*** It used to be called a bum's wine, 'brown bag' wine. It became the go-to wine for alcoholics and down and outs, because of its strong alcohol content and it was sweet. It was rebranded and relaunched in 2018, in sexy black bottles, both a Chardonnay and a red blend, and now at only 13.5% ABV. It appeals to the young and trendy rock and roll set from the West Coast.

7. ***b. Gik from Spain.*** The blue colour is a totally natural process achieved by grape skin contact with blue flower petals (1%) during the initial fermentation process; there are no chemicals used. It is an organic natural wine made in the Basque country near to Bilbao. There are now about six other blue wines being marketed in Europe.

8. ***b. Quady Wines.*** Andrew Quady was formerly a fireworks maker, and now he makes 'firework-like spectacular wines'. He started with Starboard, using the same grapes as Port, but it is illegal if made in USA to call it Port, thus Starboard. He now has a range of three sweet Muscat wines. He is seen as the leading dessert winemaker in California. Essensia, Elysium and Deviation are his dessert wines, made from the Orange Muscat grape. He also makes an Electra Moscato range, a Palomino Fino (like a sherry) and two exotic vermouths.

9. ***b. Sexy Tart.*** This is just a rude term, not a wine name/brand yet (as far as is known). a) Sassy Bitch is a brand of Chilean wines from Central Valley; there are 5 grape varieties in the range including Pinot Noir and Chardonnay. They are best premium sellers in the USA, and won a best buy award in Wine Enthusiast Magazine. c) Stu Pedasso is a red Zinfandel from Sonoma County in California, and is a highly rated wine. Other very rude wine brands are – 'If you see Kay' is a red blend from Paso Robles, California (at over £50 a bottle) and 'Fat Bastard' range is from France.

10. ***c. Veuve Clicquot.*** In 2010, a group of divers found 168 bottles of champagne in a shipwreck of a trade schooner on the bottom of the Baltic Sea, just off the coast of Finland. They had been lying there, 160 feet below the surface, for over 170 years. On opening the champagne it was very well preserved and in near perfect condition. Some of the bottles were from Veuve Clicquot, founded in 1772. They were vintages from the late 1830s. So Veuve Clicquot has now sunk 300 bottles and 150 magnums in the Baltic Sea at 50 metres depth to age for 50 years. They were placed there to age in 2014, so they will be recovered to drink in 2064.

ANSWERS TO QUIZ 72 – ODD WINE NAMES AND EVEN ODDER LABELS

1. ***a. Red. Grenache 66% Syrah 34%.*** They are from the Côtes du Ventoux in the Rhône Valley, France. It has become a real marketing success in the USA and UK. Old Git was changed to Old Fart for the American market, as the term 'Git' was not well known in the US. The rest of the words on the label stayed the same. In the USA there is a range of T-shirts, baseball caps and talking neckties, as well as a new sparkling 'Old Fart'.

2. ***b. Hungary.*** Bull's Blood is now named Egri Bikaver, which was thought to be more upmarket. The story is that over 500 years ago when the Turks were besieging the walled town of Eger after a long battle, the Eger soldiers were so brave and ferocious and their beards were dyed red (from wine), but the Turks logically thought that they were drinking bulls' blood to gain ferocity, so they retreated in disarray, and Eger town was saved; thus they called their wine Bull's Blood for 500 years.

3. ***b. Marilyn Monroe Merlot.*** This wine is very popular with wine collectors in the USA and Marilyn fans. It is from Napa Valley and the initial vintage of 1985 now sells for over $3,500 a bottle. A new vintage is released each year on 1st June, Marilyn Monroe's birthday.

4. ***a. Beaujolais.*** Pisse-Dru sounds like a rude name, but it is fresh, good quality Gamay wine – the name is an old French expression describing how readily great quality grape juice runs out of grapes that are well ripened. It translates as 'Thick Piss' which is also a French winemaker's boast to say he is particularly proud of his special wine.

5. ***c. Writer's Block.*** The name of this flagship wine from Flagstone Winery was born when SA wine laws would not allow (blocked you from) indicating if your top wine was from a single vineyard, so they called this single vineyard wine Writer's Block. It is one of the earliest single vineyard terroir wines in South Africa. It is the highest vineyard in the area, planted in ancient granite soil with added unique minerality.

6. ***b. Canada.*** In the Okanagan Valley in British Columbia, Western Canada, Blasted Church was exactly that. When they bought their vineyard land, there was an old abandoned church in the middle of the site. They therefore had to dynamite it, 'Blast', to plant the rest of their vineyard. Founded in 2002, the winery now produces around 25,000 cases from 17 hectares, and there are about six different wines in the widening range. The top wine is 'The Big Bang

Theory', and all their wine labels have illustrations of vicars and church scenes on them.

7. ***a. Pink.*** Of course Sex is a provocative pink sparkling wine with gushing bubbles – what else? It is a Brut blend of Zinfandel, Sangiovese, Chardonnay, Riesling, and Muscat – quite a blend! It is made by Mawby Winery in Michigan, on the Leelanau Peninsula.

8. ***c. Riesling.*** Dr Loosen from the Mosel in Germany makes the Naked Grape range of four wines, which started with his Riesling, and are now all best sellers in both the UK and USA. Dr Loosen has made wines of great finesse from the very steep slopes of the Mosel Valley for over 200 years, mainly from vines of over 60 years old. The Naked Grape range is Dr Loosen's entry brand from the Pfalz region, producing good value examples from pure quality grapes.

9. ***c. South Africa.*** Rude Boy Chardonnay was first launched in South Africa in 1999. Another innovative label from importers Western Wines. The back label warns, in red type, 'when this bottle of wine is chilled, Rude Boy will reveal all. Put Rude Boy in the fridge and when cold enough his white shorts disappear and he becomes a full frontal nude'. A popular brand with the young and the gay. Rude Girl has now joined him on supermarket shelves, with a surprisingly good Shiraz. Full bodied and very fruity, she's at her best at just the right temperature. And when she is warmed up enough her dress magically disappears; she is more discreet, as it is a back view and she is wearing white knickers. In 2018 Brave New Wine Rude Boy was launched, from Western Australia. It is a fresh summery blend of Grenache, Shiraz, Vermentino and Tempranillo.

10. ***b. Sicily.*** Wild Cat wine is made from Catarratto, which is a white grape variety indigenous to Sicily. In fact, it is their most widely grown grape (circa 30%). Catarratto was originally used to make Marsala sweet fortified wine. It is now also grown in other parts of southern Italy and even Australia. It makes full bodied white wines with lemon notes. There is also now a Wild Cat Riesling from Sicily.

ANSWERS TO QUIZ 73 – THE GUINNESS BOOK OF RECORDS AND WINES

1. **b. 6000 to 5500 BC.** The oldest chemical evidence of wine being made and consumed is from Georgia, in a Neolithic village excavated just 50km south of Tbilisi. The wine residue was found on the remains of large clay pots which looked like they had been used for fermentation and storage. The latest evidence shows that wine was being made and drunk over 8,000 years ago.

2. **b. Luxembourg City.** Restaurant Chiggeri in Luxembourg City has a wine list of over 1,746 different varieties of wine. To qualify, all wines on the list have had to be available for over a year. Paris is second with restaurant Tour d'Argent's wine list. London's Hide restaurant in Mayfair has the longest wine list in England. The largest restaurant wine cellar in the world is in Tampa Florida, at Bern's Steakhouse. It keeps 500,000 wines in its cellar, and has a 180 page wine list.

3. **c. 4,100 bottles.** The largest wine bottle in the world (13 ft 9 ins tall) was made and filled for a charity fundraising event in Switzerland in 2014.

4. **a. Commandaria, Cyprus.** The Guinness Book of Records traces Commandaria's wine origins back to before 2000 BC. It also has the world record for the oldest Appellation Contrôlée wine. b) Château de Goulaine in the Loire region of France dates back to 1000 AD. c) Schloss Johannisberg in Germany dates back to 1100 AD when it was a Benedictine Monastery.

5. **b. Italy.** In 2013, two Italian wine merchants were arrested in Italy for faking over 400 bottles of Romanée-Conti Grand Cru wines. French police discovered this lucrative label fraud, which it is estimated netted the fraudsters over £2 million.

6. **b. £102,000.** The specially designed bottle was a crystal decanter made by Lalique of France. Sold at a charity auction in Hong Kong, all proceeds going to the Nature Conservancy charity. Robert Parker and other wine critics had given this 1863 vintage Niepoort Port a perfect score of 100 points.

7. **b. Japan.** The NEC Systems Technology Company made the first Robot Sommelier in 2008 in Tokyo. It can taste and recommend between 30 to 40 wines, and choose the best wines to match and complement the food courses chosen by diners.

8. **a. Cyprus.** According to the Guinness Book of Records, Cyprus and its Commandaria wines first introduced restricted areas for vine planting in

1223 AD. It was almost 500 years later that Chianti introduced protected vineyard areas in mainland Europe (1716 AD). Tokaji in Hungary was next in 1730 AD. It was not until 1935 that France first introduced the wide-ranging Appellation Contrôlée system for all their wine areas and vineyards.

9. ***b. 125 million bottles.*** The vast 54 acres of wine cellars dug out for KWV Winery in Paarl, South Africa, have now become a tourist attraction. Part of the enormous cellar system is still used for storing KWV's wines, port-styles, and brandies.

10. ***c. 49 champagne bottles.*** This feat was done by a top sommelier in Moldova in 2019. He cut the tops/necks off 49 champagne bottles in 30 seconds using a special sabre sword. Just for interest, the world record for opening bottles of wine with a corkscrew is 17 bottles in 30 seconds.

ANSWERS TO QUIZ 74 – FAMOUS PEOPLE AND THEIR WINES – PART 1

1. ***a. Serge Hochar.*** From Chateau Musar in the Bekaa Valley, the best vineyard area in Lebanon. It is like a top Bordeaux château blended with the Arabian Nights exotic fantasy. Gaston Hochar, Serge's father, founded the estate in 1930, after returning from Bordeaux with vine cuttings. Serge became winemaker in 1959 and has produced fine vintages each year until he died in 2014; even throughout the 15 year civil war (1975–90). Chateau Musar is a changing blend of Cabernet Sauvignon, Carignan, and Cinsault, and is released only after 7 years of ageing in small barrels and bottle.

2. ***c. Jay Z.*** Who owns, helps blend and markets the 'Ace of Spades' luxury and very expensive champagne. Jay Z bought the Champagne House 'Armand de Brignac' in 2014 for $200million. It sells for over £250 a bottle and many rappers and black singers prefer it to Roederer Crystal. 50 Cent also owns a champagne – he launched 'Le Chemin de Roi' (The King's Path) in 2018, which sells for over £1,000 a bottle. So far Ice Cube does not own a Champagne House/Brand.

3. ***c. Emperor Sulla.*** He was the first Dictator Emperor in Roman history to seize power by force. He became the First Dictator of the First Republic in 82 BC. His large Falerian vineyards, which added greatly to his wealth by

selling to the Roman gentry, were sited in Campania and made from the white Aglianico grape.

4. *a. Gerard Depardieu.* He is a proper passionate winemaker and vineyard owner, with three wine estates. Château de Tigne is in the Loire Valley; he also jointly owns La Croix de Peyrole in Lussac St-Emilion, and owns Le Bien Decide in Herault, Languedoc. Additionally, he owns three restaurants. He is also a legendary wine drinker, and has claimed to drink up to 14 bottles a day starting with champagne before 10am. He renounced his French citizenship in 2012 and took up Russian citizenship and residency in Russia and Belgium.

5. *a. Chianti, Italy.* Sting produces six wines from his wine estate 'Il Palagio' in deepest Tuscany. His flagship wine is a Super Tuscan (IGT) of Sangiovese, Merlot and Cabernet Sauvignon named 'Sister Moon'. All the six wines are named after his famous songs. His Chianti is 'When We Dance', all have been highly praised by wine critics.

6. *b. Château Miraval.* Brad Pitt and Angelina Jolie bought Château Miraval in 2011, and partnered with the Perrin family from Château de Beaucastel (of Châteauneuf-du-Pape) to help produce the wine. Brad and Angelina got married in the Château's chapel in August 2014. Château Miraval is one of the best rosés in the Côtes de Provence region. It is made from a blend of grapes featuring Cinsault, Grenache, Rolle, and Syrah. It has also won many wine awards.

7. *c. Steven Spurrier.* He organised the famous 'Judgement of Paris' blind tasting of top red Bordeaux and Burgundy whites, pitted against the best of California's wines. California won, which was a huge upset for the French wine industry. Steven Spurrier also ran a wine shop and wine school in Paris for many years. His Dorset vineyard 'Bride Valley' had its first vintage in 2014. Sadly Steven died in early 2021.

8. *b. Michigan.* Tony Ciccone, Madonna's father, started planting his vineyards in 1995. The Ciccone Estate now produces both red and white wines. There is also a Madonna Estate wine in the Napa Valley, not owned by Madonna or her family. This is a celebrity linked wine selling for over $50 a bottle, to fans and collectors.

9. *c. 1993.* Actor Sam Neill waited until he was 45 years old before he bought and opened his Two Paddocks vineyard in Central Otago, South Island NZ. He started making award-winning Pinot Noirs from the 5 acres (2 hectares) vineyard, with his first vintage being in 1997. He now has four vineyard sites in the Otago wine area, and as well as his favourite Pinot Noirs, Rieslings and Chardonnays are also grown.

10. **b. Portugal.** Cliff Richard planted his first vineyards in 1997 on his Algarve properties at Quinta do Miradouro and Moinho. Both are only a stone's throw from the top seaside resort of Albufeira. The whole estate is called Adega do Cantor, which translates as 'winery of the singer'. Since the first vintage year of 2000, the red and white wines have been selling out fast, especially at Waitrose supermarkets. The grapes used are mainly Viognier for the white wine and Syrah for the red. His two brands of wine ranges are Vida Nova and Onda Nova.

ANSWERS TO QUIZ 75 – FAMOUS PEOPLE AND THEIR WINES – PART 2

1. **a. James Bond.** In the first 'Bond' book written by Ian Fleming, which was Casino Royale, Bond's favourite champagne was Taittinger. The James Bond of the novels was very fickle with his favourite champagne, depending on the novel it was in – Bollinger, Krug, Dom Pérignon, Pommery and Veuve Clicquot were all favourites in the books. All the Bond films since 1973 have James Bond's favourite champagne, without doubt, as Bollinger. Bond only ever drinks Bollinger, due to a deal done between the producer Cubby Broccoli and the Bollinger family.

2. **a. Geoffrey Chaucer.** He was the medieval author, who lived from 1340 to 1400 AD. In his masterpiece The Canterbury Tales, quite a few of them featured wine or mead. John Chaucer, his father, was a top London wine importer, merchant and vintner. He was also the Deputy Royal Butler looking after the wine cellars of King Edward III.

3. **c. Waitrose.** This is the first, and the only, supermarket in the UK to gain the Royal Warrant from Queen Elizabeth II. Its wines have been used consistently within Buckingham Palace and Windsor Castle, mainly for private meals.

4. **b. Mateus Rosé.** Saddam Hussein loved Mateus Rosé, the slightly sweet and gently sparkling pink from northern Portugal. He made sure that all his palaces' cellars were well stocked with Mateus Rosé. It became one of the best-selling rosé wines in the world, and the second best selling wine in the USA. Elton John, Queen Elizabeth II, Jimi Hendrix and Pope John Paul VI, were also fans of this wine.

5. **c. Marilyn Monroe.** She loved to spend time drinking champagne and especially Dom Pérignon, by far her favourite champagne. In her later years

she drank large quantities of Dom Pérignon on and off film sets. It is not absolutely proven that she did bathe in champagne, but if she did it was probably not Dom Pérignon as it takes a minimum of 350 champagne bottles to fill a bathtub and it would be a waste of her favourite. Marilyn Monroe often said 'Just give me champagne and good food, and I'm in heaven and love. That's what makes the world go round'.

6.   **b. Inglenook.** This historic California wine estate was founded by a Finnish sea captain, Gustave Niebaum in 1879. He retired from a life at sea to Rutherford in the Napa Valley to produce wines as fine as any from Europe. Almost 100 years later, a famous film director, Francis Ford Coppola bought the estate with the profits made from his Godfather films. He named it the Niebaum Coppola Winery, and produced a fine collection of good quality wines there for over 30 years. In 2011 the Coppola family renamed the whole estate Inglenook once again.

7.   **c. Pol Roger.** This family Champagne House was the favourite of Winston Churchill for most of his adult life, almost 60 years from 1907 to his death in 1965. The head of Pol Roger has estimated that Churchill drank over 42,000 bottles of their vintage champagne, from the first invoice until his death. That equates to 2 bottles of Pol Roger every day. After his death they launched a prestige champagne called Cuvée Winston Churchill. This remains their flagship wine. Its blend has 80% Pinot Noir which is as Churchill liked it, a full champagne which was good with food. Pol Roger, the racehorse, was also a winner for Churchill.

8.   **a. Chambertin.** This was Napoleon Bonaparte's favourite red wine during his whole lifetime. He said 'nothing makes the future look so rosy as to contemplate it through a glass of Chambertin'. He always took many cases on his battle campaigns abroad. His personal physician regularly prescribed it for battlefield pains and political headaches. It comes from the commune of Gevrey-Chambertin where there are nine other Grand Cru vineyards hyphenated with 'Chambertin'. Gevrey-Chambertin also has more Grand Cru vineyards than anywhere else in Burgundy.

9.   **c. Sauternes.** Daisy Fay got so drunk and sick by drinking lots of Sauternes at her wedding to Tom Buchanan, that she never got drunk again. F. Scott Fitzgerald's book The Great Gatsby was written in 1923, during Prohibition in the USA, when all alcohol was illegal. All his characters in the novel drink a lot (apart from Daisy) at the very frequent boozy parties and dinners. it is set in the prosperous (fictional) towns of East Egg and West Egg on Long Island, where the wealthy and elite spent their summers. This frequent

drinking behaviour by the wealthy was very common in Prohibition, making bootleggers like Al Capone very wealthy as well.

10. **b. Graham Beck.** His Brut NV has been affectionately dubbed 'The Presidents' Choice' as both Nelson Mandela and Barack Obama chose it as the 'bubbly' for their Presidential Inaugurations. It was also served at many State occasions and dinners, both in SA and the USA. Graham Beck's NV is a blend of 55% Chardonnay and 45% Pinot Noir, with brioche yeasty aromas, a fresh fruit palate with creamy complexity and an overall balance of fruit freshness and finesse.

ANSWERS TO QUIZ 76 – FAMOUS PEOPLE'S WINE QUOTES – PART 1

1. **a. Ernest Hemingway.** All of these three authors were celebrated drunks, who consumed large quantities of wine and all alcohol. Hemingway loved white wines, and his favourite was Sancerre from the Loire Valley. Along with his wine drinking, he also drank many cocktails. In fact he had a famous cocktail named after him in Cuba, a daiquiri called the 'Papa Doble'.

2. **c. Pliny the Elder.** He was a Roman philosopher, a naturalist, a non-fiction author and a Navy and Army Commander. Water was often polluted and was thus dangerous to drink, so many Roman nobles and citizens drank diluted wine instead, as the healthy, safer option. It was usually three parts water to one part wine. Pliny the Elder is often cited as the world's first wine critic for his writings on wine, which he graded by grape variety (Falernian were first growths), place (terroir),the vintage and winemaker.

3. **b. Dom Pérignon.** This saying, attributed to Dom Pérignon, was said when to his surprise the wine he put aside developed bubbles, and the wine bottles exploded. This is probably a widely held myth. The French believe that 'Méthode Champenoise' was discovered by the Benedictine monk named Dom Pierre Pérignon at the abbey of Hautvillers in 1697. This is now disputed by English historians and scientists who state that 30 years earlier, Christopher Merrett (of Winchcombe in the Cotswolds), who was a scientist, physician, naturalist and metallurgist discovered in 1662 'how to put the fizz into wine' by adding sugar and causing a secondary fermentation.

4. **a. Winston Churchill.** He owned many racehorses over his lifetime. One of his favourites was Pol Roger, which was named after his favourite

champagne. In fact it was the only champagne he drank for many years. It has been estimated that he drank up to 50,000 bottles of Vintage Pol Roger. After his death they created a flagship vintage champagne named after him. It was 'Cuvée Winston Churchill' using their finest grapes from their best vintages.

5. **b. 1982.** Robert Parker was the only wine critic to idolise and sing the praises of the 1982 vintage in Bordeaux, especially the Medoc and Pomerol. Thus 1982 was also famous for launching the career of the world's most successful wine critic, Robert Parker. The prices of the 1982 top classed growth wines rocketed, and it is currently still the most expensive Bordeaux vintage to buy. He introduced wine ratings based on a 100 point scale which became the norm in the USA, and he founded the wine magazine 'The Wine Advocate'. Both of these influenced the prices of newly released Bordeaux wines. For over 30 years he was the most famous and influential wine critic in the world.

6. **a. Benjamin Franklin.** Sometimes called 'the first American' and a founding father of the USA, a polymath from inventor to diplomat, he lived from 1706 to 1790. He was a lover of really fine wines and a big collector, having large wine cellars of over 1,000 bottles wherever he lived, in Paris (10 years), London (16 years) and Philadelphia for the rest of his life. He is credited for teaching Thomas Jefferson (the 3rd US President) all about French wine when they were both living in Paris, and for turning him into a connoisseur. He was also an eminent scientist and in 1752 Benjamin Franklin discovered and proved the existence of electricity by flying a kite during a thunderstorm. He tied a metal key to the kite string which conducted the electricity. For this and other achievements he also features on the American $100 bill.

7. **a. Château Cheval Blanc.** Miles Raymond, the wine enthusiast in 'Sideways', continually professes his love of Pinot Noir wines; yet his favourite wine turns out to be 1961 Cheval Blanc, a top St-Emilion Premier Grand Cru from Bordeaux. It is a blend of Merlot and Cabernet Franc, the two grapes he says he despises, especially Merlot. At the end, he drinks his 1961 Cheval Blanc out of a paper cup at a fast food restaurant; a wine selling then for over £2,500 (US$3,000) a bottle! That's style or folly!

8. **b. Napoleon Bonaparte.** Emperor Napoleon had a strong personal connection with Claude Moët dating back to 1782, when they met whilst he was at military school. It was a relationship that would last a lifetime. Napoleon's armies always marched with many cases of champagne which was collected en route from the Moët estate. It was generally drunk before and after battles by Napoleon and his generals. It is also claimed that the first ever 'sabering' of champagnes (cutting the neck off with a sword) was by Napoleon on horseback.

9. **c. Sauvignon Blanc.** This is where the top chefs in Britain go for their House white wines. Château Bauduc Sauvignon Blanc has been the' House White' at all of Rick Stein's, and Gordon Ramsey's, restaurants since the year 2001. It is from Créon in southern Bordeaux. Bauduc is owned and run by a London couple. Gavin Quinney decided to give up working in computers in 1999 for making wine in France. He bought Château Bauduc and the rest is history. His Sauvignon Blanc sells in UK shops for £11 to £13 retail.

10. **b. Salvador Dali.** He was a great wine drinker and a lover and collector of very fine wines. In the 1970s he wrote a book of favourite wines, and in 2016 it was updated and re-published as 'The Wines of Gala', a phantasmagorical and encyclopaedic journey through Mr Dali's favourite wines, with many paintings and prose written by his friend Baron Philippe de Rothschild. Dali had painted the 1958 label for Château Mouton Rothschild, and they had been friends ever since. Pablo Picasso was a very heavy drinker, and he loved Absinthe 'The Green Fairy' and lots of wine. His last words were 'Drink to me, drink to my health. You know I can't drink anymore'. Then he died.

ANSWERS TO QUIZ 77 – FAMOUS PEOPLE'S WINE QUOTES – PART 2

1. **a. Sean Connery.** Dr No was the first James Bond film, and it was so well received that it kicked off an international phenomenon, and created a new film series franchise. It was low budget, directed by a newcomer, Terence Young, and starred an unknown Scottish actor, Sean Connery. It did not sound promising, but this spy film shot and located mainly in Jamaica and London was a big commercial success. The music theme, the first shot of Bond through the barrel of a gun, and his laconic humorous yet cruel style with wit, and his love and knowledge of champagne and wine, all these were first displayed in the film Dr No and became iconic parts of the James Bond Film Franchise.

2. **c. Martin Luther.** He said that beer was made by men, wine by God because it was true in those days, (the 1500s) that if you picked grapes, crushed them and put them in a large clay pot, then fermentation would take place and wine appear. Martin Luther (1483–1546) did like wine drinking, although he was the seminal figure in the Reformation of the Catholic Church, and a rebel who shaped Protestantism, he did enjoy his earthly pleasures.

Days before he died at 62, he wrote to his wife 'you would do well to send me over my whole cellar of wine'. He drank wine and prayed, right to the end.

3. **a. W.C. Fields.** He was a lifelong lover of wines and spirits and a very heavy drinker. Unfortunately he died of cirrhosis of the liver at the age of 66, due to chronic alcoholism, which was very sad for such a funny man. He loved a liquid lunch on set or off and once said 'which weasel took the cork out of my lunch'. His father was a bartender and he started drinking early and never stopped. He also loved martinis; his version was a gin bottle in his left hand and a vermouth bottle in his right hand, then he took alternating swigs. On his deathbed he was drinking and reading the Bible; he told his friends he was looking for loopholes.

4. **a. Bottle Shock.** The film was a comedy drama, based on a true story; it was released in 2008 starring Alan Rickman. He was playing Steven Spurrier (an English wine merchant in Paris) as the true hero who changed the stuffy French Bordeaux wine elite for ever. He set up the 'Judgement of Paris' in 1976, when California wines beat the best star wines of France in a blind tasting competition. Many of the judges were French and had to lie low afterwards, as the publicity and fallout was enormous. The Californians won both the white and red trophies, with Chateau Montelena Chardonnay 1973 and Stag's Leap Cabernet Sauvignon 1973, which are now in display cases in the Smithsonian Museum in Washington DC.

5. **c. James Thurber.** He was a top New Yorker cartoonist, and a wit and writer. He was made most famous by his story 'The Secret Life of Walter Mitty' which has been made into a film twice, in 1947 starring Danny Kaye, and in 2013 starring Ben Stiller; both are worth a watch. He loved lampooning wine snobbery and wrote a humorous piece on 'How to tell a fine old wine', which punctured quite a few pompous opinions of French classic wines. It is a gem of the gentler form of wine writing.

6. **b. Pablo Picasso.** He drank a lot of wine throughout his life, although he was not a connoisseur. Every day he drank most types of ordinary 'Vin de Table' wines at meals, and for its inebriating effect, which he said made him paint more creatively. He also drank a lot of the 'green fairy' Absinthe, and often painted after he had drunk many glasses, which also fed his imagination. His love for booze also showed in paintings like 'The Absinthe Drinker' (sold for $51 million in 2010) and 'Drunk woman is tired'. His last words were 'Drink to me. Drink to my health. You know I can't drink anymore'. Paul McCartney wrote a song 'Picasso's last words' using these words in the lyrics, and recorded it with Wings just after Picasso died in 1973.

7. **b. Basil Fawlty.** Fawlty Towers was a British television sitcom broadcast on BBC2 in 1975 and 1979. Just two series of six episodes were made. The show was created and written by John Cleese and Connie Booth, who also starred in the show, and were married to each other at the time of the first series. In a poll of both TV critics and the public, it was voted the best British Television Series ever. It is a comedy series about Fawlty Towers, a hotel in Torquay, and its rude, eccentric, accident prone and put-upon owner Basil Fawlty. It was based on a real person and a real hotel in Torquay (eccentric owner Donald Sinclair and Hotel Gleneagles). John Cleese and the Monty Python team were staying there in 1971 while filming a TV episode, and he was inspired to use the Sinclairs as templates for Basil and Sybil Fawlty. John Cleese described Sinclair as 'the most wonderfully rude man I have ever met'.

8. **b. Homer.** He was a Greek classical philosopher who wrote both the Iliad and Homer's Odyssey. Wine was considered a staple of the daily diet in Ancient Greece as water was often polluted and unsafe. It was almost always drunk diluted with water, believing that it killed any germs. Wine was drunk at breakfast through to dinner and beyond; it was especially part of the Greek aristocrats social scene of feasting and festivals. Wines were not equal at all, even then the price and social standing of the wine depended on the vintage, age and grape variety, as well as where it was from and the winemaker. Bibline (fragrant white) and Pramnian (dark strong red) wines were the most lauded at Royal Palaces, along with highly prized 'straw wines' which were sweet and would age well.

9. **a. Alexander Fleming.** He was born in 1881 and became a Scottish bacteriologist who is best known for his discovery of penicillin in 1928, which started the antibiotic revolution. For his discovery of penicillin, he was awarded a share of the 1945 Nobel Prize for Medicine. The original name for penicillin was 'mould juice' and it was accidently discovered by Fleming. He came back from a holiday to his lab and found a dirty dish there with a mouldy blob growing on it; around and on this blob no bacteria were growing, so he reasoned that something in the mould was killing the bacteria, he was right. He finally called this 'mould juice' Penicillin and the first antibiotic drug was formed. The mould Juice had been used for centuries as an antiseptic by champagne workers who cut themselves while working in the deep cellars where the mould grew on the damp walls.

10. **b. James Joyce.** He was a wine lover all his life but only drank white wine, and his all-time favourite was a Swiss one, called Fendant de Sion. Sion is the capital of the Swiss Canton of Valais and the protected local grape name Fendant is exclusively reserved for wine made from the Valais Chasselas grape.

The wine is a pale bright yellow colour, with a subtle and fresh smell of lime blossom and minerals on the nose. The taste has slightly dry citrus flavours with peach, is rounded and balanced with a nice acidity. James Joyce lived in Zurich, Switzerland for some years and died and was buried there in 1941; hence his love of Swiss wines. He thought that red wine was like drinking liquid steak so avoided it. Even though his main character in Ulysses, Leopold Bloom, loved red Burgundy and drank it copiously.

ANSWERS TO QUIZ 78 – WINE DRINKING HEROES AND DRUNKS IN BOOKS AND FILMS

1. *b. Sideways.* The book was turned into a successful film of Miles and Jack going on a final wine trip, before Jack gets hitched. It is a dry comedy about two friends who are very different characters, Jack a womaniser and Miles a wine buff. It is definitely worth a watch for the humorous adventures and lots of wine along the way. c) Vertical is the second book by Rex Pickett of the friends' later road trip to Oregon's Willamette Valley for the International Pinot Noir Celebration. a) Saving Grapes is a humorous novel set in French vineyards.

2. *c. Marilyn Monroe.* Who played the sexy neighbour upstairs, tempts the married lawyer with her many charms, like dunking her chips (crisps) in champagne. In real life, Marilyn loved champagne, and dunking her potato chips.

3. *c. Spain.* American abroad Jake Barnes, and his expat friends, travel to Pamplona in north-west Spain to participate in the San Fermin Festival. They go to many bullfights, watch the running of the bulls, and relax drinking wine in the evenings. Every chapter is full of excessive wine drinking of the 'lost generation' from World War I trying to find themselves and forget the horrors of the war.

4. *b. Moët & Chandon.* Leonardo di Caprio as Gatsby was seen throughout the film drinking Moët & Chandon magnums with his friends at his lavish parties. Huge intricate champagne pyramid fountains were shown, and enormous Moët champagne bottles were poured (Balthazars at 16 bottles and Nebuchadnezzars at 20 bottles). It was not product placement, as Moët

& Chandon were taken by surprise, but delighted at all the free publicity. Historical accuracy was the film producers' reasoning.

5. *c. Falstaff.* Sir John Falstaff appeared in Henry IV Part 1 and 2, where he is a companion to Prince Hal, the future King Henry V of England, as well as being in The Merry Wives of Windsor. His death is mentioned in Henry V. He was a jovial drunk who loved his 'Sack' which is the forerunner of dry sherry. His second favourite tipple was 'Canary', a sweeter fortified wine made from the Malvasia grape (Malmsey) and imported from the Canary Islands. If not with the Prince he loved going to his favourite tavern, the Boars Head Inn, and enjoy drinking and carousing with shady characters, who were up to no good.

6. *a. Casablanca.* Rick Blaine was the owner of Rick's Cafe in Casablanca during World War II. It was a 1942 American romantic drama film directed by Michael Curtiz, with Rick played by Humphrey Bogart, with Ingrid Bergman as Ilsa Lund, in love with two men. Champagne flowed throughout. Casablanca won three Oscars (including Best Picture and Best Director) and had eight Oscar nominations.

7. *c. P.G. Wodehouse.* In his Jeeves and Wooster series of humorous novels, Bertie Wooster was a gentleman boozer of impeccable style, always helped out by his ever faithful butler, Jeeves. There were 35 short stories and 11 novels of Jeeves and Wooster, filled with jolly japes, wine, champers and frivolity.

8. *a. Sean Connery.* During Sean Connery's tenure as the first official franchise James Bond on film, for the first 11 years (1962 to 1973) his wine and champagne choice on screen was fickle yet impeccable. Sean Connery's Bond was the only one to drink Cheval Blanc and Château Mouton Rothschild, both top Bordeaux First Growths. In the seven early films, Bond drank Dom Pérignon, and in two films also Taittinger. From 1973 onwards only Bollinger champagne appeared and was mentioned in films. This was a huge product placement deal between the Bollinger family and Bond Franchise Producer Cubby Broccoli.

9. *a. Decline and Fall.* This was Evelyn Waugh's first published novel in 1928. It was well received, with the Guardian praising it as 'a great lark of a book'. Hero, Paul Pennyfeather, is laid low for life, by his drunken antics at the Bollinger Club, when he was a student at Oxford. From then on his life is all downhill, and amusingly tragic, with lots of wine drinking included.

10. *b. Gigi.* It was a 1958 Hollywood musical by MGM set in Paris, and based on a 1944 novella by Colette. Gigi as a young teenager is in training to be a high-society courtesan in her family's tradition. Her adventures and seduction attempts along the way are filled with champagne and wine drinking. a) An

American in Paris is a MGM musical also directed by Vincente Minnelli with Leslie Caron again, and also based in Paris, but this time with returning GIs from World War II. c) High Society is a 1956 musical film based in New York with Grace Kelly and Bing Crosby. A spoiled heiress must choose between three unsuitable suitors.

ANSWERS TO QUIZ 79 – THE HISTORY OF WINE

1. ***a. Armenia.*** The first ever winery was discovered in 2012, in a cave complex at the village of Areni, which is in the southern hills of Armenia. This area is still known for its wine production today. A 6,000 year old wine press, and a shallow stone large basin for foot pressing grapes was discovered. Before this latest discovery the oldest known winery was in Israel and dated from 1650 BC.

2. ***b. Diluted with water.*** All ancient Greeks drank wine often, nearly always with 1 part wine to 3 parts water. It was thought to be uncouth and barbaric to drink wine neat, without adding water. Wines in ancient Greece were often a bit sour, acidic and could be oxidised, so the alcohol content rather than the lovely taste was the important part of drinking. Diluted wine also helped to disinfect their often polluted drinking water. This was the same as the Romans did in later times.

3. ***a. In clay amphorae.*** The best wines were often stored in amphora vessels. The more ordinary wines were stored in clay jars or pots. Often herbs and spices and even salt was added to the wines to prevent them from spoiling quickly. Some Roman wines were kept for many years, heating them and smoking them over a hearth. Some were also fortified with spirit to make a sort of smoky Madeira type wine.

4. ***a. Circa 100 AD to 180 AD.*** It was very early in the second century AD that the Romans planted vineyards all across Gaul (France), especially in Burgundy, the Rhône Valley and even up to Alsace. The Gauls had been trading wines with Rome for hundreds of years before the Romans conquered them. The Gauls invented the wooden wine barrel and this was used for transporting and storing wines instead of amphorae.

5. ***a. Emperor Charlemagne.*** Charlemagne ruled most of Europe from 742 to 814. He introduced his imperial system of 17 strict wine laws on growing, making and storing wines. These were the first official wine laws or rules

introduced into the world of winemaking. Emperor Charlemagne also owned the vineyard Corton-Charlemagne in Burgundy. He ordered his vineyard workers to uproot all the red grape vines and replant them with a white grape variety (Chardonnay), because the red wine stained his beard and his wife did not like that! Nowadays, Corton-Charlemagne is one of the most prestigious white wine communes in the whole of Burgundy.

6. **b. Pope Clement V.** He was the Pope that moved the papacy from Rome to Avignon, and ruled the Papal States from there. He was Pope from 1305 until his death in 1314. During this time he was also famous for executing the Knights Templar leaders and perpetually suppressing their Catholic military order in 1312. The Classed Growth Château he owned then, and that still carries his name today, is Château Pape Clement (Château Pope Clement) from the Pessac-Léognan appellation in Graves, which makes top quality red and white wines which sell for over £200 a bottle. It is also the oldest wine estate in the whole of the Bordeaux region, and celebrated its 700th vintage in 2006.

7. **b. 1400s.** It was in the early 1400s, shortly after Madeira was discovered by accident in 1419 by the Portuguese marine explorer João Zarco, sponsored by Henry the Navigator. Madeira got its name because it was covered in dense forests, and Madeira is the word for wood in Portuguese. Settlers quickly arrived from Portugal bringing the first grape cuttings and planting vineyards almost immediately. The first grape variety brought over from Portugal was the great 'Malmsey', Malvasia grape, which to this day produces the sweetest and best Madeira wine.

8. **a. Benedictines.** All three religious orders were involved with vineyards and grape growing, from their monasteries which spread across Europe. The Benedictines were the first on the scene making high quality wine in Burgundy from circa 800 AD. They also made good wines from their abbey at Monte Cassino which is in the Lazio region near Rome. The Benedictines were called the black monks because of their black cloaks and heavy drinking behaviour. The wine drinking was notorious 'every evening rising from the table with their veins swollen with wine and their heads on fire'. They also made the famous liqueur, Benedictine, but not until 1510. The Cistercian monks took over in the 11th century as the finest winemakers, especially in Burgundy where they owned Clos de Vougeot.

9. **a. Le Pin.** This tiny wine estate in Pomerol only began in 1979 when a Belgian, Jacques Thienpont, bought the 1 hectare plot of land for 1 million Francs. It is regularly among the three most expensive wines in the world, partly from rarity value (a waiting list to buy), but it is also highly regarded by

the world's wine critics. It makes only 500 cases per annum on average. Both Le Pin and Petrus make their wines from 100% Merlot grapes. Château Lafleur is 60% Merlot and 40% Cabernet Franc, and is the oldest Pomerol estate founded in 1750, and Petrus was established in 1837. So the New Kid On The Block is now kingpin in Pomerol.

10. ***b. Port in Portugal.*** 1945 became the most incredible vintage of the 20th century for vintage Port for two main reasons. Firstly, the weather was amazing with sunshine and daily heat but with cool nights in the budding and growing/maturing months, and then a sunny and cool perfect harvest time for picking the ultra ripe grapes. Secondly, Portugal had remained neutral in the Second World War, but other European countries found that their vineyards were neglected or devastated by invasion and war, especially in 1945 the last year of World War II. The damage was worst in France, Germany and Italy. Even though the weather was amazing, growing and making the wines was a hazardous pursuit in most European countries.

ANSWERS TO QUIZ 80 – WINE GRAPE VARIETIES – PART 1

1. ***a. Red.*** Pinot Meunier is a red grape mainly used as part of the blend of a champagne. The other two grapes making up champagne blends are Chardonnay and Pinot Noir. In the champagne region they are often now calling it 'Meunier' and dropping the Pinot prefix, although it is a mutation of Pinot Noir. It has been known since the 16th century and produces lighter coloured softer wines, has more acidity, is easier to grow and ripens earlier, but on its own can be a bit bland. Currently circa 35% to 40% of all vine plantings in the champagne region are Meunier. There is now a trend to make pure Pinot Meunier champagnes – another Blanc de Noirs.

Riesling

Chardonnay

Viognier

2. ***b. Merlot.*** Currently Merlot is the most planted red grape in the whole of the Bordeaux region. It accounts for 50% to 60% of all plantings in appellation vineyards. It is especially prominent on the right bank where 70% plus of St-Emilion and 80% plus of Pomerol vineyards are Merlot. Le Pin and Petrus, sometimes the two most expensive wines in the world, are 100% Merlot. The name comes from it being very blue-black, like the plumage of the Blackbird (Merle).

Chenin Blanc

3. **b. Germany.** Riesling is by far the most planted grape variety in Germany. Riesling is a bit of an enigma – ethereal, floral and enchanting, it is also one of the world's hardiest grape varieties, with a high level of frost resistance, meaning it thrives in some of the coolest climate wine regions. The berries are small and form compact bunches on the vine, which makes them great for sweet wine production as they are very susceptible to 'noble rot'. The Rheingau, Rheinhessen, Mosel, and Nahe regions in Germany produce the most high quality Riesling wines, both dry (trocken) and sweet. Germany's Rieslings account for around 40% of all Riesling vineyard plantings in the world. a) Austria's most planted grape is Grüner Veltliner. France's most planted grape is Cabernet Sauvignon.

4. **b. Piedmont.** This is the home region of all Barolo wines made from the noble Nebbiolo grape variety. Barolo is often described as having the aromas of tar and roses, and the wines are noted for their ability to age, and usually take on a rust red tinge as they mature. Barolo needs to be aged for at least 38 months after the harvest before release, of which at least 18 months must be in wood. Traditional Barolos had a great depth of tannins which took at least 10 years to soften to make them pleasurable to drink. Nowadays, technology has resulted in faster maturing wines which are also lighter in colour, but still have the same intense flavours and long finish. It is a small region (less than half the size of Chablis) with around 300 producers making wine from 11 different communes and 170 single vineyard sites (known as 'crus') spread out over a series of three highly convoluted hill ranges.

5. **a. Galicia.** Albariño and Godello grape varieties are white, fresh grapes and the most aromatic in Spain. Galicia is a Spanish wine region in the north-west corner of Spain mainly growing white grapes. There are five DO areas and Rías Baixas is the best known. These are two of the fastest growing white grape varieties in the world, in terms of popularity (from a small base) and they were almost unknown 20 years ago, especially the Godello grape. b) Navarra produces mostly red grapes especially Tempranillo. c) Rueda produces mostly white wines from the Verdejo and Sauvignon Blanc grapes.

6   **a. Argentina.** Malbec is the traditional red grape from Argentina making over 70% of all their red wines. It is an inky purple berry that originated in the south-west of France, around the town of Cahors. Some of the Malbec Reserva wines in Argentina come from vines which are around 100 years old and produce luscious and eminently drinkable dark rich wines which are great to accompany a steak or barbecue. They also flourish on the edge of the Andes in some of the world's highest vineyards. Malbec has been the fastest growing red grape variety in the world for the last 10 years.

7. **b. Chardonnay.** Chablis wines, although very steely, dry and light coloured are all produced from 100% Chardonnay. Chablis is the northernmost Appellation (AOC) in Burgundy, and covers approximately 4,260 hectares, with 27 communes in total. There are Petit Chablis, many Village Chablis, and 40 vineyards classified as Premier Crus and 7 Grand Crus. Chardonnay grapes were first planted in Chablis in the 12th century by Cistercian monks. a) Cabernet Sauvignon is a red grape primarily from Bordeaux. c) Chenin Blanc originated and flourishes in the Loire Valley.

8. **c. Bucelas.** This is a small historic DOC wine region for white wines located north of Lisbon in Portugal. It is mainly made from the Arinto grape variety and often has a fruity zesty flavour, some have vanilla, toffee and rich wood notes as they have been oak aged. It used to be popular in England in the 19th century after the Duke of Wellington took much Bucelas back to the UK after the Peninsular Wars in 1814. a) Bonarda is a red grape grown mainly in Argentina. b) Brunello is another name for the Sangiovese grape grown in Montalcino.

9. **c. Vidal.** This is the traditional grape variety for Canadian Ice Wines from Niagara and British Columbia. It is a hybrid variety, a cross between Ugni Blanc and another hybrid variety, Rayon d'Or. It is a very winter-hardy variety that manages to produce high sugar levels in cold climates with moderate to high acidity, and it is very susceptible to 'noble rot', which makes it perfect for making Ice Wines. It takes an average of seven kilos of Vidal grapes to make a bottle of Ice Wine. Seven kilos would make about seven bottles of table wine, hence the high cost of Ice Wine. Other grape varieties are expanding their presence including Riesling, and Cabernet Franc. b) Riesling is the main variety used to make Eiswein/Ice Wine in Germany. a) Chardonnay is not used much for making Ice Wine.

10. **c. Riesling.** Some good and top quality Rieslings, especially in Alsace and Germany, can smell of petrol/gasoline in good ripe years. It is a strange phenomenon, due to a chemical compound called TDN, which forms as a result of ripeness or age. It is thus a mark of quality rather than a fault, although it is not popular with some wine drinkers. b) Muscat smells of grapes and raisins. a) Gewürztraminer smells of lychees and guavas.

ANSWERS TO QUIZ 81 – WINE GRAPE VARIETIES – PART 2

1. *c. Pinot Noir.* This thin skinned, early ripening grape variety is more difficult to grow than many others, but with sensitive wine making it can flourish in cool temperate climates like Germany and Switzerland. Since the late 1990s high quality Pinot Noirs have ever expanded into northern Europe (helped by global warming) and many New World countries. Burgundy's domination is waning; these north Europe and New World Pinot Noirs are not the same taste profile as Burgundies, but they express flavours unique to Pinot Noir, while being fresh, fruity and thrillingly different.

Zinfandel

Pinot Noir

2. *c. Uruguay.* Most of the vineyards are on clay with cool rainy conditions, and the soils and climate are not very good for ripening most grape varieties before they rot on the vine. The Tannat grape which is thick skinned, rot resistant and a tough early ripening grape has thus become kingpin, with about 30% of all vineyard plantings. More Tannat is grown in Uruguay than in any other country. It originated in south-west France in the Madiran AOC, but is now thought of as the national grape of Uruguay. Modern winemaking techniques have been able to soften the tannins to make a dark and dense yet delightfully scented red wine. It is worth seeking out.

Cabernet Sauvignon

Syrah

3. *c. Sauvignon Blanc.* This grape variety is a 'love it or loathe it grape'; many wine writers think it has become too trendy and fashionable. It can be shocking in its lime zest, brash and tangy dry personality, yet it is this nettles and passion fruit upfront nature that many drinkers love. On a hot day it can be the most refreshing of wines. The range of styles is very wide from the restrained Old World (Loire Valley) Sancerre and Pouilly-Fumé wines, full of ripeness and yet bone dry, with a slightly smoky perfume and gooseberry taste; to contrast with New Zealand's fresh wild, crunchy and slightly unripe wines, with a herbaceous yet floral aroma, and a taste of high acidity and citrus fruit.

4. *b. Franken.* This is a German wine region for quality wine situated in the north-west of Bavaria. A region rife with rolling hills, Disney-like castles, and a timber-frame romanticism which makes it one of the most fairy tale and beautiful wine areas in Europe. It has a special bottle shape for its wines called a Bocksbeutel; it looks like a Mateus Rosé bottle, but in fact Mateus copied the Franken bottle shape. The three main grape varieties are Silvaner, Müller-Thurgau and Bacchus. a) Carignan is a red grape variety of Spanish origin, but nowadays most plantings are in the south of France, Languedoc and Fitou. c) It

sounds like a disease, but it is a Greek pink skinned plentiful grape variety that was traditionally grown in the Peloponnese, making Retsina and dry whites.

5. **b. France.** The home of Syrah in Europe is the Rhône Valley from the north (Côte-Rotie, Saint-Joseph and Hermitage) to the very south with Châteauneuf-du-Pape blends and Côte du Rhônes. Syrah has expanded in the Rhône Valley and southern France within the last 20 years. It is also now grown successfully in 31 countries, but France is still the No.1 producer, followed by Australia as No.2.

6. **b. White.** The Bacchus grape variety is a double-cross, between a Silvaner & Riesling cross and a Müller-Thurgau, which was done in Germany in 1933. It was not released for commercial use in vineyards until 1972. A great name for a wine grape as Bacchus was the Roman God of Wine. Bacchus is a very popular grape in England as, with our temperate climate, the acidity levels are higher giving a more racy and zingy feel to it.

7. **b. Carmenère.** This is an ancient grape variety which was very popular in Roman times. In Chile, French, Italian, and Spanish immigrants had been making wine derived from European vine cuttings for more than 150 years. In particular, some of their Merlots tasted different from European ones, with a deeper colour and flavours with more blackberries and spice. But it was not until 1998 that with DNA tests the Chilean Government recognised that this was in fact clones of the ancient Carmenère grape and not Merlot. So Chilean wines branded Carmenère have only been around for just over 20 years. Until the 1860s, pre-Phylloxera, it used to be a blending grape in Bordeaux but it was wiped out by the disease. Now Chile produces most of the world supply of Carmenère.

8. **b. Greece.** This is a white Greek wine grape indigenous to the island of Santorini. Assyrtiko is widely planted in the arid volcanic-ash-rich soil of Santorini and other Aegean islands, such as Paros and Crete as well as on the mainland. Many of the Santorini vineyards have vines over 70 years old which are still productive and give more intensity and minerality to the wines, and Assyrtiko does not lose its acidity even if it is very ripe. It has become one of the favourite new refreshing quality white wines written about by wine professionals, but is still relatively unknown.

9. **c. Tempranillo.** This is a red grape variety widely grown to make full-bodied red wines in its native Spain. It has all these different names dependent on where it is being grown, Aragonês and Tinta Roriz in Portugal, Tinto Fino in Ribera del Duero, Cencibel in La Mancha and Valdepeñas, and Tempranillo in Rioja. Tempranillo is the fourth most widely planted wine grape variety worldwide, of which about 85% plus is in Spain where it is the most planted red grape variety.

10. **c. Sherry.** Palomino is a white grape variety mainly grown in Andalucía for Sherry production, accounting for about 90% to 95% of all Sherry vineyards in the Jerez area. It is used in the solera system to make Sherry styles from the lightest and driest finos and manzanillas to the darker and more pungent olorosos. It is often called Palomino Fino, and only really becomes exciting and vibrant when fortified and produced as Sherry. The only other two grapes allowed for Sherry are Moscatel and Pedro Ximénez, both making the sweeter Sherry styles. Palomino is also grown in Australia, California and South Africa where it is also fortified to make Sherry style wines.

ANSWERS TO QUIZ 82 – THE WINE YEAR, TERROIR, AND WINEMAKING

1. **b. September and October.** The more northerly the vineyard or the higher the vineyard, then the later the harvest. This is just because the grapes take longer to ripen. But with global warming, in some northerly regions, including Germany and the Vosges Mountains, the grape harvest is coming earlier each year and starting in late August for the first time ever.

2. **b. March and April.** Not surprisingly this is exactly six months away from the Northern Hemisphere's wine harvest timing. Again global warming is affecting the timing, and some New World wine areas are picking grapes as early as late February. This is affecting South America, South Africa and Australia.

3. **b. Burgundy.** For centuries the Burgundy region used whole bunch fermentation for both the red and white grapes. This was originally because they had no de-stemming machines, but it is now thought that including the stems adds a certain backbone to the wines. So even today, many top Pinot Noirs and Chardonnays are still made using whole bunch fermentation.

4. **a. Bordeaux (Pauillac and Margaux).** These wine areas on the left bank of Bordeaux still command the highest prices for land. The average price per hectare is at £2,000,000. This compares to only £750,000 per hectare in the Napa Valley, the most expensive part of the Californian wine growing areas. As a comparison, a hectare of good vineyard land in Rioja, Spain costs only about £30,000; and Beaujolais is only £10,000 per hectare.

5. **b. 25 to 35 years.** In most winemaking countries the lifespan of a grape vine is 25 to 35 years, after that their volume of grape production decreases

and it becomes uneconomic, so they are grubbed up and replanted. Also, with old vines pests and diseases can take their toll. Some vineyards in the world making top quality expensive wines, do so with vines up to 100 years old. This is because even though the yield is very low, the juice is more concentrated and thus makes fine wines with more nuances, character and finesse.

6. *b. White grapes that ferment on their skins.* The skins are left in the fermentation process for about three to four weeks, and thus impart a very light orange colour and extra tannins to the must. Orange wine is tipped to become a new in-trend with younger wine drinkers. Some wine experts are saying in a few years' time it will overtake rosé wines in popularity (rosé wines are usually made from pressing red grapes very gently, and then removing the skins). Some restaurants are already printing special Orange wine sections on to their wine lists. Decanter wine magazine has had a front cover and many articles devoted to Orange wines in 2020.

7. *c. Spain.* Spain for the last 20 years and has had more land devoted to vineyards than anywhere else in the world. Spain has 970,000 hectares of vineyards. China is second with 800,000 hectares of vineyards, many of these producing table grapes to eat, rather than wine. France is now third with an area of 780,000 hectares of vineyards producing wine. China is the only country where vineyard areas are growing at 10% plus per year. In all the other top ten wine producing countries the area under vineyards is declining slowly each year.

8. *b. 300 bottles.* A (French) barrique holds 225 litres of wine. This is equivalent to 50 UK imperial gallons or 25 cases of 12 bottles of wine each, so 300 bottles. In fact one tonne of grapes produces about 700 to 740 bottles of wine, or fills about 2.5 barriques. Nowadays barriques are used worldwide; traditionally they were used in the fine winemaking of Bordeaux and Burgundy, and constructed from Tronçais and Vosges oaks, which have a very tight grain that lets less air in.

9. *c. When a fungus triggers Noble Rot, to make grapes sweeter.* Botrytis is a fungus that rots the grapes turning them into near raisins which then intensify the flavours and sweetness. This 'noble rot' occurs after cool, wet conditions then turn dry with extra heat and humidity. The most famous dessert wines made using noble rot are Sauternes and Barsac from the Bordeaux region. It is expensive to make as it takes five times as many shrivelled grapes to make a bottle of these dessert wines, compared to using normal fresh grapes.

10. *a. A process to remove the sediment from a wine.* This method removes impurities from the must or wine and helps to clarify it.

It is done during the early fermentation process in barrels or tanks and has been undertaken for many centuries. Fining is adding a substance to the wine or must during fermentation that will flush out elements that may affect the clarity, aromas and tastes of the final wine. Nowadays, for many mass produced wines a very fine metal mesh is used to filter out impurities. Traditionally egg whites, isinglass and gelatine were used as natural fining agents, and still are by many top red wine producers.

ANSWERS TO QUIZ 83 – WINE LABELS AND WINE LAWS

1. **b. Greece.** It started with very basic labelling, just the name of the winemaker stamped on one of the arms of the clay wine Jar, and often the vineyard region stamped on the other arm. This was started in Greece in circa 4000 BC, so labelling of wines has been around for over 6,000 years. The Egyptians were the next wine vessel labellers with stamps put on their amphorae to distinguish the best wines; this occurred in circa 2000 BC.

2. **b. Champagne.** Labels were tied onto the necks of the bottles of Dom Pérignon in 1668, the champagne produced by Moët & Chandon. It was named to commemorate the Benedictine monk who is often cited as the founder of champagne.

3. **a. England.** In the country estates and townhouses of the British upper classes and aristocracy, wine was bought in small barrels from wine merchants and stored in their cellars. The butlers or householders then hung metal wine labels (often silver) around the necks of bottles or decanters, to identify their contents before they were presented at table.

4. **c. 1798.** This was the year Bavarian born actor, then Czechoslovakian printer Alois Senefelder invented lithography printing. It started as an accidental discovery when he put some greasy crayon drawings on slabs of limestone and found that he could then print the designs when rolling on ink and pressing paper down onto them. From then on rectangular paper labels could be printed cheaply and in large quantities.

5. **b. Champagnes.** This was because of the high price and special celebratory nature of champagne. To enhance the luxury feel and look, it was felt worthwhile to use gold and silver colours on the labels, and individual designs for the champagne houses on the top capsule.

6. **c. 1950s.** Before that date wineries could put what they liked on their wine bottle labels. From that year on, strict laws were introduced on naming the grapes used, stating the growing region and there was a prescribed minimum information level. It started in France first, then was quickly adopted by the other European major wine countries.

7. **b. Château Mouton Rothschild.** The first time this happened was in 1924, and then every year from 1945 onwards a different famous artist has designed and painted the label design for each vintage. The artists have total freedom in their choice of design and are paid by the gift of cases of their own designed Château Mouton Rothschild. Pablo Picasso, Marc Chagall, Andy Warhol, Jeff Koons, David Hockney, Salvador Dali and many other famous artists accepted the honour. So far 75 famous artists have designed/painted a wine label for Château Mouton Rothschild.

8. **b. Leeuwin Estate.** This top winery, based in Margaret River, Western Australia, launched its Art Series wines in 1980. Every year a different Australian artist is invited to paint the label picture. So far there are over 40 different Art Series vintage wine labels. Leeuwin Estate also has an Art Museum at their winery with over 250 paintings of Australian art.

9. **b. California.** Big Ass Red from Milano Winery in Mendocino also produce a Big Ass Blonde white wine and, along with White Trash White from Harper Hill Vineyards, these wines are positioned as good fun party wines aimed at younger drinkers. They are both blends of Italian grape varieties.

10. **b. Placomusophiles.** Most of the famous and prestigious champagne houses design a different top metal cap for each of their champagne variants. This practice started back in 1844, and there are now over 30,000 different cap designs to collect.

ANSWERS TO QUIZ 84 – OPENING, KEEPING, AND SERVING WINE

1. **c. 18th century.** The Reverend Samuel Henshall invented and patented the first ever corkscrew in 1795. It is a nice link between the clergy and wine. It was only in the late 17th century that wine was kept in bottles; before that wines were kept in barrels, stone and clay vessels and even animal skins. Corks were not used until mid 18th century; previously cloth, leather or wooden stoppers were used.

2. **c. 90% + are screw top bottles.** Cork closures are now only used for New Zealand wines in some high quality Bordeaux blends, and Cabernet Sauvignon. Until recently New Zealand used to export wines to the UK with corks, and to other countries with screw caps. The UK was one of the last countries to accept screw caps as acceptable closures for good quality wine. Nowadays, worldwide, over 50% of white wine and almost 40% of red wine have screw cap closures. This is because people do not store wines for long and it is three times more expensive for producers to use a cork stopper. Many top Bordeaux Châteaux are experimenting and testing the long term ageing of their wines using screw caps.

3. **b. Portugal.** Portugal has always dominated the wine cork trade worldwide with their wide plantings of cork oak trees. Some of these cork oaks can live for 300 to 500 years, and their thick barks are stripped off every 9 to 15 years, to produce wine bottle corks. A tree has to be at least 25 years old before the first cork stripping is done. Spain is the second largest cork producer, 20% globally. Amorim Company, founded over 150 years ago in Portugal, is the largest producer of cork in the world, selling around 4 billion wine corks a year.

4. **b. Pinot Noir.** This is often the palest and lightest coloured red wine in the world. The grape variety has a very thin skin and thus imparts less colour to the wine when being fermented. Both Syrah and Malbec have much thicker darker skins, which when fermented can produce young wines that are almost purple black and dense looking.

5. **a. Drink youngest available.** Most New Zealand Sauvignon Blancs are ready to drink as soon as they are bottled, most do not improve after two years. Fresh is best. They are made to drink early, and if kept over 5 years they can lose their zing, tingling acidity, lemon freshness and grassy-lemongrass flavours, and become rather bland and flat. Even so, some top New Zealand wineries do produce Sauvignon Blancs that will age for 10 years plus, examples are Astrolabe, Dog Point, Sacred Hill, Spy Hill and Yealands Estate.

6. **b. 18C to 21C (65F to 70F).** This is the perfect temperature range to serve a fine and mature red wine at, including Bordeaux, Barolos and

Châteauneuf-du-Papes. This is traditionally called 'room temperature', which helps open up the complex aromas and soften the tannins. If served too chilly, under 16C or 60F, then the nose (aromas) will be blunted. If the red wine is served too warm at a restaurant then do not hesitate to ask for an ice bucket for your red wine.

7. **c. Syrah or Shiraz.** The range of flavours are more elegant and lean from Syrah, with black pepper and spices. The New World Shiraz (most still from Australia) is more overt, rich, dark, dense and almost sweet with rounded tannins, and fruit driven. Merlot is very rounded and smooth, slightly sweet and plummy, with a nose and taste of blueberry fruits. Pinot Noir is usually a light and pale red with a taste and nose of cherries and raspberries, juicy and fruity with much less tannin.

8. **b. Master Sommelier.** Both qualifications are very difficult to achieve, and can take many years to complete successfully. The first Master Sommelier examination was held in London, in the United Kingdom in 1969. The Court of Master Sommeliers now operates mostly in the UK and USA. There are fewer Master Sommeliers in the world with between 250 and 260 individuals currently working in restaurants or the wine trade, compared to about 400 Masters of Wine worldwide. The pass rate of applicants annually is between 3% and 8% for both qualifications. The Master Sommelier is usually a more practical exam and many holders work in the restaurant trade; while the Master of Wine exams are more academic, and many MWs work as highly paid wine buyers for major supermarkets and wine merchants, as well as being wine writers and wine critics. There are currently only 3 to 5 people working in the wine industry who are holders of both qualifications.

9. **c. A wide, pale or colourless rim at the top.** The depth of this pale or colourless rim widens with age and is especially prominent with mature fine Bordeaux reds or Barolos. More wines today are drunk too late than too early, as wine technology means that most wines are ready to drink when bought, or within two years. Only the very fine traditional wines will improve greatly over ten years old, and many of these will mature for another 20+ years.
a) Lees is a sediment at the bottom, which are remaining dead yeast cells from the fermentation process, not necessarily a sign of age, just often of minimalist winemaking, not a wine fault. b) Legs, tracks down the side of a glass often indicates higher alcohol content; it is glycerine – a sign of viscosity and a higher alcohol content.

10. **b. 18 years to 24 years.** This is the safest age range for a top classed growth Bordeaux to ensure it is fully mature and not fading. You can be lucky, if it is from a very ripe great vintage like 1982, it will still be at its best over 40

years later. Many classed growths are made to be drunk much earlier with a more modern approach to the needs of wealthy wine drinkers, who no longer have the patience to store the wine and wait decades. This more approachable winemaking has accelerated in both Pomerol and St-Emilion, even with the top growths, as the higher Merlot content means that these wines can naturally mature at a faster rate and be mature and ready to drink after 5 years or so.

ANSWERS TO QUIZ 85 – BUYING AND SELLING WINE

1. ***a. Berry Bros. & Rudd.*** This is Britain's oldest wine and spirits merchant, and one of the ten oldest family-run businesses in the UK. It was founded by the Widow Bourne in 1698 at 3 St. James's Street, London, which today is a Grade II listed building still used as the company's headquarters. It also has extensive cellars there for wine tastings. It has the Royal Warrant and shares the title as the Queen's Wine Merchant with b) Justerini & Brooks, also in St James's Street but not founded until 1749, 51 years later than BBR. It was family owned, but is now part of Diageo's drinks empire. c) Lay & Wheeler is one of the oldest provincial wine merchants, founded in 1854 in Colchester, Essex.

2. ***c. 65 to 74 years.*** Maybe surprisingly the 'retired age group' drinks the most wine, especially red wine. They also spend more on all alcohol per week. They drink more wine in a home environment than on-trade at pubs or clubs. The age group that drinks the least wine is the youngest group of the under 30 year olds. This is also because around 45% of them do not drink wine at all.

3. ***a. Acker Merrall & Condit.*** This USA, New York based auction house leads the pack in wine sales by value with $108 million in overall sales in 2019, followed by b) Sotheby's at $98 million and c) Zachys at $80 million. Acker Merrall & Condit usually outsells Sotheby's by 10% to 20% per annum; Sotheby's used to be the leader but is now in second place because of the exploding increase in wine auction sales in the USA. Of worldwide wine auction value sales, the USA now accounts for 45% to 50%, while Hong Kong and Shanghai are 2nd accounting for 25% to 30%, and London and Geneva markets were 3rd at 10% to 12%. Online wine auctions continue to grow at the fastest rate, at 30% per year, and are now at circa 15% of all wine auctions by value.

4. **c. 70% to 80%** of all wines are bought by consumers in the top eight UK supermarkets (Tesco, Sainsbury's, Morrisons, Waitrose, Asda, Co-op, Aldi and Lidl). It has been this way in the UK for more than a decade, with supermarkets accounting for 7 to 8 out of every 10 bottles sold. The average price for a bottle of wine bought was just under £6 in 2020. Price is very important for wine sales in supermarkets, with 90% of wines sold at under £9. For buying finer wines of £15 and above, the specialist wine merchants and wine chains like Majestic come into their own and account for almost all the sales, most of them being from France, Bordeaux, Burgundy or Rhône, and Barolos and Brunellos from Italy. Some prestige wines are sold as En Primeur wines, or newly released wines stored in bonded warehouses for longer term maturing or investment.

5. **b. 6 Bottles.** A Rehoboam holds 4.5 litres of champagne, but very confusingly, an exact large bottle of 4.5 litres filled with Bordeaux wine is called a Jeroboam (everywhere else a Jeroboam is 3 litres). Big bottle sizes are all named after Biblical kings (Methuselah, Salmanazar, Balthazar, Nebuchadnezzar, Melchior (18 litres), and Solomon (20 litres, 26 bottles). Rehoboam is named after the biblical King who was the son of Solomon and the grandson of King David.

6. **c. Hardy's from Australia.** It has been the number one selling brand in the UK for over 5 years. It was founded in 1853 by Thomas Hardy, 'the Father of the South Australian Wine Industry' and is still family run almost 170 years later. In 2003 it became part of Constellation Brands, and it now exports to over 60 countries, and accounts for 25% of all Australian wine produced. Annually it sells circa £275 million to £300 million of Hardy's wines in the UK. Barefoot Brands used to be No.1 in the UK but is now No.2, while still being the biggest selling wine brand in the USA.

7. **b. UK.** The UK by far consumes the most Prosecco on the planet. Consumers in the UK drink about one third of all the Prosecco produced in Italy. The British are thus fuelling the extraordinary growth in production, up over 50% in 5 years. The UK now drinks around 150 million bottles a year. Prosecco is made from the Glera grape variety, with the best (DOCGs) coming from the cool climate Veneto region of north-east Italy, especially in the Valdobbiadene and Conegliano areas, where they grow in alpine conditions in steep valleys.

8. **c. Sauvignon Blanc.** This is the UK's favourite grape variety, and second is b) Pinot Grigio. Dry white wines dominate the on-trade (pubs and restaurants) as well as the off-trade sales (home consumption). This white grape preference has changed greatly over the past 30 years, when there were only the Loire versions of Sancerre and Pouilly-Fumé, both expensive wines with very small sales, and often thought of as too dry. UK tastes have changed over

the past 20 years from medium sweet to dry, and New Zealand Sauvignon Blancs burst upon the scene along with Australia, Chile, Argentina, Italy, Spain and USA. They now all export good value and high quality Sauvignon Blancs to the UK.

9. *c. The Wine Society.* It was founded in 1874 as a co-operative/mutual organisation for wine lovers, who had to become 'Lifetime Members' to purchase the wines. Each member owns one share of the company. Their objective from the start was 'to introduce foreign wines hitherto unknown'. This is still their mantra today with their very large catalogue of unusual and small producer wines. They have always been mail order or then online retailers, as they have no retail shops. They now have the largest wine warehouse in Europe and there are over 140,000 active members annually buying over £100 million of wines, so on average a member spends £715 per year.

10. *a. 1 to 3 years.* Most red wines are now made to drink almost immediately, the year after the vintage as soon as they are bottled. Excess tannins are extracted in the process to soften the wines; sometimes a dose of must is used to sweeten as well. It is difficult to find a red wine in a UK supermarket that is over 3 years old. They are designed to sell quickly at between £5 to £9 a bottle and to be ready to drink immediately. Very few UK consumers store wine for more than a year or two. Only a very small minority buy fine wines En Primeur, and then store them in bonded cellars (mainly top Bordeaux Châteaux) for 10 plus years, and then finally drink them when they are fully mature.

ANSWERS TO QUIZ 86 – WINE TASTING AND FOOD MATCHING

1. *a. 2 to 5 years.* If a red Bordeaux wine is a deep, dense purple colour, opaque and looks a little thick then it would usually be 2 to 5 years old. An almost black and opaque colour indicates it is from a good vintage with hot sunny weather when the skins become thick and full of colour pigments; a cooler vintage will usually produce a paler colour wine. A red Bordeaux after five years begins to turn a ruby red colour as it ages, and it goes paler and has orange tints at the edge of the glass. The older it gets the less opaque it is and the more red brick it becomes as it reaches maturity. When past its prime it will become a dull brown colour.

Fruit Aromas
Herb Aromas
Earth Aromas
Other Smells
Intensity

SMELL

2. **c. Sauternes.** All three of these wines would turn amber and grow darker, when over 30 years old. But Sauternes would become a dark amber, old gold colour. The better the vintage year the darker the amber colour of the Sauternes. Very few white burgundies nowadays are made to last more than 10 years. It used to be safe to keep a Grand Cru Chablis or Montrachet for 15 to 20 plus years, but unless you know your Burgundy winemaker, it has become a lottery whether it will still be drinkable.

3. **b. Sauvignon Blanc.** The taste profile of being grassy, nettles, zingy and crisp, lime and green apples is close to New Zealand's very fresh, acidic and citrus style. This is very different from the taste profile of Sauvignon Blancs from its birthplace in the Loire Valley. Sancerre and Pouilly-Fumé, which are the most famous Sauvignon Blancs from the Loire, are more restrained and elegant, with less acidity and citrus lime bite. A Sancerre can be silky and mineral with a nose of guava, peach and apple. Across the river the Pouilly-Fumé can have an almost smokey gunflint nose, with more rounded citrus and savoury flavours. So Old and New World Sauvignon Blancs are poles apart in their taste profile.

4. **c. Syrah or Shiraz.** These names are for the same red grape variety, Shiraz is mostly used for Australia and Syrah elsewhere. It produces full-bodied wines with brisk acidity, firm tannins, and highish alcohol levels of 13% to 15% ABV. Syrah/Shiraz has a wide taste profile but is the only wine that displays white and black pepper on the nose and palate. It can be described as being peppery with spicy herbs and herbaceous notes, sometimes smokey and always with red and black fruits.

5. **c. Robert Parker.** He is a US wine critic. His wine ratings on a 100-point scale and his newsletter The Wine Advocate are influential in American wine buying and throughout Europe and the Far East, and are therefore a major factor in setting the prices for newly released Bordeaux wines. He has had no formal wine training or education and is said to have been born with a million dollar nose and palate. Robert Parker's affirmed independence with regard to wine producers and the wine trade is the key to producing unbiased, credible reviews that are trusted by both consumers and professionals. Parker is responsible for altering the taste of Bordeaux fine wines, reducing the tannic structure and elegant austerity and helping create wines which are more fruit driven and smoother. In July 2020 Michelin bought a 40% stake in The Wine Advocate, and the future partnership between the Michelin Guide for fine dining and Parker's Wine Advocate's guides to finest wines will be a powerful aid to enhance food and wine experiences.

6. **c. Jeroboam.** The theory is that in larger bottle sizes the ratio of liquid to oxygen is assumed to govern the ageing process. With a much smaller ratio

of oxygen in the neck to the wine content, the reactions that comprise the ageing process will take place more slowly and somehow in a more stately fashion. Slowly ageing in larger bottles seems to be more beneficial for red tannic wines than any other types. A strange anomaly is that a Jeroboam bottle size in Bordeaux is 5 litres while a Jeroboam bottle in champagne is 3 litres. Thus the slowest to mature red wines is in a Bordeaux Jeroboam, within which a 20 year old fine Bordeaux Château Classed Growth will seem to be only around 12 years old compared to if it had been stored in a 75cl bottle.

7. *a. b. c. Chenin Blanc, Gewürtztraminer, Sauvignon Blanc.* All are correct as they go well with Thai Curries. Most sommeliers would choose Gewürtztraminer, but also mention 2 or 3 other choices including these and either Riesling or Grüner Veltliner. When matching wines with Thai Green Curry it is important to find a wine that can handle the aromatic components and hot spice. That is, lemongrass, ginger, coriander etc. and the richness of coconut milk. The wine must also be able stand up against the heat from the bird's eye chillies used in Thai Green Curry paste. It is best to choose an aromatic wine with a touch of sweetness and high acidity.

8. *c. Sauternes.* The classic pairing for foie gras is a Sauternes wine. With an abundance of residual sugar, backed with plenty of acidity and the unique profile of botrytis, this wine has the natural ability to enhance any foie gras-based dishes. It sounds counter-intuitive to match a sweet white wine with a fat enhanced red liver of a goose or duck, but is has been the traditional match for hundreds of years in France, and it works. a) Chardonnay does not work well because it can seem to be acidic and metallic, especially Chablis. b) Pinot Noir is too delicate a red to stand up to, or enhance, the fatty structure of foie gras, and in France a red wine is never served with it.

9. *a. Fillet or Rib Eye Steak.* A top mature Malbec Reserva wine is the best match of these three alternatives. Malbec is now the signature grape variety of Argentina, from obscurity to international fame in two decades. It produces a rich, ripe, jammy and juicy wine with soft tannins. The mature Reservas are big, bold and spicy, with dark plum and cassis fruit notes, which goes well with all red meats but especially beef steak. b) Grilled pork chops are paired better with a lighter red wine such as Pinot Noir or Sangiovese. c) Roast leg of lamb is a classic pairing with either a top quality Rioja or a Merlot based Bordeaux blend, such as a St-Emilion or Pomerol. These are not wine matching rulings just the summation of recommendations from Master Sommeliers.

10. *b. To test for any flaws especially cork taint.* You should taste or just smell a wine before it is served to you in a restaurant, because about 5% to 8% of wines with corks can be tainted by TCA (2,4,6-trichloroanisole). If it

is (corked) off, it will smell slightly of cardboard, wet socks or just smell musty. It will also often taste mouldy and muted with fruit flavours dulled down and the wine is left bland; it will not harm you, just be unpleasant to drink. Many New World quality wines, both reds and whites, in restaurants have screw caps instead of corks. In that case, just examine the label as some restaurants may try to palm you off with a lesser vintage or younger wine (if they have run out of the vintage on the wine list), If it is wrong you can ask for another wine. If it looks ok then say 'just pour', don't bother to go through the tasting ritual as it is an over 1,000 to 1 chance that the wine will have a flaw. You may not like it but that is a different problem. Other wine flaws to look out for are oxidised wines (only in older wines); too much oxygen exposure can turn the wine to a Sherry like taste or vinegar. Other rare flaws are fizzy bubbles (secondary fermentation occurring), Sulfur overuse, which tastes like a burnt match or a burnt rubber smell, in worst cases smells of rotten eggs.

ANSWERS TO QUIZ 87 – WINE BRANDS AND WINE BASED DRINKS

1. *c. Le Piat d'Or.* IDV (now Diageo) manufactured this wine to match the British wine drinkers' tastes of the 1970s. The British palate back then was for wine that was sweet and smooth, for both reds and whites. For the Le Piat d'Or blend, grape varieties with very low tannin content were used and grape juice (must) was then added to Le Piat d'Or during fermentation; this made it smooth and a little sweet with no rough edges. The bottle   DARK HORSE
    shape was also unique to stand out on the shelves. It was a cross between a Perrier bottle and an Indian club. With its gold label it looked like a special purchase. The large TV advertising budget had a slogan, 'The French adore Le Piat d'Or', which was extremely effective, but it was never sold in France.
    a) Black Tower was a successful German Liebfraumilch from the 1970s, similar to Blue Nun. b) Jacob's Creek was a top selling Australian brand, but not launched in the UK until 2004.

2. *b. Sainsbury's.* They launched their 'Taste the Difference' brand range of wines and food in the year 2000. It was the first upmarket brand range for a supermarket in the UK, and was very successful from the start. There are now well over 50 different wines in the Taste the Difference range, which often get very good reviews from wine critics. a) Morrisons launched their 'The Best'

brand of House Wines in 2005, to compete with Sainsbury's. c) Waitrose do not have an upmarket House Wines range.

3. **b. Sémillon & Merlot.** There is a Lillet Blanc and Rouge version of the wine based aperitif, which is 17% ABV and very popular in France, but not that well known in the UK or USA. It was founded in 1872 by the Lillet brothers in Podensac village in the Graves area of the Bordeaux region. It was sold as a Tonic Wine for many years, because of the quinine content. Both the red and white versions are 85% Bordeaux wines and then 15% of orange liqueur, and herbs, quinine and spices are added. Lillet is produced as a Bordeaux wine, with tank and barrel fermentation, fining, racking and filtering before ageing and bottling. Lillet is usually served on ice with a slice of orange, or lemon or lime peel.

4. **a. Barefoot.** This is by far the largest wine brand in terms of volume and value in the world, annually selling over $700million of wine. It was started in California in 1965, and its name refers to the free-spirited method of crushing grapes barefoot. The original winery was bought by E & J Gallo in 2005, the largest wine company in the world. b) Great Wall is an enormous wine brand made and sold mainly in China. c) Sutter Home is the second largest wine brand in the USA.

5. **c. Yellow Tail.** This brand was launched by the Casella family in 2000, and is based in Yenda, New South Wales, Australia. Its name comes from the yellow-footed wallaby which also features on all its labels. It has a wide range of white and red grape-named wines including Chardonnay and Shiraz and 10 or more others. By 2005 it was the most imported brand into the USA. It out-sold all the imports of French wine combined, accounting for 11% of all their imported wines. It is now the fourth largest wine brand in the world, exporting to over 80 countries and represents 8% by volume of all wine produced in Australia.

6. **c. Pernod Ricard.** Dubonnet was launched in 1846 in Paris by Joseph Dubonnet, and was bought by Pernod Ricard in 1976. It was originally produced to sell to the French Foreign Legion as a medicinal wine to ward off Malaria, because of its quinine content. It is a blend of red fortified wines mixed with secret herbs and quinine; it is aged in oak barrels before being released and bottled. Only in the United States is Dubonnet produced and marketed by Heaven Hill Distilleries of Bardstown, Kentucky. The French made version is 14.8% alcohol by volume and the US version 19% and sweeter with less quinine added. It was, and is now, one of Queen Elizabeth II's favourite cocktail drinks, either as gin and Dubonnet or Dubonnet and bitter lemon.

7. **b. Hirondelle.** It was one of the biggest selling wine brands in the 1970s in the UK. There was a red, and a white both medium dry, and a sweeter white

dessert version was launched. The actual grape varieties were never revealed on the label. The white version is thought to be made from a Muscat variety from Italy and Hungary. The red was made from various grape varieties sourced from Italy, Hungary and Austria. The brand name means swallow in French.

8. *c. Provence.* Noilly Prat, which is called the original French vermouth, has been made in Marseille for over 160 years, very near the sea and aged in oak barrels and left outside in all weathers to age gently. The salt, sea air, and wood impart complex flavours to this subtle vermouth with an ABV of 18%. Joseph Noilly, a herbalist, developed the first formula in 1813 and sold it locally for many years. Then his son Louis Noilly and his son-in-law Claudius Prat set up the company that became Noilly Prat in 1855, moving the business to Marseille where it remains to this day. There are now four types of Noilly Prat available, but the original dry white version is still by far the most popular. The company is now owned by the Bacardi-Martini family of brands.

9. *c. Torres.* It was founded in Penedès near Tarragona, Spain, in 1870 by Miguel and Jaime Torres. It has now celebrated its 150th Anniversary and is still run by the family. It is one of the largest wine companies in Spain exporting to over 140 countries. They also have wine estates in California and Chile, as well as in many of the major wine regions of Spain. The winery was destroyed by bombing in the Spanish Civil War and they had to rebuild from scratch. World War II helped their sales as most French and Italian wines could not be exported, due to German occupation; therefore Torres exported increasing volumes to the USA and UK. In 1970 their Coronas Black Label won the Wine Olympics in Paris, which also boosted their sales and reputation further. They have been voted the best wine brand in the world and for 9 years in a row also been voted the best European Wine Brand. b) Calvet is a French wine company founded in 1818 in Hermitage in the Rhône, then expanded to Burgundy and to Bordeaux. Nowadays its signature wines are value-priced red Bordeaux AOC. a) Antinori is the most famous name in Italy for top quality wines, originally from Tuscany. The influence of Piero Antinori on modern Italian winemaking has been profound, with the invention of Super Tuscans onwards.

10. *a. Concha y Toro.* The wine estate was founded in Santiago, Chile in 1883, and has grown to be the largest South American wine producer by far. It has over 10,000 hectares (25,000 acres) under vine and exports to over 140 countries, and has become the company with the most planted vineyards in the world. It sells over 15 million cases, or over 180 million bottles, per annum and is the 3rd biggest wine brand in the world. b) Cono Sur is the 3rd largest brand in Latin America with 3 million cases per annum, and Santa Rita is next with 2 million cases produced per year.

ANSWERS TO QUIZ 88 – ICONIC WINES OF EUROPE

1. *c. Vieux Telegraphe.* This Châteauneuf-du-Pape wine estate is one of the most celebrated and often the most expensive especially in good vintages. It has been in the Brunier family ownership since 1898. Its name comes from a telegraph tower on the vineyard's highest hill, built in 1793 by Claude Chappe, the inventor of the Telegraph communications system. a) Château de Beaucastel and b) Château Mont-Redon are also top Châteauneuf-du-Pape wine estates.

   PETRVS
   POMEROL

2. *b. Château Palmer.* A third growth in Margaux, it is said by many wine critics to have the most perfumed potent nose of blackberries and strawberries. It is also a wine of voluptuous power and complexity, and which is less than half the price of first growth Château Margaux.

3. *c. Domaine de la Romanée-Conti.* Often called DRC, it has its own AOC, and is a Grand Cru red Burgundy from the Vosne-Romanée commune. It is often one of the world's most expensive wines due to its quality and rarity. The wine uses vines which are over 50 years old with very low yields. It takes three vines to make one bottle of Romanée-Conti.

4. *c. Château d'Yquem.* It is literally in a class of its own; it is the only 'Premier Cru Superieur' of Sauternes, Barsac, and Bordeaux. With careful storage, bottles can last well over a century in perfect condition. Robert Parker gave the 1811 Château d'Yquem a perfect 100 points, when tasted in 1996. A bottle of 1811 sold for over £75,000 at London's Ritz Hotel in 2011, which was exactly 200 years after it was made.

5. *c. Le Pin.* Its first vintage was 1979, and its vineyard area has expanded by 100%, and it now produces wine from 5 acres (2 hectares) of gravel, clay and sandy soils. Le Pin is still microscopic even by Pomerol standards. Thus its circa 8,000 bottles of 100% Merlot sell for astronomic figures, mainly in the Far East and the USA. It is owned and managed by Jacques Thienpont, who is Belgian. It is often the most expensive red wine in the world; the 1982 vintage was selling for over £10,000 a bottle.

6. *a. Mosel.* The Mosel wine region has 7 of the 10 most expensive wines made in Germany, the other 3 are all from the Rheingau region. It is Germany's oldest wine growing region with production dating back to Roman times. It is also the world's steepest wine growing region with over 50% of vineyards situated on inclines of over 30° and is home to the world's steepest vineyard, the Bremmer Calmont which has an incline of 65°. A highest quality example of Mosel's top Rieslings is Egon Muller Scharzhofberger Riesling Trockenbeerenauslese, from the Muller family owned estate, founded

in 1797. It is the most expensive German wine because of many factors, including scarcity, and care in production. The wine is made from individually handpicked berries to produce a luscious dessert wine. Top vintages sell for over £24K a bottle, and is only 6% ABV. Answer b) The Nahe region produces everyday, very drinkable, good value wine. Answer c) The Rheingau region has changed recently from producing dessert wines to over 80% of wines being dry (Trocken).

7. *a. Domaine de la Romanée-Conti.* The 1945 vintage sold for $558,000 dollars according to the Guinness Book of Records, a world record for a single bottle. It was sold by Sotheby's auction house in New York on 13th October 2018.

8. *b. Dominio de Pingus.* Both Pingus and Vega Sicilia are made from 100% Tempranillo grapes in the Ribera del Duero wine region. Pingus is the 'new kid on the block' wine, launched in 1995 by Peter Sisseck, a Dane, who is owner, winemaker and manager. This micro winery produces only about 5,000 bottles per annum, and thus its extreme rarity and quality has helped make it the most 'consistently' expensive Spanish wine over its 25 year period of production. Answer a) Alvaro Palacios L'Ermita (Priorat) is the top single vineyard of old Garnacha vines, part of the larger Palacios Estate. L'Ermita is sometimes the most expensive wine at auction; it is grown on a 60° slope and produces around 5K bottles per year. Answer c). Teso La Monja (Toro) was founded in 2007 by Marcos Eguren, who is considered to be one of the finest winemakers in Spain. The wine is made from very old Tempranillo ungrafted vines. It is now one of the top wines of Spain.

9. *c. Tignanello.* This is the first ever Super Tuscan wine created by Piero Antinori in 1971. Tignanello thus started the long running trend of IGT Super Tuscan wines made with Bordeaux grapes, often with the addition of Sangiovese the red grape of Tuscany. Tignanello was also the first Tuscan wine to be aged in barriques, and not to have doses of white wine added to the red must. It is predominantly Sangiovese (75% to 85%, varies by vintage) with 15% to 25% Cabernet Sauvignon and 5% Cabernet Franc. It now has its own unique DOCG area. The average production varies between 40K and 80K bottles per year. Sassicaia IGT from Tenuta San Guido vies for being the oldest Super Tuscan; it is grown in its own DOC Bolgheri by Piero Antinori's uncle. But for over 30 years it was only bottled and drunk by the family. It was released first for sale in the mid 1970s, and in a 1978 Decanter blind tasting against top Bordeaux blends (from Bordeaux and 11 countries) it was awarded first place. Sassicaia is usually 85% Cabernet Sauvignon and 15% Cabernet Franc, with no Sangiovese. Average production is 180K bottles.

10. **c. Salon.** Salon champagne is a tiny champagne house on the Côte des Blancs. It only produces 50,000 bottles, when it declares a vintage, which is on average three or four times a decade. Salon produces the only wine in the world not to be made every year, just when there is exceptionally good weather. In the other 6/7 years of a decade that they don't make Salon, the grapes are sold off to other champagne houses. The quintessential blanc de blancs (100% Chardonnay) champagne is made using vines over 40 years old, which result in a rich yet delicate wine with complex aromas of fruit and flowers. In 1989 Salon was sold to Laurent-Perrier and since its first commercial vintage in 1920, in the next 100 years it only declared 41 vintages. It is a truly special and unique Chardonnay champagne which costs on average £700 a bottle.

ANSWERS TO QUIZ 89 – ICONIC WINES OUTSIDE EUROPE

1. **a. California.** Screaming Eagle was founded in 1986 by former real estate agent Jean Phillips, it epitomises low-production, exclusive Napa winemaking. The first vintage was in 1992 and thus the $500,000 bottle was the first Imperial made by the winery. With just 57 acres (23 hectares) of vineyards, and an annual production of around 500 cases, it has become a cult wine with a 10 year waiting list to buy from the winery. Robert Parker gave its first 1992 vintage a near-perfect 99 out of 100 rating. The winery would then receive the magic 100 Parker points for its 1997 vintage, as well as its 2007, 2010, and 2012 bottlings. It is thought that this is the world record for the most 100 point vintages awarded to a single wine estate.

2. **a. Château Lafite Rothschild.** They were the European pioneer investor and vineyard buyer in Chile. Los Vascos was launched in 1988, on land where vines had been growing since 1750. Replantings of Cabernet Sauvignon were introduced and now they account for 85% of all the vineyard's grape varieties. Los Vascos now produces around 300,000 cases (3 to 4 million bottles) of Cabernet Sauvignon per year. In Argentina in 1999, Lafite teamed up with family Catena to launch Domaine Caro, the best of Europe and Argentina with signature wines combining Cabernet Sauvignon and Malbec into flagship blends. Château Lafite Rothschild are also the pioneers of the finest wines in China, Domaine de Long Dai was planted in 2009 and its first vintage was 2017.

3. **a. $30,000.** Royal DeMaria Ice Wines are the most expensive in Canada
    and the world. In 2006 a half-bottle of 2000 Chardonnay Ice Wine was sold
    for $30,000 to a Saudi Arabian Prince. This 2000 vintage is also the most
    awarded Ice Wine in the world having twice won the trophy for 'the best
    Chardonnay in the world'. It has also won four gold medals at the Bordeaux
    Vinexpo world wine event. Joseph DeMaria started the wine estate in 1998
    with no previous winemaking experience. As owner and winemaker, his
    Royal DeMaria is the only estate in the world to specialise exclusively in the
    production of Ice Wine. Four grape varieties - Vidal, Riesling, Chardonnay and
    Cabernet Franc make his most sought after Ice Wines. Queen Elizabeth II and
    billionaires like Richard Branson are customers.

4. **a + b +c.** A trick question, all three are correct, as all three are owners of
    Cloudy Bay. The most correct answer is probably LVMH as they are the holding
    company of both the other two. Veuve Clicquot actually bought Cloudy Bay
    in 2003, but it is now part of LVMH as is Moët & Chandon. The Cloudy Bay
    estate lies in Wairau Valley, Marlborough which is at the northern tip of New
    Zealand's South Island. It takes its name from the most easterly point of the
    valley, which was named Cloudy Bay by the explorer Captain James Cook in
    1770. Since David Hohnen founded the estate in 1985 it has been the flagship
    NZ Sauvignon Blanc, but nowadays there are many new competitors for the
    top spot. They now also produce Pelorus sparkling wine, Chardonnay, Pinot
    Noir, Merlot and Cabernet Sauvignon.

5. **a. 1930s.** Gaston Hochar was only 20 years old when he started Chateau
    Musar by planting Bordeaux type grape varieties in the southern Bekaa valley
    in 1930. His son Serge Hochar became Decanter magazine's first ever Man
    of the Year in 1984. The red wines taste like exotic first growth Bordeaux,
    and differ every year in blend and taste. Their 180 hectares are all organic
    and their reds are neither fined nor filtered; it is minimalist winemaking at
    its best. Gaston Hochar, the great-grandson of the founder, and named after
    him, is now chief winemaker and family manager of the winery. Other family
    members are all involved in exporting, and the commercial side. It is still truly
    a family business. Both the top red and white wines (also a rosé now) are high
    quality and slow in the fermentation, production and maturing process, taking
    at least seven years at Chateau Musar before the wine is released. The 2012
    white Chateau Musar was only released in 2020, as was the 2013 red.

6. **c. Shiraz.** Penfolds Grange Bin 95 is at least 95% to 100% Shiraz
    dependent on the vintage weather, (the additional 5% to 0% is Cabernet
    Sauvignon). It is the iconic wine of Australia and often called the 'Southern
    Hemisphere's only First Growth', putting it on a par with Château Lafite and
    Margaux in terms of quality. Grange's reputation as one of the world's most

celebrated wines continues to grow today. On its 50th birthday in 2001, Grange was listed as a South Australian heritage icon, while the 2008 Grange vintage achieved a perfect score of 100 points by two of the world's most influential wine magazines.

7. ***b. Rio Negro in Patagonia.*** Noemia is the most expensive Malbec wine in the world, and not grown in Mendoza or Cahors. It is produced in extreme and unusual circumstances of geography and wine growing. Patagonia's Rio Negro Valley is the setting of this small but beautiful winery, 620 miles south of Buenos Aires in the middle of the desert. This extreme winemaking is made possible by irrigation channels excavated by British colonists in the 1820s. The climate is bone dry with just seven inches of rain each year and it is in one of the most southerly wine areas in the world. Hans Vinding-Diers is the Danish, South African born, Bordeaux-trained winemaker at Noemia. He is a perfectionist and has restored ancient pre-Phylloxera vines to make his flagship Malbec.

8. ***a. Cornwall.*** The most southerly and westerly county of England has less than a dozen commercial vineyards, but has some very high quality ones, especially Camel Valley, between Bodmin and Padstow. Camel Valley has become the first English wine producer to be granted a royal warrant, and their sparkling wines are often served at State Banquets held at Buckingham Palace. Their 2013 Camel Valley Brut sparkling wine is served in British Airways First Class, and is the House English sparkler for Fortnum & Mason.

9. ***a. Muscat.*** It makes one of the most luscious dessert wines in the world. The renowned 'Groot Constantia Grand Constance' is South Africa's oldest wine established in 1685 by the first Governor of the Cape, Simon van der Stel, and is the finest example of the famous 'Constantia Wyn' as drunk by Emperors and Kings, from Napoleon and Frederick the Great of Prussia to Louis Phillipe (King of the French). All vied for their share of Constantia in the 18th and 19th centuries. It was Napoleon's lifetime favourite and deathbed wine on St Helena. Muscat is one of the oldest and widest spread wine grape varieties in the world, throughout history making sweet dessert wine, but also dry versions, or even high quality fortified 'Liqueur Muscats' in Australia.

10. ***a. Casa Madero.*** It was founded in 1597 and is the oldest winery in the Americas. Felipe II, King of Spain, authorised the planting of the vineyards in August of that year, in order to make wine and brandy for the invading and then ruling Conquistadors, and it has operated continuously since 1597. It is also Mexico's most awarded winery, winning more than 900 medals for its wines in international competitions. The vineyards and winery of Casa Madero are located in the Sierra Madre Mountains in the northern state of

Coahuila. They are planted at a 5,000 ft altitude which makes it possible, with the cool climate, to make such fine wines with finesse in such a hot country. They make both red and white wine, including 15 separate wines (of 3 quality levels). Their Gran Reservas are Chardonnay, Shiraz, Cabernet Sauvignon, 3V Bordeaux Blend, Merlot and Malbec.

ANSWERS TO QUIZ 90 – MATCH ICONIC WINES OF THE WORLD – PART 1

1. ***d. Lebanon, Bekaa Valley.*** In 1930, Chateau Musar was established by purchasing land and planting Bordeaux type grape varieties in the Bekaa Valley. The winery and offices are located in Ghazir, 15 miles north of Beirut overlooking the Mediterranean, which is a 2.5 hour drive from their vineyards in the Bekaa Valley in the far south. The reason is in the turmoil of Lebanon being formed, the Hochars' wanted to be sure that their wine business would be in the Christian area near Beirut. The southern Bekaa vineyards benefit from an altitude of around 1000 metres and the subsequent cool nights serve to lengthen the crucial ripening process. Both the top red and white wine (also rosé now) are high quality, and slow in making and maturing, taking at least 7 years at Chateau Musar before release. The 2012 white Chateau Musar was only released in 2020, as was the 2013 red.

2. ***c. USA, Washington State.*** Chateau Ste Michelle is Washington State's oldest winery formed from land purchased from a lumber baron in 1912. It is also the largest (2 million cases per year) and the most acclaimed winery in Washington, with more award-winning wines. It is situated in a historic chateau near Seattle. Chateau Ste Michelle produces over 800,000 cases of Riesling wine per year, making them the largest producer of premium Rieslings in the world. The winery owns several estate vineyards in Eastern Washington including the Canoe Ridge vineyard in the Horse Heaven Hills AVA, the Cold Creek vineyard and Indian Wells vineyards in the Columbia Valley AVA. These are all top Riesling growing areas, planted at high altitude and having cool weather.

3. ***b. France, Bordeaux.*** Château Montrose, the well-known second growth of Bordeaux's St-Estèphe Commune was formed in 1778 and makes very expensive quality Medocs that need extensive ageing to be at their best. In fact Château Montrose produces some of the longest-lived wines in the

entire Bordeaux region. Montrose's wine is typically a blend of 65% Cabernet Sauvignon, 25% Merlot and 10% Cabernet Franc and is matured in oak barriques (30% new) for 18 months. The 1990, 2009, and 2010 vintages were rated at 100 points (perfect) by Robert Parker.

4. ***a. Australia, Barossa Valley.*** Château Tanunda calls itself the icon of the Barossa, which many wine critics agree with. Château Tanunda was the birthplace of the Barossa Valley wine industry established in 1890. It is on the site of the valley's first vines planted in 1845, as well as then becoming Barossa's first winery. The Geber family have been making wines there continuously for the last 130 years. Château Tanunda are world-renowned for their Old Vine wines. Their signature 150 year old vines wine called 1858 Field Blend, and the 100 year old, Old Vine Shiraz, and 100 year old Everest Old Vine Grenache and Shiraz, are treasured by wine critics and exported to wine collectors in China, the USA and Europe. Most of their wine production is red wine, leading with Shiraz, Cabernet Sauvignon and Bordeaux blends. Château Tanunda has now become the largest Château in the Southern Hemisphere. The Château also has an international standard cricket pitch that hosts the annual Masters games that traditionally feature some of the legends of Test cricket.

5. ***e. Chile, Cachapoal Valley.*** The first vineyards of Chateau Los Boldos were planted 100km south of Santiago in the foothills of the Andes in 1948. The estate itself, and Chateau Los Boldos, was then founded there in 1991, with 170 hectares of vineyards of Sauvignon Blanc, Merlot, Cabernet Sauvignon and Syrah. This little-known Chilean wine region has long played second fiddle to its more celebrated neighbours, Maipo (to the north) and Colchagua (to the south); but now with its varied terroir it is coming into its own on the International wine stage.

6. ***h. Vidal.*** This grape variety is the predominant grape making Canadian Ice Wine in both Ontario and British Columbia. It's a hardy hybrid grape that has great resistance to freezing temperatures, has high natural acidity and creates lots of sugars, and is thus ideal for growing Ice Wines in Canada and the north-eastern United States (Finger Lakes area). Vidal can also make dry white table wines, but its best use is in creating luscious and intense Ice Wines which are both floral and fruity, and sweet, with a balance of intense acidity.

7. ***j. Sangiovese.*** Chianti, in the Tuscan region of Italy, has one predominant grape which is Sangiovese. Since 1996 the blend for Chianti and Chianti Classico has been 75% to 100% Sangiovese, with up to 10% Canaiolo and up to 20% of Merlot, Syrah or Cabernet Sauvignon. Since 2006 the use of white grape varieties added to the blend has been prohibited. The Sangiovese grape has dark berries and thick skin and is the most widely planted grape variety

in Italy, especially in Tuscany. It often has a flavour profile of sour red cherries with earthy aromas and medium tannins with high acidity.

8. *f. Chardonnay.* Chablis from the north of Burgundy is often said to be the Chardonnay with the most finesse and elegance. Because of its austere fruit freshness with minerality and crisp acidity, many people do not know that Chablis is a Chardonnay. Chablis has been an enormous success worldwide; 50 years ago there were only 400 hectares of Chablis, now there are 4,900 hectares. This is probably the largest expansion in France of any Appellation area. Chardonnay is the most popular white grape (Airén the most planted) in the world. Chardonnay has arguably the widest taste profile of any grape variety; from the bone dry Chablis style to the richer, classically hazelnuts, creamy and minerally intense dry whites of the Côte de Beaune. In the New World, Chardonnay varies from the melon, apple and grapefruit cool climate styles (NZ), to the more tropical fruit salad styles with flavours of peach, mango, lime and pineapple (originally an Australian style).

9. *g. Tempranillo.* Rioja is a wine region in north-central Spain, 20 miles south of Bilbao. There are 64,000 hectares of vineyards divided between three provinces on the Upper Ebro river. Rioja produces around 300 million litres (400 million bottles) of wine per annum, of which 90% is red and the rest is a mixture of white and rosés. The dominant grape is Tempranillo, which can also have Garnacha, Graciano, and Mazuelo added to the Rioja blend. Rioja was also the first wine region in Spain (in 1926) to establish a DOC area with all the rules and regulations. Now Tempranillo is grown in many other countries, although still about 85% is in Spain, where it is still their flagship grape variety.

10. *i. Touriga Nacional.* The Douro Valley wine region is allowed to use up to 40 grape varieties for making both Ports and still red wines. Touriga Nacional is not the widest planted grape, but it is the variety with the iconic reputation. Despite its low yields from its very small thick skin grape berries, it is increasingly used for both table wines and Port blends in the Douro, and now also in the Dão region. Most Port blends for Vintage or Tawny or LBV are made from up to 5 different grape varieties, led by Touriga Nacional. Its importance in a Port blend is often compared to French Cabernet Sauvignon in a Bordeaux blend. Both grapes display bold dark fruit flavours with hints of spice. It is Portugal's iconic grape and has the best claim to world-class status.

ANSWERS TO QUIZ 91 – MATCH ICONIC WINES OF THE WORLD – PART 2

1. **e. Sauvignon Blanc.** Cloudy Bay on the northern tip of New Zealand's South Island was founded in 1985 by David Hohnen, who was the famous Australian pioneer winemaker from the Margaret River Valley, where he established Cape Mentelle in 1976. Cloudy Bay gained worldwide fame for its very intense and concentrated grassy and zingy fresh Sauvignon Blanc wines. They also now make a Chardonnay, Merlot, Pinot Noir and even a Cabernet Sauvignon. It Is now owned by Veuve Clicquot, the prestigious Champagne House and part of the LVMH Group.

2. **a. White Zinfandel.** Blossom Hill White Zinfandel is juicy and smooth and easy to quaff. It is just a sweeter, lighter coloured version of a rosé wine, usually produced in California. They used to be referred to as Blush wines, but lately the name has reverted to White Zinfandel. Carol Thorup was Blossom Hill's first winemaker, starting in 1992. Her belief was there was too much complication and snobbery about wine – while it is just about an enjoyable taste. So she created a range of fruity wines, from juicy red berries to zesty citrus and wonderful watermelon flavours. There's a whole world of taste in Blossom Hill wines at a very competitive price. It is now extremely popular in the USA and sold copiously in UK supermarkets.

3. **b. Merlot.** Petrus from Pomerol in the Bordeaux area is one of the top five red wines in the world and now 100% made from Merlot grapes. It was virtually unheard of 30 years ago and It was only when the Moueix family bought a half share in the property in 1962 that its true potential began to be fully realised. The Petrus vineyards are just under 12 hectares (30 acres), and the vines are unusually old and are only replanted after they reach 70 years old. The grapes are hand harvested only in the afternoon, when the morning dew has evaporated, so as not to risk even the slightest dilution of quality. The grapes are then fermented in cement vats and the wine is aged in 100% new oak barrels for 22–28 months. It is bottled unfiltered, and Petrus will age for many years producing a concentrated, creamy, smooth, yet rich and powerful complex red with black fruit flavours. In an average year only 4,000 cases are produced, the rarity rockets the price and for the stunning vintage of 1982 a bottle of Petrus sells for over £3,500.

4. **c. Malbec.** Catena Zapata was founded in 1902 by Italian immigrant Nicolas Catena and now his grandson Nicolas Catena Zapata (Nicolas Catena) runs the whole enormous Catena enterprise of quality wines in Argentina. As a real

pioneer, he introduced European winemaking techniques to Argentina, including the introduction of Malbec, and vine growing at high altitudes above 1,400 metres. He is known worldwide for spearheading the re-emergence of Malbec – the French varietal that had been almost completely forgotten by the rest of the world, and making it into the iconic grape variety of Argentina. In 2009, Nicolas Catena became the first person from South America to receive the prestigious Decanter Man of the Year award for producing world-class Malbecs.

5. *d. Pinotage.* Kanonkop in South Africa, based in the foothills of the Simonberg Mountains near Stellenbosch, is one of the top wine producers of Pinotage, which is grown almost exclusively in South Africa (98%). This variety is a crossing of Pinot Noir and Cinsault, first bred in 1925 but not used commercially until 1943. At its best it makes a red wine which is rich, concentrated, and dense with a flavour of black and red fruits, spice and chocolate. Kanonkop makes the best Pinotage in the world, called Black Label. This is a Single Vineyard using old vines planted in 1953.

6. *h. Prosecco, Sparkling.* Adriano Adami has been producing Prosecco Valdobbiadene DOCG and Prosecco Treviso DOC for over 90 years and is regarded as one of the top Prosecco wineries. Prosecco is made from the Glera grape, the best comes from the Valdobbiadene region in north-east Italy. It is the sparkling success story of the last 10 years. The UK consumes the most Prosecco in the world, almost one-third. UK consumption, driven by supermarket sales has more than doubled in less than 10 years. UK consumers now drink over 130 million bottles per year.

7. *i. Champagne, Sparkling.* Nicolas Feuillatte champagne is the region's largest co-operative. It is the oldest union of producers of champagne with 82 winemaking cooperatives representing more than 5,000 winegrowers and vineyards. It is situated on a hill in Chouilly overlooking Epernay. The Nicolas Feuillatte brand was created in 1976, and now produces about 15 million bottles of champagne per year, from 8% of all vineyards. It is the best-selling brand of champagne in France, and the third biggest global brand, just behind Moët & Chandon and Veuve Clicquot, both owned by LVMH.

8. *f. Barbaresco, Red.* Angelo Gaja took over the company, which is located in Barbaresco in Piedmont, in 1970. He is widely credited with transforming the image and quality of Italian wines as a whole. His fine wines now compete with the top wines of Burgundy and Bordeaux in terms of price and quality. Gaja has been producing wines for over 160 years. It now produces over a million bottles of high-quality wine per year. Their top Barbaresco and Barolo sell for over £300 a bottle. Both these wines are made from the Nebbiolo

grape, producing similar wines which are pale red, yet full-bodied and elegant with notes of dark cherries and an earthy finish.

9. *j. Rioja, Red.* Marqués de Riscal, along with Murrieta, were pioneers of Rioja back in the 19th century, when the wines were distinguished by long oak barrel ageing. They have evolved over two centuries and are now summer fruit packed, silky, elegant and jammy reds which can be drunk when released at 5 years old. Riscal, one of the oldest bodegas, now produces around 1 million bottles a year. 90% of all Riojas are red and most are made from a blend of three grape varieties, Tempranillo, Garnacha and Graciano. Rioja wine region has three levels of quality starting with Crianza wines, then Reservas and then finally Gran Reservas, which can age for decades. Rioja now produces an average of 360 million to 400 million bottles per year, and the UK imports about 50 million bottles, which is 40% of all Spanish wines consumed in the UK.

10. *g. Burgundy, White.* Jean-Marc Brocard has been making top quality white Burgundy from the Chardonnay grape in Chablis since 1973. It was by happy accident he married a vineyard owner's daughter and inherited the vineyard. He was an innovator from the start using more stainless steel and now ceramic eggs for fermenting, thus making even fresher more balanced fruity wines with elegance. Their Domaine covers over 200 hectares, and produces Village Chablis, Premier Cru and Grand Cru Chablis which are all elegant and fresh, with elements of mineral and citrus fruit flavours. Most of the wines are now biodynamic. Chardonnay is originally from France's Burgundy region, where almost all white Burgundies are now Chardonnay. The best white Burgundies are powerful and rich, with complex fruit flavours and notes of earth and minerals. Chablis is the most northerly of the white Burgundy regions.

ANSWERS TO QUIZ 92 – WHITE WINES OF THE WORLD

1. *a. Château-Grillet.* Since 1936, Château-Grillet has had its own appellation, and is the stand-out wine produced in the well-known Condrieu appellation in the northern Rhône, and is made from 100% Viognier grapes. Viognier is now grown in many countries around the world, but the northern Rhône is its spiritual home and, in particular, Condrieu and Château-Grillet.

2. **Bacchus.** The Roman God of Wine. Bacchus is one of the best-known white grape varieties used in the production of English wine, and is very popular amongst most of the leading wine producers in England. The wine is fresh, dry, elegant, and aromatic. In riper years, it can develop tropical fruit flavours.

3. **c. Austria.** Located north-west of Vienna, Kamptal is one of the leading Austrian wine regions and is positioned next to other top regions such as Wachau, Kremstal, and Wagram. Several grape varieties are produced in the Kamptal region, with Riesling and Grüner Veltliner being the most important. The region is named after the River Kamp that runs through it.

4. **b. Santorini.** The island of Santorini lies about ninety miles due north of Crete, in the Aegean Sea. Its production of top quality Assyrtiko white wine, made from grapes grown on volcanic ash-rich soil, has won countless international wine awards. Assyrtiko is one of Greece's most famous and successful wines. On Santorini, sun-dried Assyrtiko grapes are also used to make the sweet wine, Vinsanto.

5. **a. Chateau Montelena.** In the famous 1976 tasting competition in Paris, organised by the well-known wine writer, Steven Spurrier, who had a wine business there at the time, top Californian red and white wines were tasted blind against top French wines, by an eminent panel of judges. Seen by most people at the time as a foregone conclusion (the French would easily win), the results shocked the world of wine when, not only did Chateau Montelena 1973 Chardonnay, from California's Napa Valley, win the white wine section, but Stag's Leap 1973 Cabernet Sauvignon, also from Napa, won the red wine section!

6. **b. Marlborough.** Cloudy Bay takes its name from a bay named by Captain Cook in 1770, at the northern tip of Marlborough, on the South Island of New Zealand. Their Sauvignon Blanc, launched in 1985, was their flagship wine and is still the grape variety that they are most associated with today. Cloudy Bay Sauvignon Blanc was the wine chosen by the New Zealand Prime Minister, John Key, in 2014 to serve to the Duke and Duchess of Cambridge during their royal tour of the country.

7. **c. Franken.** This region begins about twenty miles east of Frankfurt, and borders the wine regions of Baden and Württemberg. Contrary to the norm in Germany, Franken produces better wine from Silvaner grapes than it does from Riesling. Silvaner is widely planted in this region, and has a close affinity with the clay-limestone soil of Franken. Its food-friendly, light acidity character has become increasingly popular with winegrowers.

8. **a. Porto.** Produced in Portugal's northernmost province of Minho, Vinho Verde is made right up to the banks of the River Minho, which separates

Portugal from the province of Galicia in Spain. To the south, the production area runs a little further on from the city of Porto. 'Verde', meaning 'Green', refers to the fact that these are young wines, meant for drinking early, and are fresh, crisp, and lively.

9. **a. Torrontés.** In recent years, Torrontés has been a hugely successful white wine in Argentina and, indeed, it is increasingly being grown elsewhere in the world. It's produced all over Argentina, and its character varies, depending on where in the country it is grown. Essentially, it has a light peach, apricot, and rose petal aroma, with a fresh, smooth texture and moderate acidity on the palate.

10. **a. Baja California.** Located in the far north-west of Mexico, the state of Baja California is the heartland of the Mexican wine industry, producing around 85% of all Mexican wine. The peninsula of Baja California is over 700 miles long, but the winegrowing area is concentrated in the very north of the peninsula, close to the border town of Tijuana. The largest concentration of Mexico's new wave of enterprising and progressive vintners is in the Guadalupe Valley, part of the Ensenada Valleys, about an hour's drive south of the Californian border.

ANSWERS TO QUIZ 93 – RED WINES OF THE WORLD

1. **Moulin-à-Vent.** Arguably the best of the ten Beaujolais cru, Moulin-à-Vent, windmill in French, made from the Gamay grape variety, is also a more full-bodied and tannic Beaujolais, partly because of the crumbly pink granite soil, with seams of manganese. It's situated towards the northern end of the Beaujolais wine region, with Chénas, Juliénas, and St-Amour above it.

2. **a. Pinot Noir and Cinsaut.** Historically, the Cinsaut grape was called Hermitage in South Africa, hence the name Pinotage. It was created in 1925 by the first professor of viticulture at Stellenbosch University, Abraham Izak Perold, who wanted to produce a grape that combined the sturdiness of Hermitage with the difficult-to-grow Pinot Noir, in order to create a grape that benefited from both characters. Today, Pinotage is increasingly being grown in other parts of the world, but its origins lie in South Africa.

3. **c. Australia.** Known as Australia's 'First Growth', Penfolds Grange is produced predominantly from the Shiraz (Syrah) grape variety, with a little

Cabernet Sauvignon. It's officially listed as a Heritage Icon of South Australia, and is sourced mainly from the Barossa Valley vineyards, with smaller amounts from Magill Estate and McLaren Vale.

4. *c. Touriga Nacional.* Also grown to produce wine in other Portuguese wine regions, particularly the Douro and Dão, Touriga Nacional is an important grape variety in the blends to produce Port, along with Touriga Franca and Tinta Roriz grapes. Touriga Nacional is a thick-skinned grape, rich in colour and tannins. It adds to the structure of Port with its intense, floral, and fruity flavours.

5. *b. Austria.* The wine region of Burgenland wraps itself around Lake Neusiedl in north-east Austria, close to the Hungarian border. It's home to Austria's greatest sweet wines, and also home to some of the country's best Blaufränkisch red wine. It's a late ripening grape, characterised by prominent tannins with balanced acidity. Blaufränkisch is generally seen by Austrians as their finest red wine.

6. *a. Pinot Noir.* Oregon produces a huge range of grape varieties, but the one that this state is world-famous for is their cool climate, high quality, Pinot Noir. The vast percentage of Oregon's Pinot Noir is produced in the iconic Willamette Valley, which is home to many hundreds of wineries.

7. *c. Rhône Valley.* Château de Beaucastel is one of the biggest wine estates in the Châteauneuf-du-Pape region of the southern Rhône Valley. It is also one of the very top producers. The Perrin family have run Château de Beaucastel for several generations, and is currently run by four Perrin brothers.

8. *a. Lake Garda.* Produced in the province of Verona, around part of the eastern shores of Lake Garda, close to the lakeside town of Bardolino itself. The light red wine of Bardolino is produced from Corvina, Rondinella, and Molinara grapes, the same ones as nearby Valpolicella.

9. *b. Malbec.* Despite its roots being French, and mainly in Bordeaux, as well as Cahors, it was Argentina that really put this grape on the map as a single varietal and, indeed, in a reverse role it was Malbec that put Argentine wine on the map! The country has been producing high quality full-bodied, plump and juicy Malbecs since the 1990s, and Argentina is now seen as the Malbec capital of the world.

10. *c. Lebanon.* Chateau Musar is made in the well-known Bekaa Valley, where most Lebanese wines are produced. If anyone with a knowledge of wine was asked to name one producer from Lebanon, they would doubtless say Chateau Musar. It's a famous wine, first produced by Gaston Hochar, and then by his son, Serge Hochar, who died in 2014, and now by Serge's son, also called Gaston. His blend of Cabernet Sauvignon, Cinsault, and Carignan produces a wine of superb quality.

ANSWERS TO QUIZ 94 – SPARKLING WINES OF THE WORLD

1. *Taittinger.* Comtes de Champagne is the family-owned house of Taittinger's top-of-the-range prestige champagne. It's available in both Blanc de Blancs and Brut Rosé styles. Created in Taittinger's Gallo-Roman chalk cellars under the former Saint-Nicaise Abbey in Reims, Comtes de Champagne is sought after around the world by collectors, investors, and drinkers alike.

2. *Prosecco.* Produced from the Glera grape variety, Prosecco is made in north-east Italy, in the Veneto and Friuli Venezia Giulia regions. The sparkle is usually achieved by using the Tank Method of secondary fermentation, which is quicker and cheaper than the traditional champagne method where the secondary fermentation takes place in bottle over a much longer period. The finest, and more expensive, versions of Prosecco usually come from the top quality DOCG region of Conegliano Valdobbiadene.

3. *a. Tasmania.* The Jansz vineyard is located in the Tamar Valley in northern Tasmania. The vineyards lie in the heart of the Pipers River region, an area known as 'Sparkling Tasmania'. Jansz is produced by the traditional, and more expensive, Champagne Method of secondary fermentation in bottle. Tasmania has a worldwide reputation for producing excellent sparkling wine, and Jansz is seen as the best-known.

4. *b. Penedès.* Cava is mainly produced in Penedès in Catalunya, and the three most important grapes are Macabeo, Parellada, and Xarel-lo. Two producers dominate production, Codorníu and Freixenet. Cava is closer to champagne than, say, Prosecco, because it's usually made using the traditional method of secondary fermentation in bottle, as opposed to Prosecco being mainly produced by the cheaper carbonated Tank Method.

5. *False.* The name 'champagne' is legally protected around the world. It is often used generically by people to mean sparkling wine, but to call it champagne it has to be produced in the strictly delimited champagne region of France, which starts roughly ninety miles east of Paris, with the two main cities being Reims and Epernay. There are three main grape-growing regions in the champagne district – Montagne de Reims, Vallée de la Marne, and Côtes des Blancs.

6. *a. Pinot Meunier.* This grape is often regarded as the least noble of the three main grapes used to produce champagne, the other two being Pinot Noir and Chardonnay. But it accounts for about a third of plantings in the region, and is often blended with either one or both of the other two leading

grapes by the different champagne houses, to add its particular character to their house styles.

7. *c. Charmat Method.* The sparkle can be achieved in sparkling wine by using the Tank, or Charmat, Method of secondary fermentation, which is quicker and cheaper than the traditional champagne method where the secondary fermentation takes place in bottle over a much longer period. The large stainless steel tanks trap carbonation in the wine, which produces the sparkle.

8. *a. Lombardy.* Produced by the traditional, or champagne, method of secondary fermentation in bottle, Franciacorta is a high quality sparkling wine made in Lombardy, between the shores of Lake Iseo and the city of Brescia. Grape varieties used are two of the classic champagne grapes of Pinot Noir and Chardonnay, plus Pinot Blanc. It has the top Italian wine status of DOCG (Denominazione di Origine Controllata e Garantita).

9. *b. Taittinger.* Launched in 1987 in the Napa Valley, as a joint venture with the Kopf family of Kobrand Wine & Spirits, Domaine Carneros is produced in one of California's oldest and most celebrated viticultural areas. Taittinger and Kobrand created a high quality terroir-driven sparkling wine, using traditional methods of production. The Chateau at Domaine Carneros is considered to be one of the most beautiful wineries in North America.

10. *c. Jasmine Monet.* The grapes that produce Jasmine Monet sparkling wine are selected from the company's own vineyards in the Gualtallary district of Tupungato, in the famous Uco Valley region of Mendoza. This region is renowned for its ideal combination of climate and soil for the production of high quality vines. Produced from the classic Pinot Noir and Chardonnay grapes, Jasmine Monet sparkling wine is 100% organic.

ANSWERS TO QUIZ 95 – SWEET DESSERT WINES OF THE WORLD

1. ***a. Bordeaux.*** They are the world famous great classic sweet dessert wines of France from the Communes of Sauternes and Barsac, part of the Graves region of Bordeaux. All the wineries in the area can be labelled appellation Sauternes, but many now choose to call themselves Barsac, when it is their village/commune such as Château Coutet and Château Climens. All these dessert wines are made from the Sémillon grape, sometimes blended by the addition of a little Sauvignon Blanc. They are late harvested, after 'noble rot' has shrivelled the grapes and concentrated the sugars within. If 'noble rot' does not occur they are just sold as Bordeaux Whites, but this is an unusual occurrence nowadays. The wines have great finesse and complexity, including soft acidity to balance their sweetness.

2. ***b. Royal Tokaji Essencia 2008.*** This wine from Tokaji is the only one ever to be bottled in a special crystal decanter of 1.5 Litres. It sells to collectors or billionaires at £35,000 each. It is from the village of Mad in Hungary. Royal Tokaji was started by Hugh Johnson and two partners back in 1990. It takes over 180 litres of shrivelled 'raisined' grapes to make a 1.5 litre of Essencia decanter, and over 200 hours to pick them; that is equivalent to over 400lbs of grapes and then 10 years plus ageing per 1.5 litre decanter. a) Scharzhofberger Riesling Trockenbeerenauslese sells for over £5,000 a bottle, while c) Château d'Yquem Sauternes sells on average for £300 to £600 a bottle depending on the vintage.

3. ***b. Riesling.*** Almost all of New Zealand's sweet dessert wines are made from the Riesling grape. The best NZ sweet wines are made from grapes influenced by 'noble rot', Botrytis Cinerea; a few are just super ripe and a tiny minority are Ice Wines. Increasingly other grape varieties are now being used, including Gewürztraminer, Chenin Blanc and Sauvignon Blanc.

4. ***c. Sicily.*** Marsala is a large wine port in the west of Sicily, and Marsala is also the sweet fortified wine produced there since 1773. In that year John Woodhouse, a Liverpool trader, visited Marsala by accident, because a storm at sea forced him to take refuge there. At the local tavern he tried the wine, which he liked. He decided to buy a cargo of barrels of the wine, to take on his ship back to Liverpool. To ensure that the wine did not spoil on the long sea trip back to Liverpool he added brandy to each barrel. These newly imported fortified wines became so popular that he returned to Marsala and started a Marsala fortified wine business. Woodhouse Marsala became a firm favourite and was supplied to the British Navy, and the victory of the Battle of Trafalgar was toasted by Lord Nelson with Marsala. So Marsala, the Sicilian dessert wine

was discovered, produced and exported to the UK by British trading companies for 60 years until 1832 when a local Sicilian company, Vincenzo Florio, entered the market and now dominates the top quality production of Marsala.

5. **b. Muscat.** This has been the grape grown for dessert wines on the Constantia estates (Klein and Groot) since it began vintages in 1685. The legendary Klein Constantia 'Vin de Constance' was the favourite wine of kings and queens of Europe, and the Tzars of Russia during the 18th and 19th centuries. It was the absolute favourite of Emperor Napoleon in his later years and which he drank on his deathbed on St Helena.

6. **b. Mosel.** The Mosel Valley produces the largest quantity of quality dessert wines in Germany, including Eiswein (Ice Wine). The other top dessert wines it produces are Trockenbeerenauslese, and late harvest Rieslings. In 2019 global warming meant that no Ice Wine could be made at all in Germany. This was because the temperature in winter never fell to $-8°C$ required by law. c) Rheinhessen is the largest of the 13 German wine regions, but it makes mainly dry and medium table wines. a) Baden is the most southerly wine region which is making excellent quality Pinot Noir. Red wines are now approaching 50% of Baden wine production.

7. **c. Vin Santo.** This translates as holy wine in Italy. It originates from Tuscany and is made from many grape varieties especially Trebbiano and Malvasia. They are usually called straw wines as the grapes are dried on straw mats outside in the sun until they become like raisins. Fortified Vin Santo does exist but it is always called 'Liquoroso'. a) Banyuls is a south of France fortified sweet wine which has been made since the 13th century. b) Malaga is a fortified wine made from Pedro Ximénez and Muscat grapes.

8. **a. Canada.** Almost 90% of the world's production of Ice Wine is now made in Canada. Germany used to dominate by value and volume, but global warming and changing fashions in wine caused Germany to refocus on other dessert wines, late harvest dried berries selection Trockenbeerenauslese. Ice Wine by law has to be picked at under -8°C, when the berries are all frozen. In 2018 no Ice Wine was produced in Germany because the temperature did not fall low enough. In Canada when the temperature reaches under -8°C, grape picking by hand starts and the frozen berries are gently pressed to exude about 20% sugar liquid and the rest of 80% are ice crystals and disposed of. It takes at least 4 to 5 times as many grapes to make a bottle of Ice Wine compared to a normal table wine.

9. **a. Furmint.** This is the dominant grape variety in the Tokaji region, accounting for almost two thirds of vineyards. The loose bunches and thick skins make the variety perfect for producing 'Botrytised' dessert wines. After

'noble rot', the berries have very concentrated and elegant sugars left over to gently extract as liquid gold. Furmint also makes very good dry white wines that are increasingly being produced and being exported. The sweet and dry wines are light coloured, well balanced with fruit and zesty acidity.

10. **a. Botrytis Cinerea.** A horrible name for a process that helps produce the world's most luscious, concentrated, distinctive quality sweet dessert wines. This 'noble rot' magic grey fungus infects the grape bunches, produces a furry mold-cover, then shrivels them up, and concentrates the sugars within. It helps create wines with unique finesse and a balance of honey sweetness that is never cloying. There is always a residual dry bite of acidity with the finish. Prime examples are Sauternes and Tokajis, especially Essencia.

ANSWERS TO QUIZ 96 – FORTIFIED WINES OF THE WORLD

1. **b. Bual.** A sweeter style than both Sercial and Verdelho, but less sweet than Malmsey, Bual is a dark and fragrant Madeira, with balanced acidity. So an ideal choice for a dessert wine. In Madeira itself, Bual is a popular choice for accompanying a cheeseboard, with sweet fruit preserves, or with dark chocolate.

   DUBONNET

2. **a. Ratafia.** Ratafia de Champagne is a fortified wine produced in the champagne region. The juice of Pinot Noir, Chardonnay, and Pinot Meunier grapes are fortified with Marc de Champagne, or an eaux-de-vie from the region. It's a typical Champenois aperitif.

3. **b. Commandaria.** Grown around fourteen designated villages on the lower slopes of the Troodos Mountains in Cyprus, Commandaria is a sweet dessert wine made from sun-dried Mavro and Xynisteri grapes. Producers have the option to fortify or not to fortify. Production is said to date back to the ancient Greeks, and in the twelfth century Richard the Lionheart described it as the wine of kings and the king of wines.

4. **b. Andrew Quady.** Producing his fortified wine called Elysium, meaning 'a state of eternal bliss', from Black Muscat grapes since the 1980s, Andrew Quady is justly proud of his award-winning dessert wine. It marries extremely well with various cheeses and desserts and, indeed, can be delicious in cocktails.

5. **Cognac.** A fortified wine from Cognac in France, Pineau des Charentes is a blend of the Charente region's grape juice, and cognac brandy itself. It

is usually drunk as an aperitif. Ageing can be for a period of months, or for years, depending on the producer. Though well-known in its region of origin, Pineau des Charentes is much less familiar elsewhere in France and, indeed, in other parts of the world.

6.   *a. Palomino.* Predominantly cultivated in the Jerez region of south-west Spain, where around 95% of the total vineyard area is used to produce sherry. Palomino, full name Palomino Fino, is the primary grape variety for producing Manzanilla, Fino, Amontillado, Oloroso, and Palo Cortado sherries.

7.   *a. De Krans.* Widely known as one of the leading Port-style wine producers in South Africa. Because of the worldwide protection of the Port name, De Krans' wines are called Cape Ruby, Cape Tawny, Cape Vintage etc. De Krans Port-style wines are of consistently high quality, and from one of the most innovative cellars in South Africa.

8.   *c. Tinta Roriz.* Along with Touriga Nacional and Touriga Franca, Tinta Roriz is the third main grape variety used in the production of Port. It is known as Aragonês in the large Alentejo wine region, east of Lisbon. It is also used to produce wines in different parts of the Iberian Peninsula, where it has varying names, as well as in other parts of the Douro Valley to make table wine.

9.   *a. France.* Originating in France, Dubonnet was created in 1846 by Joseph Dubonnet, a chemist and wine merchant from Paris. He formulated his Dubonnet fortified wine to help make quinine more palatable to French soldiers confronting Malaria in North Africa. It is a sweet wine-based aperitif, a blend of fortified wine, herbs and spices.

10. *b. Mavrodaphne.* Most often used for the production of sweet fortified wine in Greece, Mavrodaphne grapes are also used to make decent red table wine. Indigenous to the Northern Peloponnese region in northern Greece, this fortified wine was first produced in about 1850. It has been described as a subtle dessert wine with strong similarities to a tawny port.

ANSWERS TO QUIZ 97 – PINK, BLUSH, AND ORANGE WINES OF THE WORLD

1   *a. France.* In fact France produces 30% of the world's pink or rosé wines. Just four countries account for 85% of all the rosé wine in the world. These are France, Spain, USA and Italy, and in that order of production quantities. Provence in the south of France grows 60% of all French rosé/pink wine. Between the years 2002 and 2017 French rosé production grew by over 60% and is still growing. Rosé wine is usually made by using red grapes, and allowing skin contact for 2 to 20 hours during early fermentation. The length of contact is dependent on the depth of pink colour wanted.

2.   *c. Fermenting with white grape skins included.* This Orange wine method is the same as the fermentation process for red wine where the grape skins are also left within the vats or barrels. The white grape skins are left in contact with the must or grape juice for up to two months depending on the depth of amber or orange tinge wanted in the final wine. This is a very ancient way of making wine and was done this way in Georgia using clay vessels, over 5,000 years ago.

3.   *a. Grenache.* Red grape varieties are used worldwide to produce rosé or pink wines. Thin skinned grape varieties (Grenache or Pinot Noir) produce a very light colour called 'eye of the partridge' or 'onion skin', a slightly pink off-white colour, if time of skin contact is also kept to a minimum. Darker thicker skin grape varieties produce a dense rosé that can almost resemble a red wine. Almost 90% of Provence wine is rosé, and the lead grape variety is Grenache, often blended with 2 or 3 other red grape varieties.

4.   *b. Georgia.* Orange wines date back well over 5,000 years especially in Georgia, where many wine experts say they originated. It was natural, simple winemaking using large subterranean clay vessels, called Qvevris, which they still use in Georgia to this day. Orange wine outside of Georgia was very rare until 10 years ago, and only resurfaced as a new trendy wine when young winemakers in northern Italy, Croatia and Slovenia became passionate about making and selling it.

5.   *a. b. c. Blush Wines, Pink Wines, Vin Gris.* All the answers are right, as all very light coloured rosé wines have these three interchangeable names. Vin Gris which translates as 'Grey Wine' is usually used for the palest rosé wine made in France. It is often made from Pinot Noir or Gamay. Blush wines are nearly all from the USA, usually medium sweet and often made

from Zinfandel grapes and also Grenache and Merlot. Pink Wine is the slang name for any of these wines, but often used for darker coloured rosé wines.

6. **b. Provence.** This wine region in the south of France still produces the majority of French rosé wines. There are three distinct wine areas within Provence, and each terroir produces its own unique flavours. Because of the enormous growth in popularity of rosé wine worldwide over the last 10 years, many vineyards in Provence were dug up and replanted with varieties which make a better quality rosé wine. Nowadays almost 90% of Provence wine production is rosé.

7. **b. 1970s.** It was Sutter Home in the 1970s that first coined the name Blush Wine. Sutter Home's winemaker, Bob Trinchero, first called the very light pink wines 'Blush' which were almost 'Blanc de Noirs' and previously labelled as White Cabernet or White Merlot and White Zinfandel. Up until the late 90s Blush was the popular term for any light pink American wine, which gobbled up 22% of all wine consumed in the USA. It was not until the early 2000s that French rosé wine from Provence started taking over. The popularity of Blush wine has decreased rapidly in the USA,and most pink wine is now called rosé. Blush as a wine name has always been largely unknown outside of North America.

8. **a. Guigal Tavel.** Tavel is from the southern Rhône just across the river from Châteauneuf-du-Pape, and the most southerly appellation in the Rhône Valley. It was favoured by France's 'Sun King', Louis XIV, and praised by Balzac. Tavel is France's most famous rosé although, it must be said, not now always its best, it now depends on who makes it. The wines are full-bodied and dominated by Grenache and Cinsault; they should be fresh and aromatic and seemingly fruit driven, while being bone dry. Maison Guigal, based in Ampuis in northern Rhône, near Condrieu, is judged to be the best Rhône valley wine producer for at least the last 30 years. The appellations of Côte-Rôtie and Condrieu, where the company was at one time responsible for about a third of all production, are still the core of their business, but they have branched out to make top quality Rhône wines from the north to the very south where their Tavel Rosé is of exceptional quality. b) Château Miraval is a top quality Provence rosé owned by Brad Pitt and Angelina Jolie. Wine Spectator even named it the best rosé in the world. c) Whispering Angel, made by Sacha Lichine, has become the most popular Provence rosé in America.   .

9. **c. Zinfandel.** White Zinfandel, which is the red Zinfandel grape very gently pressed. Skins are then ejected from the early fermentation process, and is then called Zinfandel Blush wine, and it sells over 6 times as much wine by volume as red Zinfandel wines in the USA. Sutter Home, the inventor of Zinfandel Blush, is still the number 1, with 30% by volume and sales of over

$100 million. The wine is medium sweet and very fruity with watermelon and strawberry on the palate. Nowadays Zinfandel Blush is also being made in Puglia Italy (where the Zinfandel grape variety originated) and exported to the USA. Surprisingly, Cabernet Sauvignon, a relatively dark and thick skinned grape, is the 2nd largest variety producing Blush wines.

10. *c. Louis Roederer Cristal Rosé.* The world's most expensive pink/rosé champagne is Louis Roederer's Cristal Rosé (circa £350 per bottle). It also achieves the highest quality score of all rosé champagnes in many international competitions. Rosé champagne is made by one of two methods, either adding a little still red Pinot Noir (5% to 15%) to the blend, called 'Assemblage' or the more difficult method for top champagnes of allowing skin contact for a very limited time called 'Saignee' (bleeding), which is the method for Roederer Cristal Rosé. Rosé champagne is usually more expensive than Brut champagnes, as it is often more fiddly to make and it has an extra allure, with an amazing range of colours, from pink to copper to orange to salmon, and every shade in between. Dom Pérignon is the second most expensive rosé champagne, and Krug Rosé is often the third or fourth most costly.

ANSWERS TO QUIZ 98 – MATCH REGIONS/COUNTRIES WITH THEIR PRIME GRAPE VARIETIES

1. *h. Shiraz.* Situated in South Australia, about thirty five miles north-east of the state capital, Adelaide. South Australia is the most important wine state in Australia, producing around half the nation's wines, and the Barossa Valley is one of the country's most important wine regions. Many different grape varieties are grown here, but the grape that the Valley is most famous for is Shiraz (Syrah). The often ungrafted vines here (this state has not yet encountered Phylloxera) produce a rich, earthy, spicy and delicious Shiraz.

2. *d. Pinot Noir.* This is the famous red Burgundy grape variety, particularly throughout the Côte d'Or, composed of Côte de Nuits in the north, and Côte de Beaune in the south. It is also grown all around the world, and is highly successful in regions such as New Zealand's Central Otago, and USA's Oregon. But its ancestral home is Burgundy.

3. ***i. Sangiovese.*** Widely planted in Italy, but native to Tuscany, where it is the base grape for Chianti, and the only permissible grape for the famous Brunello di Montalcino. The name Sangiovese means 'Blood of Jove', Jove being a Roman name for Zeus. Pockets of Sangiovese plantings can be found elsewhere in the world, but nowhere is more associated with this grape variety than Tuscany.

4. ***b. Assyrtiko.*** The island of Santorini lies about ninety miles due north of Crete, in the Aegean Sea. Its production of top quality Assyrtiko white wine, made from grapes grown on volcanic ash-rich soil, has won countless international wine awards. Assyrtiko is one of Greece's most famous and successful wines. On Santorini, sun-dried Assyrtiko grapes are also used to make the sweet wine, Vinsanto.

5. ***j. Malbec.*** Despite its roots being French, and mainly in Bordeaux, as well as Cahors, it was Argentina that really put this grape on the map as a single varietal and, indeed, in a reverse role it was Malbec that put Argentine wine on the map! The country has been producing high quality full-bodied, plump and juicy Malbecs since the 1990s, and Argentina is now seen as the Malbec capital of the world.

6. ***g. Sauvignon Blanc.*** For most people, New Zealand, especially the Marlborough wine region, is the country that immediately comes to mind when the white grape of Sauvignon Blanc is mentioned. Crisp and refreshing, and best drunk relatively young, it is also one of the UK's favourite white wines. It is grown extensively around the world, and can vary enormously in character, but it is the personality of New Zealand Sauvignon Blanc that is most associated with this grape variety.

7. ***f. Cabernet Sauvignon.*** The Médoc is arguably the most famous red wine district in the world, and is home to many of the greatest wine names in Bordeaux, including all the First Growth clarets, except Château Haut-Brion which is in Pessac-Léognan. Generally seen as the noblest of all red grape varieties, Cabernet Sauvignon is the anchor in the 'Bordeaux Blends' produced in the Médoc.

8. ***a. Grüner Veltliner.*** This white grape variety is primarily grown in Austria, but is also increasingly being planted in other countries around the world. However, it is Austria's most significant white grape variety and is, indeed, the country's flagship wine. It can easily be said that Grüner Veltiner put Austrian wine on the map, similar to Malbec putting Argentine wine in front of the world's eyes.

9. ***c. Chasselas.*** Easily the most planted grape in Switzerland, Chasselas is particularly prevalent in the western, French-speaking, part of the country.

Chasselas is grown in some other countries in the world, but Switzerland is its true home. Its exuberant and powerful nature is well suited to the cool mountainous weather of Switzerland's alpine slopes.

10. *e. Chenin Blanc.* Sometimes called 'Steen' in South Africa, Chenin Blanc is the first grape variety that comes to mind when one thinks of South African white wine. It is still the most widely planted grape variety in South Africa, though many other grapes are now competing for that space. Today, Chenin Blanc is also increasingly grown around the world.

ANSWERS TO QUIZ 99 – FINALE OF GENERAL WINE QUESTIONS – PART 1

1. *c. Mâconnais.* Pouilly-Fuissé is a white wine produced at the southern end of the Mâconnais wine region, which is positioned between Côte Chalonnaise to the north, and Beaujolais to the south. The wine is made around the twin villages of Pouilly and Fuissé, using Chardonnay grapes. The quality of Pouilly Fuissé varies, depending on producer, from rather bland to rich and succulent.

2. *South Island.* Canterbury is a wine region situated just north of Central Otago, and spread inland around the city of Christchurch, the capital of New Zealand's South Island. The character of the region's Pinot Noir and Chardonnay has been compared in style to that of wines from Burgundy. Good quality wine is also produced in the region from Riesling and Sauvignon Blanc grapes.

3. *a. Umbria.* The region of Umbria is in central Italy, lying between Tuscany and Lazio. Orvieto is the best-known white wine of the region and, even though a small amount of semi-sweet and sweet wine is produced, the vast majority of Orvieto is dry, made largely from Trebbiano Toscano (called Procanico locally) and Grechetto grapes.

4. *b. Sercial.* There are four main wine styles/grape varieties produced on the island of Madeira, which range from sweet to dry as Malmsey, Bual, Verdelho, and the driest being Sercial. Verdelho, in particular, is growing in popularity and plantings in some other parts of the world, especially Australia. Sercial vines are generally grown on Madeira's highest vineyards, and are harvested comparatively late. This wine can be an ideal aperitif.

5. **a. Napa Valley.** Situated just north of San Francisco, the world-famous Napa Valley wine region is home to many top wine producers, not least of which is Stag's Leap Wine Cellars. Located towards the southern end of Napa Valley, east of Yountville, Stag's Leap will forever be iconic for winning the famous 1976 Paris Tasting, now known as The Judgement of Paris, where top Californian wines were blind-tasted in a competition against top French wines, and Stag's Leap 1973 Cabernet Sauvignon won the red wine section, much to the shock of the wine world at the time, as top French wines were believed to be unbeatable.

6. **c. Koblenz.** The source of the Mosel river is in the Vosges Mountains, across the border in France, and the river is lined with vines all the way to meeting the Rhine at Koblenz. All the best Mosel wines are produced from the Riesling grape, and on the steep slopes down towards the river.

7. **a. Victoria.** Located in the state of Victoria, about an hour's drive north-east of Melbourne, the Yarra Valley is a region producing high quality wine. It has many micro-climates, so different parts of the region are ideal for certain grape varieties. Some excellent Cabernet Sauvignon, Riesling, and Shiraz wines are produced, and the Valley also makes superb Pinot Noir and Chardonnay, which are often used here to produce some excellent sparkling wines.

8. **Toro.** The Toro wine region is in the far west of Castilla y León in north-west Spain. The town of Toro itself is only about 40 miles east of the Portuguese border, and lies close to the Duero river, which becomes the Douro when it enters Portugal. Toro is mainly a red wine appellation, and the main grape variety is Tempranillo, known here as Tinta de Toro.

9. **Pinotage.** This red grape is a crossing of Pinot Noir and Cinsaut. Cinsaut used to be known as Hermitage in South Africa, which explains the 'age' part of Pinotage. Even though it is now also grown, usually in small quantities, elsewhere in the world, it is South Africa that immediately comes to mind when one sees or hears the name Pinotage. Character of the wine can vary, depending on viticulture and vinification, but it is usually a fruity, full-bodied wine.

10. **b. River Danube.** Passing through most of Austria's most important wine regions, the River Danube flows through Wachau, Kremstal, Kamptal, Wagram, and Traisental, before running through the middle of Vienna, and the Wien wine region. Then it skirts Carnuntum before reaching Bratislava and continuing on through Slovakia. On its way through Austria it sweeps past steep vine terraces stretching over rolling hillsides, where most of the wine produced is from Riesling and Grüner Veltliner grapes.

ANSWERS TO QUIZ 100 – FINALE OF GENERAL WINE QUESTIONS – PART 2

1. *a. Northland.* The sub-tropical climate of Northland, right at the top of New Zealand's North Island, results in warm spring temperatures, and hot dry summers, which allow the grapes to ripen early, creating full-bodied and rich wines. Part of Northland is the Bay of Islands, where New Zealand's first vines were planted in the early nineteenth century.

2. *c. Sanlúcar de Barrameda.* Manzanilla sherry, along with Fino, is the lightest and driest of all sherries. It tends to have a slightly salty tang, owing to the sea air carried from the nearby Atlantic Ocean. The town of Sanlúcar de Barrameda, around which the Palomino grapes for producing Manzanilla are grown, is in Andalucía and sits at the mouth of the Guadalquivir river, where it runs into the Atlantic.

3. *c. St-Nicolas-de-Bourgueil.* Generally a lighter red wine than its neighbour, Bourgueil, owing to its sandier soil. Situated in the central Loire Valley, the wine is produced either predominantly, or entirely, from Cabernet Franc grapes, and tends to be medium-bodied in character.

4. *True.* Situated in north-east Italy, between Emilia Romagna and Marche regions, the tiny country of San Marino, with a population of just 34,000, has a small wine industry. Unsurprisingly, given its proximity to Tuscany's eastern border, only about ten miles away, Sangiovese is the preferred red grape here. Local white grapes include Ribolla and Biancale, as well as Moscato Bianco for sweet and sparkling wines.

5. *b. Ontario.* Canada is the world's largest Ice Wine producer, and Ontario, particularly in the Niagara Peninsula, is by far the biggest maker of Ice Wine in the country. Often called Canada's 'liquid gold', Ice Wine is produced by pressing grapes that are frozen solid, and have a huge intensity of sugar, resulting in a wine that is sweet and luscious.

6. *c. St-Amour.* Located above both Juliénas and Chénas, St-Amour is the most northerly Cru in the Beaujolais region. As well as being the northernmost Cru, just south of the Mâconnais, it is also one of the smallest. Produced from the Beaujolais grape variety, Gamay, St-Amour has one of the lightest styles out of all the Beaujolais Crus. Character, though, can vary due to the variety of soils in the region, which include clay, granite, limestone and slate.

7. *The Andes.* As well as running between Chile and Argentina, the Andes is the world's longest continental mountain range, at about 4,500 miles long, and also runs through Venezuela, Columbia, Ecuador, Peru, and Bolivia. The

terroir in the vineyards on either side of the Andes has a direct bearing on the type of Argentine and Chilean wines produced there.

8. **b. Turin.** Capital of Piedmont, Turin is situated in the north-west corner of this wine region, home to the famous wines of Barolo and Barbaresco, produced from the noble Nebbiolo grapes, and Barbera, from its eponymous grape variety. As well as being the home of Italy's car industry, and famous for its chocolate, Turin is also where vermouth was invented.

9. **Margaret River.** Situated in Western Australia, about 170 miles south of the State's capital city, Perth, Margaret River is the most important wine region in the State, and one of the most important in Australia, producing some of the greatest Cabernet Sauvignon and Chardonnay wines in the world. It is a relatively young wine region, as the first vines were only planted here in the late 1960s, with the first wines emerging in the early 1970s.

10. **a. A treetop champagne bar.** A champagne treehouse in the middle of woods near the town of Verzy, just south-east of Reims in the champagne region, the Perching Bar offers expansive views over the surrounding countryside. Approximately twenty feet above the forest floor, and accessed through several suspended walkways, you have the option of sitting inside the bar in comfortable swings with your glass of champagne, or standing outside with your drink, admiring the views.

ABOUT THE AUTHORS

RODDY BUTTON

Roddy started his career working for a centuries-old wine company in Bristol. His responsibilities included the enjoyable task of decanting and tasting wines from the 'Directors Bin', some of which dated back to the late 19th century.

When the business was taken over by a large wine and spirit company, Roddy moved to London to work on the marketing and advertising of various wine and spirit products.

Having successfully completed all the Wine and Spirit Education Trust's exam courses, right through to Diploma, Roddy is now an AIWS, Associate member of the Institute of Wines and Spirits.

Roddy is passionate about wine and, along with Mike Oliver, his co-author of The World of Wine Quiz Book, as well as The Wine Quiz Book, and Wine: 101 Truths, Myths and Legends, regularly attends international wine tastings in London, as well as travelling every year to different wine regions to meet producers and taste their wines.

MIKE OLIVER

Mike's interest in wine began at university where he was a member of the wine tasting team, a role that sparked a lifelong involvement in the wine trade.

During his career, Mike has advertised many international brands of wines and spirits, a position which has regularly brought him into close contact with international wine producers.

He frequently takes part in trade and consumer wine tastings in London and, on one occasion, narrowly lost out on the Wine Taster of the Year Award to well-known wine expert Oz Clarke.

Mike's passion for wine has made him an enthusiastic collector of both new and antique wine books.

With his co-author of The World of Wine Quiz Book, The Wine Quiz Book, and Wine: 101 Truths, Myths and Legends, Roddy Button, Mike makes regular trips abroad to visit wine regions and meet winemakers, from local farmers to internationally celebrated estates and families.

BRIAN WHITEHEAD – DESIGNER

Brian is responsible for The World of Wine Quiz Book's design, art direction, typography and is the artist who created all the black and white drawings and illustrations in the book.

Brian graduated from art school and started his career as a graphic designer specialising in design, typography and books.

Over the years Brian has been a graphic designer, illustrator, photographer and an art director in advertising agencies in London and New York. He has also designed and produced many books and edited magazines on art.

Latterly he has turned to art education and is now a London University Senior Lecturer taking students to BA(Hons) and MA level in Graphic Design and specialising in typography, illustration and design in the creation of books.

Brian's interest in fine art and design has fused together with his love of wine to help make this wine quiz book lively and unique.

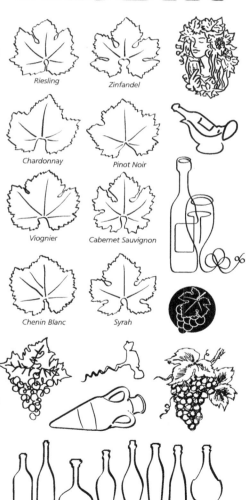

Riesling

Zinfandel

Chardonnay

Pinot Noir

Viognier

Cabernet Sauvignon

Chenin Blanc

Syrah

SOURCES AND BIBLIOGRAPHY FOR THE WORLD OF WINE QUIZ BOOK

Both writers, Roddy Button and Mike Oliver, have used multiple sources for all the amplified answers. All the facts are at least triple checked from different sources, including wine reference books and the original websites of wine estates/producers. Also, official websites of government wine statistical bodies have been consulted.

Bibliography (40 of the main source reference books used to check wine facts)

Johnson, Hugh and Robinson, Jancis — The World Atlas of Wine 8th Edition

Johnson, Hugh — Story of Wine

Johnson, Hugh — Pocket Wine Book 2020

Robinson, Jancis — The Oxford Companion to Wine

Robinson, Jancis — Wine Grapes

Robinson, Jancis — How to Taste: A Guide to Enjoying Wine

Robinson, Jancis — Wine Course: A Guide to the World of Wine

Robinson, Jancis — American Wine

Clarke, Oz — Wine A-Z

Clarke, Oz — Wine Atlas

Clarke, Oz — Encyclopedia of Wine: An A-Z Guide to the Wines of the World

Clarke, Oz — World of Wine: Wines Grapes Vineyards

Clarke, Oz — Grapes & Wines

Stevenson, Tom — The Sotheby's Wine Encyclopedia

Stevenson, Tom — Christie's World Encyclopedia of Champagne & Sparkling Wine

Cobbold, David — Larousse Wine

Kolpan, Steven — Exploring Wine

Sohm, Aldo — Wine Simple

Joseph, Robert — French Wines

Brook, Stephen — The Complete Bordeaux

Coates, Clive — The Wines of Burgundy

Edwards, Michael — The Finest Wines of Champagne

Strang, Paul — South-West France: The Wines and Winemakers

Jeffs, Julian — The Wines of Spain

Radford, John — The New Spain

D'Agata, Ian — Italy's Native Wine Grape Terroirs

Rosso, Gambero — Italian Wines 2020

Krebiehl, Anne — The Wines of Germany

Mayson, Richard — Portugal's Wines and Winemakers

Metcalfe, Charles — The Wine and Food Lover's Guide to Portugal

Brook, Stephen — The Wines of Austria

Barty-King, Hugh — A Taste of English Wine

Skelton, Stephen — The Wines of Great Britain

Adams, Geoff — Greek Wine

Laube, James — Wine Spectator's California Wine

Brook, Stephen — The Finest Wines of California

Goldstein, Evan — Wines of South America

Evans, Len — The Complete Book of Australian Wine

Gibb, Rebecca — The Wines of New Zealand

James, Tim — Wines of the New South Africa: Tradition and Revolution

Websites Visited for Information Gathering, Fact Finding and Checking

For fact checking the 'Amplified Answers' for the 1,000 questions, well over 100 websites were visited. The main original source was always the wine region's or wine estate's own website, then facts were independently checked with at least two other sources. Any Wikipedia facts were always very carefully checked with two or three separate authoritative sources.

The top 25 general source wine websites used were: Decanter, The Wine Society, Wine-Searcher, Vivino, Wine Business, Wine Spectator, The Drinks Business, Drinks Retailing News, Wine Folly, Jancis Robinson, Harpers, Vincarta, Wine & Spirits, Averys, Berry Brothers & Rudd, Corney & Barrow, Justerini & Brooks, Majestic, Berkmann Wine Cellars, The Wine Economist, Wine Enthusiast, VinePair, Tim Atkin, Wine-Pages, Robert Parker Wine Advocate.

Official wine websites of countries and wine regions were also used extensively, such as these 25 reference websites: Austrian Wine, Wines of Germany, German Wines, Italian Wine Central, Hungarian Wines, Wines of Greece, NZ Wine, Wine Australia, Wines of Lebanon, Vins-France, Wines of Chile, Koshu Japan, Swiss Wine, Wine Romania, Discover California Wines, Rioja Wine, Vini di Puglia, Dao Wines, Wine Tasmania, Champagne, Vinho Madeira, Bourgogne Wines, English Wine Producers, DO Rueda, VQA Ontario.

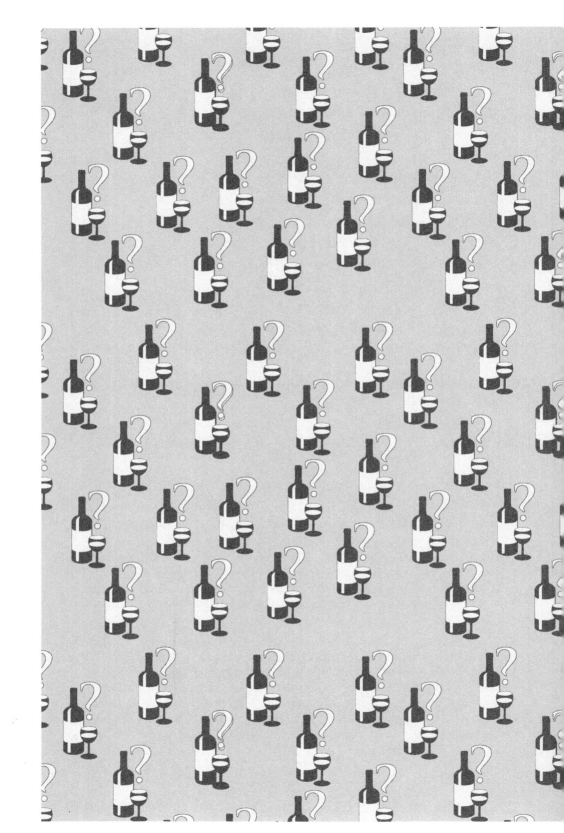